J.C. LAMBE.

2

Resilient Computing Systems

Editor

T. Anderson

COLLINS
8 Grafton Street, London W1

Collins Professional and Technical Books
William Collins Sons & Co. Ltd
8 Grafton Street, London W1X 3LA

First published in Great Britain by
Collins Professional and Technical Books 1985

Distributed in the United States of America
by Sheridan House, Inc.

Copyright © T. Anderson 1985

British Library Cataloguing in Publication Data
Resilient computing systems.
1. Electronic data processing
I. Anderson, T.
001.64   QA76
ISBN 0-00-383039-X

Printed and bound in Great Britain by
Mackays of Chatham, Kent

Contents

Preface   iv

1. Fault tolerant computing (*T. Anderson*)   1

2. Hardware fault tolerance (*W. C. Carter*)   11

3. Design fault tolerance (*P. A. Lee and T. Anderson*)   64

4. Reliable communications (*M. Morganti*)   78

5. Resilient real-time systems (*H. Kopetz*)   91

6. Robust distributed programs (*S. K. Shrivastava*)   102

7. Software safety (*N. Leveson*)   122

8. Software reliability prediction (*B. Littlewood*)   144

9. Commercial resilient systems (*A. P. Smith*)   163

10. The Tandem Non-Stop system (*C. I. Dimmer*)   178

11. The MOMENTUM high resilience system (*A. P. Smith*)   197

12. The STRATUS computer system (*D. Wilson*)   208

13. August Systems industrial control computers (*J. Wensley*)   232

Index   247

Preface

A *resilient* computing system is capable of providing dependable service to its users over a wide range of potentially adverse circumstances. The two key attributes here are dependability and robustness. Computing system *dependability* refers to the quality of the delivered service such that reliance can justifiably be placed on this service, and serves as a generic concept encompassing notions of reliability, maintainability, availability, safety, functionality, performance, timeliness, etc. A computing system can be said to be *robust* if it retains its ability to deliver service in conditions which are beyond its normal domain of operation, whether due to harsh treatment, or unreasonable service requests, or misoperation, or the impact of faults, or lack of maintenance, etc.

Of course, the ideal computing system would be *infallible*, but this would require its construction to be *flawless* and its operation to be *invulnerable* – rather a tall order with current technology. Nevertheless, two trends are likely to ensure that future computing systems will be more resilient than at present. First, the continuing expansion of applications for computing systems will increase demand, and second, the sustained decline in hardware costs is stimulating supply.

There are many applications of computing systems where the property of resilience is highly desirable, ranging from ballistic missile defence systems down to washing machine controllers by way of nuclear reactor shutdown systems, avionics in civil aircraft, railway interlocking, medical systems, electronic funds transference, military intelligence systems and university computing facilities (for example). Indeed, everyone would like a robust system on which they could depend, and so resilient computing systems are a highly attractive and commercial proposition.

This book is designed to supply information and guidance on key topics relating to the provision of resilience (Chapters 1–8), and to describe some of the commercially available systems which are marketed on the basis of their resilience properties (Chapters 9–13).

The first three chapters address the subject of fault tolerance in computing systems; Chapter 1 provides an overview of the basic concepts and principles while Chapters 2 and 3 discuss the provision of tolerance to physical and design faults, respectively.

Chapters 4–6 address topics relating to the provision of resilience in distributed and real-time systems. Chapter 4 examines techniques for achieving reliable communication between processors and processes, Chapter 5 deals with the additional problems engendered by the imposition of real-time constraints on a system, while Chapter 6 presents an approach to the construction of robust software for a system of autonomous processing nodes.

The next two chapters concentrate on software, where so many of the problems lie. Chapter 7 discusses techniques whereby the safety properties of software can be established; Chapter 8 shows how software reliability models can be judged on the basis of their predictive capabilities.

Chapter 9 reviews the commercial market place for packaged resilient computing systems, and this is followed by four chapters which describe resilient systems which are in volume production: Tandem, MOMENTUM, STRATUS and August systems.

The material presented in the above chapters should be of interest to all involved in the design, construction, modification or use of computing systems, save those who do not require resilience as an attribute of their system. Thus, if you are an implementor or a user of a computing system for which frequent and regular breakdowns are of negligible consequence, you may safely ignore this volume. Others do so at their own risk.

In conclusion, I would like to thank the contributors to this book, eleven colleagues whose names may be found on the Contents page. I hope I will not be thought invidious if I especially thank Bill Carter for his detailed and comprehensive exposition of hardware fault tolerance techniques.

And finally, my thanks go to Bernard Watson of Collins for his precision, persistence and patience – cardinal virtues for a commissioning editor.

T. Anderson

CHAPTER 1

Fault tolerant computing

T. Anderson
(Computing Laboratory, University of Newcastle upon Tyne)

In recent years the commercial significance of fault tolerant computing systems has increased markedly. However, it should not be thought that the techniques of fault tolerance constitute a recent innovation. In the mid 1950s von Neumann worked in this area, and subsequently many computer manufacturers have made use of fault tolerance to improve reliability (e.g. IBM's 370 series), and since 1971 an international symposium on fault tolerant computing (FTCS) has been held annually.

In the following sections we attempt to summarise the basic principles on which strategies for fault tolerance can be founded, placing additional emphasis on the need for a structured approach and on coping with design faults. It must be stressed that the treatment here is extremely condensed. A much more detailed presentation, from which this material is largely derived, can be found in *Fault Tolerance: Principles and Practice* by T. Anderson and P. A. Lee, published by Prentice-Hall International in 1981.

CONCEPTS AND TERMINOLOGY

A continuing source of difficulty in discussing issues relating to the reliability of systems and the provision of fault tolerance is the absence of any agreed terminology for the relevant concepts. Indeed, the concepts themselves are perhaps a little more elusive than many people realise. In this overview it will be necessary to sacrifice some of the subtleties in the interests of brevity, but we hope, nevertheless, to indicate the need for care and consistency.

First, let us examine the notion of reliability itself. It is essential to distinguish situations in which undesirable behaviour from a system can be attributed to deficiencies within that system from those situations where the deficiences are external to the system, either in the form of untoward circumstances in the environment of the system, or arising from misunderstanding by users. (Misplaced reliance on a system is no justification for criticising that system as unreliable.) The only way in which the required distinction can be made is to have available (at least in principle) an authoritative specification which prescribes what the behaviour of the system should be in all circumstances. Ideally, of course, as well as being complete, specifications should be consistent, unambiguous, formal, etc., so that they can always provide a standard against which the behaviour of a system can be judged.

Given the existence of a specification we can define a *failure* of a system to occur whenever that system deviates from its specification. The *operational reliability* of the system is then simply the historical record of any occurrences of system failure. Of more significance is our ability to construct an assessment of the *predicted reliability* of a system; this will usually be based on estimating the parameters of some reliability model of the system. If a single numeric measure of reliability is required this is most often taken to be the MTBF (mean time between failures) or the failure rate for the system.

When a system is unreliable in its behaviour, two separate but related concepts should be distinguished. These are the *event* of doing something 'invalid' (which we have already termed a failure) and the *condition* of being in an 'invalid' state. For some time before a system failure the internal state of a system will have been erroneous. That is to say the state will have contained *errors* – erroneous values to which the eventual failure of the system can be attributed. Furthermore these errors must have been generated by internal failures within the system, failures either of component subsystems or a failure of these components to interact correctly. In turn these internal failures can be attributed to errors within the components or the design of the system. These internal errors will be referred to as *component faults* and *design faults* to avoid confusion with errors in the state of the system itself.

The terminology adopted above identifies a chain of causality in the malfunctioning of a system. Faults can be present in either the components or the design; the manifestation of these faults introduces errors into the system state; these errors can lead to a subsequent failure of the system. In physical systems (hardware), faults can be introduced from external sources (e.g. cosmic rays) or by physical deterioration (e.g. rust). Abstract systems (software) usually remain in their original 'pristine' condition.

RELIABILITY ENGINEERING

The traditional approach to achieving reliability in computing systems has been based largely on *fault prevention*, the goal of which is to prevent system failure by ensuring that no faults can be present when the system is in use. Fault prevention has two aspects, and these are referred to as *fault avoidance* and *fault removal*.

Fault avoidance concerns the selection of techniques and technologies which aim to avoid the introduction of faults during the design and construction of a system. Examples of its use are the adoption of design methodologies to cope with the complexities of hardware and software designs, and the selection of reliable components and proven interconnection technology for system construction. Of course, fault avoidance should not be expected to succeed in completely avoiding the presence of faults.

For this reason, fault removal techniques are necessary to validate the implementation of a system and remove any faults which are thereby exposed. Testing, of hardware or software, is by far the most prevalent validation method, and can be applied with various degrees of sophistication. However, informal (and, to some extent, formal) verification techniques are also employed, not to confirm the total absence of faults (a largely pointless exercise) but to identify the presence of faults so that they can be removed. Of course, fault removal should not be expected to succeed in completely eradicating faults.

For this reason, *fault tolerance* techniques may be needed to provide a last line of defence. By incorporating redundant elements in a system it may be possible to cope with the effects of faults and avert the occurrence of failures or, failing that, at least to warn a user that errors have been introduced into the state of the system. The provision of tolerance to anticipated hardware faults has been a common practice for many years. A relatively new development is the proposal that it may be possible to tolerate unanticipated faults (i.e. faults whose consequences cannot be predicted) such as design faults in either hardware or software.

It is certainly the case that a wide range of techniques is available for enhancing the reliability of computing systems. Furthermore, many of these techniques can be at least partially automated through the provision of tools to assist the designers and developers of systems. For instance, we are beginning to see the introduction of unified development environments for software construction (e.g. the Programmer's Workbench on UNIX and the various proposals for an APSE (Ada Programming Support Environment)).

However, the ability to engineer the reliability of a system is not so much a consequence of the availability of techniques for improving reliability as it is dependent on information concerning the cost-effectiveness of those techniques. In order to construct a system which will have a given level of reliability, within a fixed budget and adhering to project timescales, the reliability engineer needs to be able to select appropriate reliability techniques for that system and apportion the amount of effort to be devoted to each technique. At present such judgements are often made on an *ad hoc* basis, guided to some extent by previous experience. For software systems the approach is all too often simply to write the software and then exhaustively test it – that is, to continue testing until either the tester or the budget is exhausted.

Only when we have data on the cost-effectiveness of techniques for fault avoidance, removal, and tolerance in relation to specific classes of system will it be possible to make a rational determination of the best mix of those techniques. In the absence of such data (as is the case for software techniques) we would argue for a more eclectic approach than is currently adopted. Different techniques can be expected to provide coverage for different classes of fault, if only because they depend upon different assumptions. The law of diminishing returns (and its quantitative variant, the 80:20 rule) suggests that optimal solutions are rarely obtained by placing all one's eggs in one basket.

A well engineered approach to building highly reliable systems is likely to be based on striving to attain perfection, but simultaneously acknowledging that imperfections will remain, and therefore fault tolerance will be needed to cope with them.

FAULT TOLERANCE

The policies and mechanisms utilised in a system to provide fault tolerance can be divided into two categories. The first of these concerns *error treatment* and covers three phases, each dealing with a different aspect of coping with the presence of erroneous values in the state of the system. We will refer to these phases as *error detection*, *damage assessment*, and *error recovery*. In some situations it may be sufficient merely to deal with errors as and when they are discovered lurking in the system state; however, a more thorough and comprehensive approach to fault tolerance will also endeavour to provide *fault treatment* in order to root out the source of the errors. Again, three phases of fault treatment can be identified, which we will refer to as *fault location*, *system repair* and *continued service*.

These six constituent phases form the basis of most, if not all, strategies for fault tolerance. It should be noted that there can be considerable interplay between phases, which tends to blur their identification in a particular system. The order in which the phases are undertaken may also vary from system to system. For simplicity in what follows we will address each of the phases separately.

ERROR DETECTION
The starting point for all fault tolerance strategies is the detection of an erroneous state; the success of those strategies is critically dependent upon the effectiveness of the techniques for error detection. Unfortunately, the detection of errors is highly system dependent – only in the special case of *interface checks* can a general mechanism be proposed. An interface between components in a system can always be characterised in terms of a set of abstract objects together with their associated operations. Interface checks are concerned with confirming that a requested operation is legitimate and permissible, and whether the operands are compatible and valid. Ideally the interface checks should form the initial stage of an *exception handling* mechanism, which, when an error is detected, will *signal* that something untoward has occurred. Such a mechanism could then be augmented by any other specific checks that are built into the system. Based on the many forms that these checks take in actual systems the following classification is proposed:

- Replication checks – an alternative implementation of the system is used as a check for consistency.

- Timing checks – the use of a clock to confirm that the system adheres to imposed timing constraints
- Reversal checks – when the relationship between inputs and outputs is one-to-one it may be possible to calculate from the system output what the input should have been
- Coding checks – redundant data is maintained in a fixed relationship with the system data so that data corruption can be detected
- Reasonableness checks – a determination that a value or set of values satisfies some criterion of acceptability
- Structural checks – checks on the structural integrity of data aggregates.

DAMAGE ASSESSMENT

When an error is detected, much more of the system state may be suspect than that initially discovered to be erroneous. Invalid values may already have spread within the system and an assessment must be made of the extent of the damage. Strategies for this purpose must rely on assumptions about the structure of the system, since these will determine the possible flows of information. Constraints which maintain system structure and prohibit undesirable information flow provide the basic means for *damage confinement* and are usually the most significant factor in assessing the spread of damage. These constraints make possible the identification of *atomic actions* within the internal activity of a system, for example as depicted by the curves A and B in Fig. 1.1. (The vertical arrowed lines indicate information flow between components.)

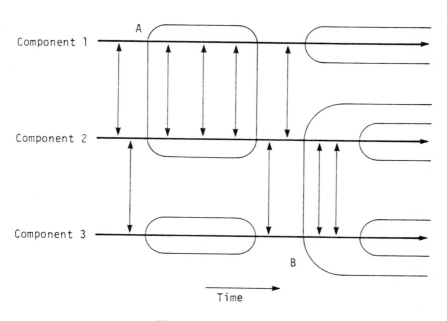

Fig. 1.1 Atomic actions.

The activity of a group of components constitutes an atomic action if no information flows between that group and the rest of the system for the duration of the activity. Atomic actions may be planned when the system is designed, or (less often) dynamically identified by exploratory techniques after the detection of an error. Planned atomic actions must be maintained by imposing constraints on communication within the system. These constraints can be explicit – e.g. physical separation or electrical insulation – or they may be enforced by a *protection mechanism* which controls access to shared data – e.g. the use of locking schemes in database systems to support transactions.

ERROR RECOVERY

After an error has been detected and an assessment made of the damage it is then necessary to eliminate the errors from the system state by means of error recovery techniques. Two approaches are available, known as *forward* and *backward* error recovery. Forward error recovery attempts to make further use of an erroneous state by making selective corrections to remove errors. This can certainly be very efficient, but is system specific and only appropriate when dependable and accurate predictions can be made of the location of errors. In contrast, backward error recovery relies on restoring the system to a prior state, thereby discarding all of the current erroneous state. State restoration is a more profligate approach and can be expensive to implement, but has the enormous advantage that it can be used to recover from errors generated by any fault whatsoever, including the unanticipatable damage caused by design faults.

A further advantage is that this approach can be provided as a mechanism. Backward error recovery mechanisms fall into three categories: *checkpointing* mechanisms, which save a copy of all (sometimes part) of the system state, *audit trail* techniques, which record all modifications made to the state, and *recovery cache* mechanisms, which compromise by incrementally forming a copy of just that part of the state which is changed. The provision of these mechanisms in a single-level, single-process system is relatively straightforward, but is more difficult for hierarchical systems or those containing concurrent processes. Distributed systems introduce further problems (and further opportunities too, of course). Solutions can be linked to the notion of an atomic action, which is said to form a *restorable action* if all components within the action retain the ability to perform a mutually consistent state restoration, as illustrated in Fig. 1.2, where a '[' indicates a possible restoration point.

FAULT LOCATION

Errors are merely the symptoms produced by a fault, so although error treatment can remove the immediate danger of a failure it may still be necessary to attempt to treat the fault to prevent it from continuing to damage the system state. Only if the fault is transient, or if the system can cope with recurrent fault manifestations, will error treatment alone be

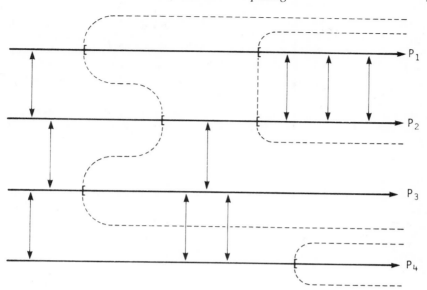

Fig. 1.2 Restorable actions.

adequate. Before a system can deal with a fault, some assessment must be made of the fault's location. Initially the only information available for this purpose is information derived from the characteristics of the generated errors. Exploratory techniques to supplement or refine this information usually rely on the use of *diagnostic checking*. A diagnostic check is performed by invoking a component with a set of inputs for which the correct outputs are known, and comparing the actual outputs obtained. The overheads incurred in diagnostic checking are high and can have a very disruptive impact on the system. This can be avoided if the system was constructed to have excess capacity, since components can then be taken out of service for diagnosis and only returned if given a clean bill of health.

SYSTEM REPAIR

The fault location phase will result in a determination that one or more components are faulty. Repair of the system then consists of performing some reconfiguration, usually to avoid making further use of the faulty components. For this to be possible the interconnections between components must be dynamically switchable. The simplest reconfiguration strategy is to have stand-by spares available to replace faulty components. A more flexible alternative is to utilise all spares from the outset as a means of enhancing performance; disabling faulty components then results in a *graceful degradation* in the standard of service provided by the system. If a global reconfiguration is required this can be achieved by starting from a trusted minimal system and bootstrapping up to a fully working configuration by systematically incorporating only those components which satisfy their diagnostic checks. Critical components known as the *hardcore* of the system are responsible for applying diagnostics and performing reconfiguration. The ability to reconfigure a system on-line is a very potent one, and should only be used with circumspection. Precautions must be taken to ensure that the switching mechanisms are not activated inadvertently. Many systems do not attempt to provide fully spontaneous reconfiguration and instead rely on manual intervention either to initiate or to effect repairs.

CONTINUED SERVICE

The final stage of fault tolerance is to return the system to normal operation. In hardware systems a *retry* is frequently attempted – this is sometimes referred to as the use of *temporal redundancy*. Software systems can provide considerable flexibility of action, essentially since a transfer of control is easily made to any designated restart point. One important decision which has to be made when a system is restarted is whether the internal activity of suspect components can be resumed. If this is not allowed then all such activity is effectively terminated when fault tolerance is invoked (of course, this does not necessarily mean that the components are prevented from undertaking any subsequent actions). It can certainly be argued that solutions based on a *resumption* model for continued service are likely to be more complex (and therefore more risky) than those which simply accept the limitations of a *termination* model.

STRUCTURED APPROACH

The need to adopt a structured approach to the design of systems is widely accepted as being essential if complexity is to be kept under control. This is particularly important for the design of fault tolerant systems; an unstructured approach could easily reduce system reliability by introducing more faults than those to which tolerance was being provided.

Figure 1.3 suggests a coherent way in which the provisions for fault tolerance could be built into a system, in a framework which minimises the impact on system complexity. Three classes of exceptional situation (i.e. in which some fault tolerance response is needed) are identified. *Interface exceptions* are signalled when interface checks determine that an invalid service request has been made to a component. These must be dealt with by the part of the system which made the invalid request. *Local exceptions* are signalled when a component believes that it has detected an error that its own fault tolerance capabilities should deal with. Lastly, a *failure exception* is the means by which a component notifies the system that, despite the use of its own fault tolerance capabilities, it has been unable to provide the service requested of it (thus the component has failed, but acknowledges its failure).

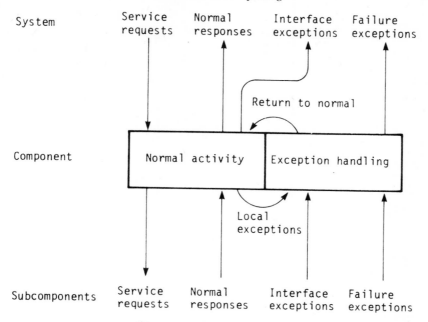

Fig. 1.3 Ideal component.

DESIGN FAULT TOLERANCE

The difficulty in providing tolerance for design faults is that their consequences are unpredictable, and on-line repair can only be achieved if *design diversity* has been built into the system in advance. Two proposals have been made for tolerating faults in software; these are known as *recovery blocks* and *N-version programming*. A simple generalisation of these two approaches is shown in Fig. 1.4.

Each redundant module endeavours to provide a result which the adjudicator will accept. Each module is independently designed and may utilise whatever algorithm and local data its designer selects. The adjudication module may base its decision on predetermined criteria, on a comparison of the results from the separate modules, or on some combination of these. (Redundancy may also be incorporated within the adjudicator.) The N-version programming scheme has an adjudicator which is essentially a voter accepting the majority decision – the scheme is directly analogous to the hardware technique of TMR (triple modular redundancy) and as such parallel execution of the modules is usually assumed. The recovery block scheme has an adjudicator which applies an acceptance test to each of the outputs from the modules in turn, in a fixed sequence. The outputs from the first module to pass the test are accepted. In order to permit sequential execution of the modules, the recovery block scheme normally assumes the availability of backward error recovery.

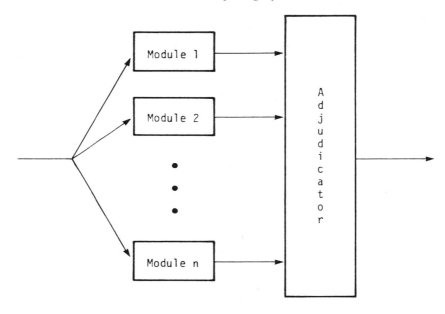

Fig. 1.4 Design diversity.

FAULT TOLERANT SYSTEMS

A number of computer systems have been developed which incorporate a high degree of fault tolerance. Most of these systems have been designed to meet very high standards of reliability for certain special purpose applications. Of particular significance are: the Jet Propulsion Laboratory STAR computer, designed as a prototype for unmanned deep space missions of 10 or more years duration; the BBN Pluribus interface message processor for the ARPANET; the Bell System's ESS No 1A telephone switching system with a permitted down-time limit of two hours over a 40 year period; and SRI International's SIFT prototype computer intended for avionics applications requiring a failure rate below 10^{-9} per hour.

The commercial success of the Tandem Corporation's Non-Stop systems has led to a pullulation of new (and old) companies marketing a range of general purpose computer systems offering high availability systems to different sectors of the market. These include ITL's MOMENTUM, STRATUS/32, August systems, and (last but never least) IBM's System D.

It is an encouraging sign that the fundamental trade-off of cost *vs.* performance is now (perhaps belatedly) being increasingly influenced by a perception that computer systems will in future need to provide a quality of service comparable to that available from other electronic consumer goods. We can therefore look forward to when highly reliable general purpose computer systems (both hardware and software) will be the norm, and can surely expect fault tolerance to have a major role in bringing this about.

CHAPTER 2

Hardware fault tolerance

W. C. Carter

(*IBM T. J. Watson Research Center, Yorktown Heights, N.Y.*)

As indicated in the previous chapter, computer system operational life is viewed by its users as alternating between two states. The first is valid operation in which a specified system service is delivered. The second is interruption of the service for maintenance. As Avizienis (1978) points out, the speed of modern logic circuitry (pico seconds) has so far outstripped the speed of manually controlled maintenance (hours) that only inclusion of effective system resiliency can return the speed of service restoration to within a few orders of magnitude of the speed of normal operation. The economic benefits to be gained from system resiliency are obvious. Measurements of the field experience of the ESS 1A system (Toy, 1978) assign computer system interruptions to one of the four categories shown in the pie chart of Fig. 2.1(a). A view of the interaction between these categories is shown in Fig. 2.1(b) (Hsiao, 1981). This figure indicates, in a different way than in the first chapter, the hierarchy of levels in a dependable computer system, and the necessity of the efficient design of the request/normal response/exception response/error chain.

To accomplish such design, this operation-interruption alternation must be quantified and measured with respect to the life cycle. This quantification depends upon a set of detailed definitions of the events which characterise the transitions between system operation and interruption. These events are system failure and restoration. System failure occurs after deviation from the system specification. Failure begins with a failure of a system level, producing an incorrect part of a system state. As defined in the previous chapter, this incorrect part of a system state is an error, and a fault is the adjudged proximate cause of an error. A fault is thus an abstraction or model of the effect of a failure at some level of a computer system. The system is restored by performing the system modification indicated by the fault finally adjudged responsible for the error. To complete the restoration, a viable fault-free part of the resilient computer system must be validated, then made available. Such restoration is the survival attribute of the system (Avizienis, 1978), because the return from erroneous to specified behaviour assures the survival of the system activities. These activities continue during valid operation, as long as the integrity of the system data and information and correctness of the system procedures are assured as not being interrupted by the effects of fault

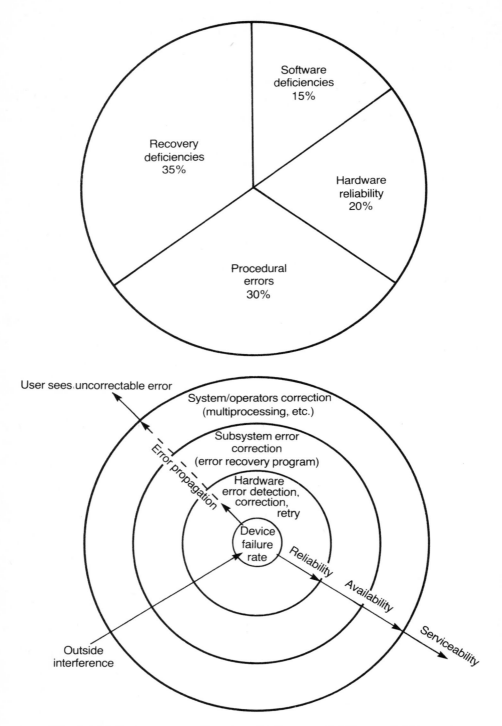

Fig. 2.1 (a) System outage allocation. (b) System reliability, availability and serviceability.

occurrence. During the life of a system, improvements and modifications will be made to many hardware or software system components, because of normal learning and evolution (Isaacson, 1980). This evolution will result in decreased price or increased functionality of these components. To take proper economic advantage of these opportunities, as well as system restoration because of error, resilient systems must be designed so that valid operation can continue while such updates and modifications are made.

In the systems to be considered, faults are expected and normal, and must be tolerated. As shown by Fig. 2.1, faults may be caused by adverse physical phenomena causing a change in physical parameters, by design defects in hardware or programs, by interaction mistakes by humans in repair or in normal operation. The presence of such faults means the existence of latent errors, waiting to cause harm to the system after their activation by the proper conditions. Avizienis (1977) classified faults by their duration – permanent, intermittent, or transient; by their value – determinate or indeterminate; and by their extent – local (independent) or distributed (correlated, multiple). A more detailed discussion of physical faults can be found in Breuer and Friedman (1976) or in Siewiorek and Swarz (1981). Faults caused by humans have the same characteristics, and are much more difficult to study.

This chapter will survey and briefly describe the hardware techniques useful in preventing too frequent system failures and lengthy interruptions due to the occurrence of faults. System initialisation prepares for system operation by validating system integrity after fault removal. The first section will discuss fault avoidance, fault models, techniques for fault detection and removal, and system validation. System operation begins in its optimum mode, but after an error is detected may recover to continue in a full or degraded mode. The second section will discuss the determination of system integrity to permit full operation, and the preparation necessary for successful recovery to degraded operation. The third section will describe error elimination and restoration of a valid operational status.

DESIGN TO AID VALIDATION OF SYSTEM INTEGRITY

No matter how dependable the system, unfortunately faults will occur during system operation. After fault removal, the system must be certified to be fault free before operation is reinitiated. The design techniques to aid this validation of system integrity will be surveyed in this section. Circuits and their faults will be described using a simple model, and their characteristics determined. These characteristics are used to define the basic fault handling methods. Next, the modifications necessitated by VLSI will be considered.

Two representations for computer system circuits are commonly used. Boolean algebra is the basic algebraic representation. Boolean functions will be written as $F(X_1, X_2, \ldots X_n)$ and manipulated according to the rules of Boolean algebra. Ramamoorthy (1967) first formally proposed a structural theory of computer description, using a directed graph as his basic model. The graph model is intuitively appealing, and a natural way to represent a system as a hierarchy of interconnected levels. Partitioning or segmenting the system into a number of smaller subsystems is easy. Moreover, this circuit description leads very naturally to a representation of a combinational logic circuit described by Boolean algebra as an acyclic graph with nodes representing the logic functions and arcs representing interconnecting circuit lines.

In the early 1950s the first specific model connecting faults and errors used such a Boolean graph representation (Eldred, 1959). The fault model was an arc (logic gate input or output) set at 1 (respectively 0) no matter what the Boolean logic value of the line should become when the function was evaluated for a set of input values. Failures of the logic functions at the nodes are represented as equivalent faults on the output arcs. The faults are determinate (values 0 or 1), local (independent), with duration of at least one clock cycle (synchronous machines). This fault model, called the single stuck-at-fault model, is still widely used. Modifications, designed to overcome the effects of VLSI causing its obsolescence, will be described later.

Figure 2.2 shows two Boolean graph circuit models. The simple circuit represents $f = ab + bc$, with functional transformation as shown. The faults a (or c) equal 0 modify the transformation into bc (ab) respectively. These faults are detected by only one of the eight input combinations $(1,1,0)$ and $(0,1,1)$ respectively, while $b = 0$ causes three changes in f's output. Similarly, the AND gate failure which makes lines 3 or 4 equal to 0 causes one output change, while the opposite fault making these lines equal to 1 causes five changes in output value (the output is always 1). The IBM 704/709 add/carry circuit has similar characteristics, which can be easily verified. There are 6 input and 44 circuit faults possible, and 65.9% of these faults are detected by only one of the eight input combinations; 13.6% are detected by three of eight; and 20.5% are detected by four of eight. Because of the carry output, 13 of the faults will cause multiple errors in the computer outputs.

Clearly faults in combinational circuits cause the transforms implemented by these circuits to change slightly, rather than becoming completely erroneous, causing intermittent errors in computer outputs. Errors occur only after the application of the input pattern which causes the fault to affect the output. The error is active only if the result of the functional transformation is used. Experience confirms that faults are discovered at a rate roughly proportional to the number of different input patterns encountered during a period of system operation. Memory and computer controls have similar characteristics.

To determine if faults which can produce errors exist, and locate these faults, tests are used. A test for a circuit is a sequence of patterns for the circuit inputs, together with the corresponding circuit output vectors. A system is tested by applying tests to each circuit (preferably to several

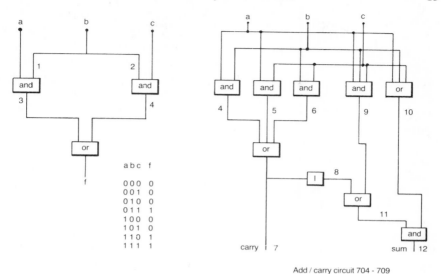

abc f

000 0
001 0
010 0
011 1
100 0
101 0
110 1
111 1

Add / carry circuit 704 - 709

Fig. 2.2 Two Boolean graph circuit models.

circuits simultaneously). Tests can be classified by their input pattern sources as *deterministic* (each pattern tests some specific faults), *exhaustive* (all Boolean combinations are applied to the inputs of each circuit), *random* (the input patterns are generated by a random number generator). As shown by Fig. 2.3, after tests have been determined they must be applied to the circuitry under test and the results gathered and analysed.

The input pattern source may be a file of data (Carter *et al.*, 1964), or a generator for exhaustive testing (McCluskey, 1982), or a feedback shift register (David, 1980). There are three standard methods of applying the tests for validation of system integrity. First, use the computer itself and its normal instructions (self-test); second, augment the computer circuits with maintenance and I/O circuits and use an independent processor to apply the tests, then record and analyse the results; third, augment the computer circuits with maintenance circuitry and use this circuitry to perform independently controlled built-in-self-test. Test treatment may be comparison with either the computed results, or the response of an adjudged good unit, or a compacted datum called a signature. Signatures may be produced by counting methods (Fujiwara and Kinoshita, 1978), or by the

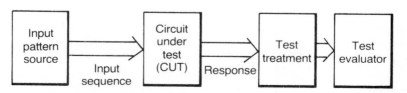

Fig. 2.3 General testing scheme.

content of a LFSR (Benowitz, 1975). The test evaluation depends upon the goal of system testing. The current goal, validation that a system is ready to operate, uses two types of tests. The first, detection, is designed to determine if a fault exists; its output simply is YES or NO. The second, diagnostic, has as output, for each fault f_i covered, a list of m_i replaceable units, one of which is adjudged to contain the failed component modelled by the fault. Detection test effectiveness is measured by the coverage, which is the percentage of possible faults (in the fault model) which the test detects. Diagnostic test effectiveness is measured by the coverage and by the diagnostic resolution, which is the average value of the m_i.

Eldred (1959) generated his tests by hand, then applied them using a self-test routine. The classical work on devising methods to generate deterministic test patterns automatically was done by Armstrong (1966) and Roth (1966) for single stuck-at faults. In both methods a fault was assumed to exist on an input or the output of a logic element represented by a node in the graph. Node failures result in the output being stuck-at a value. In Roth's notation, D stands for the value which is 1 in the good circuit and 0 in the bad; $\bar{D}$ stands for the opposite values. Using Fig. 2.2, find a test for the AND gate with output 6 stuck-at-0. To test for an erroneous node value of 0, the value of line 6 must be represented by a D. To show the fault, line 6 must be 1 in the correct circuit, so the node inputs b and c must both be 1. Propagate $b = c = 1$ to the circuit inputs and make all implications. These determine the value of line 10 to be 1. Both methods follow these techniques, determine the line values which produce the appropriate node output, and propagate these values back to the circuit inputs to determine part of the input pattern for the test. Next, the D logic value determined by the fault must propagate to a circuit output so it can be observed.

Armstrong's method propagates the D logic value down a single path to the output, using Boolean logic equations with D ($\bar{D}$) as a variable. In the example, the D will not be propagated through the OR gate unless lines 4 and 5 are 0. Propagating these values backward shows that line a must be 0. Now the value D appears on the output 7, and all necessary values for the test pattern to be applied to the circuit inputs have been determined. Roth's method propagates a D through the OR gate and another D through the inverter (line 8), since line 6 fans out to both nodes. The inverter changes the D to a $\bar{D}$, which propagates to output 12. Thus, in fact, both circuit outputs would be erroneous. The test pattern found is $a = 0, b = c = 1$. By examination of the circuit, it is easily seen that this pattern also detects the single faults line 8 s-a-1, line 9 s-a-1, line 11 s-a-1, and the a input to the AND gate with output 9 s-a-1. Such a process is called *logic fault simulation*, and is used to reduce the number of test patterns which must be used to form a test (Roth *et al*, 1967a). Armstrong's method is efficient, but it does not always succeed (Schneider, 1967). Roth divided his algorithm into two parts: D-DRIVE, propagate Ds down all lines possible, then determine what choices of variable values will let some

*D*s proceed; and CONSISTENCY, make the implications from this choice. Continue alternating the two steps. If a test exists for a stuck line, the algorithm will find it eventually. The fault analysis of a circuit is simplified, and the number of patterns necessary for a test is reduced, if the faults whose effect on the circuit is the same are grouped into classes of indistinguishable faults (Schertz and Metze, 1972; McCluskey and Clegg, 1971).

Using the algebraic model, let F be a Boolean function with inputs X_1, X_2, ..., X_n, primary outputs $f_1, f_2, \ldots, f_m$. Let G be an internal net with a single input g. Express G as a function of the X_i, and the f_j as functions $f_j = F_j(g, X_1, \ldots, X_n)$. The problem of test generation for g s-a-v can be stated as one of solving the two following sets of Boolean equations (Sellers *et al.*, 1968a; XOR stands for exclusive or):

$$G(X_1, \ldots, X_n) = \bar{v} \tag{1}$$

$$F_j(1, X_1, \ldots, X_n) \text{ XOR } F_j(0, X_1, \ldots, X_n) = 1 \tag{2}$$

for at least one j, $i \le j \le m$ and $X_i = 0$ or $X_i = 1$ for $1 \le i \le n$. The search for a test pattern is thus a search of the n dimensional 0–1 space defined by the variables $X_i (1 \le i \le n)$ for points which satisfy the above set of equations (Goel, 1980a). Generally the search results in finding a k-dimensional space ($k \le n$) such that all points in the subspace will satisfy these equations. This algorithm is complete and the corresponding program is more efficient than Roth's. Ibarra and Sahni proved in 1975 that such algorithms are NP-complete.

To apply circuit tests and analyse the results, self-test programs were introduced with the ENIAC. Scola (1972) published a bibliography containing over 1000 references to articles describing such routines. However, the necessary information is often not accessible to direct program control, the addressing resolution problem. The interval between points at which the system status can be determined is a complete instruction time, the timing resolution problem (Carter *et al.*, 1964). Thus the testability and diagnosability of a circuit network depend upon its observability, i.e. the amount of information on its internal states which can be transmitted to its primary output points, and its controllability, i.e. the extent to which these internal conditions can be controlled by applying signals to the primary inputs of the network (Ball and Hardie, 1969). The observability and controllability of a network may be improved by adding extra circuitry. Hayes (1974) proved that if enough extra control logic is added to a network N, the resulting network N* requires only five tests to detect all single and multiple faults. Automated techniques to balance testability and the amount of extra logic were developed by Chang and Heimbigner (1974) Microprograms, called from self-test routines (Carter *et al.*, 1964) can be designed to have control of all or most of the unit latches (Hackl and Shirk, 1965). Since one unit cycle corresponds to a micro-instruction execution, the state status resolution problem is solved. Access to sufficient data is possible by adding a small amount of circuitry. However, for both techniques, running on the same computer is a serious disadvantage when an error has occurred.

Instead of a CE console, Hitt (1971) introduced a universal system service adapter which allowed external equipment to be used to test the IBM S/370-155. Evenson and Troy (1973), Chang *et al.* (1973) and Fox (1975) describe the maintenance units which assist in performing system initialisation, testing and diagnosis, and real-time status observation. These are some of the tasks now performed by units variously called maintenance processors (Liu, 1984), processor controllers (Reilly *et al.*, 1982), monitor computers (Avizienis, 1981) and watchdog processors (Lu, 1982).

Since the 1960s, the following practical difficulties have hindered the development of test generation routines. First, a logic circuit is logically redundant if a gate is not necessary for the logical functioning of the circuit; obviously the effects of the failure of such a gate can not be simply determined. Unfortunately circuit redundancy is sometimes necessary to eliminate races and hazards (Eichelberger, 1965). Friedman (1967) showed that a set of test patterns generated using the single stuck fault assumption detected all detectable faults for circuits whose design is redundant so that races and hazards are not present by Eichelberger's criteria. Because of necessary redundancy or latency, faults may be present on more than one line. Call a fault involving *m* lines a multiple fault of multiplicity *m*. Because of the increased density of logic in VLSI chips, to ensure satisfactory reliability these chips should have tests which cover many multiple faults as well as single faults. Some statistical studies (Goldstein, 1977) have shown that in a LSI chip, multiple faults of sizes at least up to 6 must be tested to ensure its pragmatic reliability. Finding tests for multiple faults is much more difficult than finding tests for single faults, but some methods exist (Hayes, 1971; Bossen and Hong, 1971). However, the practical experience of the last 10–15 years is that a test set designed to detect only single stuck faults has usually detected most multiple stuck faults as well. In 1980, Agarwal presented a theory which provided quantitative greatest lower bounds on the multiple fault coverage capability of single fault detection test sets for combinational networks. His theory predicts generally good coverage except for some circuits with reconvergent internal fanout, the major stumbling block for the simple generation of tests.

The second classical problem is generating tests for sequential circuits. The technique usually used involves cutting the feedback loop lines, replacing the sequential circuit by an iterative circuit, and generating tests step by step through this iterative circuit, beginning with the first copy and propagating results, replacing a time sequence by a space sequence (Putzolu and Roth, 1971). Because this model is inadequate, the generated patterns may not be test patterns, and in addition they may introduce races and hazards in the circuits. Simulation is used to determine if a good test pattern has been generated, using a three valued simulator like Eichelberger's (1965). Other simulation routines go to even greater lengths to model the circuit and the effects of circuit timing (Syzgenda, 1972). The books by Breuer and Friedman (1976, 1978) treat such methods very well and, with the Proceedings of the IEEE Test Conferences, provide other references.

Because of the difficulty and cost of generating tests, and the time necessary for computer system maintenance, systems began to be designed with aids for testing and diagnosing their circuits. The IBM System/360 was designed so that test patterns needed to be generated only for combinational circuits (Carter *et al.*, 1964). For LSI, Williams and Angell (1973) suggested that the latches on a chip be connected as a shift register as well as normally. The shift registers can be easily tested, and only two extra inputs per chip are needed (in general). In the IBM system called Level Sensitive Scan Design (Eichelberger and Williams, 1977) the shift registers and sequential logic structures are designed so that their correct operation is not dependent on signal rise and fall time or on circuit or wire delay. However, as VLSI circuits become larger, the cost of generating and applying combinational circuit tests becomes more important. Goel (1980b) showed that if G is the number of gates in a circuit, the cost for test pattern generation for combinational circuits grows as G^2, and the cost for fault simulation grows at a rate between G^2 and G^3, depending upon the method used. Thus, at best, the minimum test pattern generation costs grow as G^2. Most of this time is spent in determining tests for a relatively few circuits which are difficult to test. In addition, the time for testing logic using deterministic tests grows as G^2.

Techniques to add hardware to enhance testability (Grason, 1979; Goldstein, 1979, 1980) analyse the interconnection paths of the circuit to evaluate measures of testability and to determine where modified circuit design or added hardware might be best used to enhance testability. Savir (1983) showed that the controllability of a fault g ($\bar{g}$) is the probability that an input pattern picked at random will set the value of the fault to $\bar{g}$ (g). He proved the observability of a fault g to be the probability that an input pattern picked at random will propagate the effect of the fault to a primary output. By solving the Boolean algebraic equations (1) and (2) he proved that the tests to detect a given fault lie in the intersection of the set of vectors that control the fault and the set of vectors that allow the fault to be observed. These measurements improve the previous techniques by taking reconvergent fanout into account.

For VLSI circuits, faults requiring a different model occur frequently (Wadsack, 1978); the physical fault of two wires shorted together, which depends upon the design process and the circuit layout, is the prevalent fault mode. Tests may not only not detect these faults, but such faults may affect the detection of stuck faults. Depending upon the circuit technology, shorts act as logical AND or logical OR; the circuit function is thus changed from $f(a,b,...)$ to $g(a,c,...)$. Another example (Davidson, 1982) is the current switching problem which may occur when more than a specified number of outputs simultaneously change value, due to an input change.

Timoc (Timoc *et al.*, 1983) identified and modelled the logical behaviour of some of the most frequent failures in bipolar and MOS technologies. They defined the prevalent failures in bipolar technology to be: open connections, shorts, and piped transistors with excessive collector-to-emitter leakage current. The open connector was modelled as a single stuck fault, the short as a logical AND fault, and the piped input transistor as a multiple stuck fault. Test patterns can be generated, but under the multiple stuck fault assumption. Some other failures in MOS technology are much more complicated (Banerjee, 1983; El-ziq, 1983). Algorithms which would permit efficient test generation are not available. An effective method for generating test patterns for faults in FET circuits has been developed (Roth *et al.*, 1984) by following the methods used in defining the Boolean fault model. A function-preserving, failure-preserving transformation of a FET switching network into a Boolean graph is defined. The Boolean graph is generated in linear time, and the graph has the same failure and logic function as the original switching network. Tests for stuck faults can be generated for this network, and it is easily proved that these are tests for shorts and opens in the original switching network.

In addition, VLSI has caused changes in circuit design verification. Formerly, designers would design a computer, build it, debug it, then correct the remaining errors on the testfloor (Monachino, 1982). With VLSI, the engineer is dependent on a manufacturing entity for building the customised chips, chip mounts or modules, and boards, and for reworking these items during the building and testing phases. With these dependencies, the initial hardware delivery of a module design was estimated to take a minimum of six months. An average of thirty working days was estimated for reworking each design change. Since thousands of changes are likely in a large project, a design could be obsolete by the time it was ready for shipment. Roth (1977) proposed a hardware verification system to overcome such difficulties. Monachino used and extended this idea so that the logic functionality of the design could be verified, the timing constraints could be checked, and the progress of the design verification status could be monitored to select a time to commit the design to hardware. Furthermore, the status of the system validity can be determined as engineering changes, function enhancements and feature additions change the original design.

Following Roth, Smith *et al.* (1982) in Boolean comparison use two representations of the logic design which purportedly describe equivalent sequential machines with the same state assignments. A one-to-one correspondence is defined between the latches, the primary inputs, and the primary outputs of the two representations. The Boolean comparison programs then determine whether or not the functions driving each corresponding pair of latches or outputs in the two representations are Boolean equivalent. If this equivalence is satisfied, it follows that the operating sequences of the two machines described by the representations are identical, if the timing sequence is correct. If the system uses a clocked design, and timing constraints are checked by a timing analysis program (Hitchcock *et al.*, 1982), assurance can be given that the functions driving each latch determine the next state behaviour with correct timing. This completes the proof that if both machines are placed in corresponding initial states and corresponding input patterns are applied at each clock interval, their operating sequences are identical, and their outputs agree at each clock interval. As an example, for the IBM 3081, Boolean comparison is performed between detailed hardware logic diagrams of the machine and the hardware logic representation compiled from a hardware description language represented by hardware flowcharts which describe the same machine. These flowcharts describe the operation of the hardware at each clock interval by describing the logical behaviour of the latches and outputs in terms of the input and latch values available at each clock interval. For speed and efficiency, the detailed implementation of the physically realised machine is normally quite different from the compiled form of the intervening combinational logic.

Clearly the correctness of the flowchart representation must be established by other techniques, such as simulation or hardware implementation. To improve the speed of specification validation, special purpose programmable highly parallel hardware machines have been constructed (Pfister, 1982; Abramovici, 1982). For example, the Yorktown simulation engine is a special purpose, highly parallel programmable machine for the gate level simulation of logic. It can simulate up to one million gates at a speed of over two billion gate simulations per second; it is estimated that the IBM 3081 processor is simulated at the rate of 1000 instructions per second. Monachino (1982) states that verifying the flowchart correctness by simulation was more efficient than expected. The number of design errors discovered early in the design was proportional to the number of test cases that were developed and the amount of computer time spent on running the verification package. Moreover, logic simulation, though cumbersome at times, was less expensive than physical hardware debugging.

The considerable expenses of deterministic test generation, and concomitant storage of test inputs and test outputs, prompted a search for alternatives. Rault (1971) proposed *random testing*. The principle of random testing is as follows: a random input sequence is applied simultaneously to both a circuit under test and a reference circuit. The outputs are compared. The input patterns are generated by hardware, usually using a linear feedback shift register (LFSR). More inclusive classes of patterns may be generated using a store and generate test generator (see Abrulhamid, 1983). Rault gave an analysis of this testing procedure, establishing an heuristic relationship between test length and a measure of test quality. This is a difficult problem, as Shedletsky (1977) showed when he proved that if stuck-at faults are considered then determining accurate measures of test quality is a problem that is as difficult as test generation. David (1976) defined the result of a test to be right if it indicates that a fault exists when the circuit is faulty. He then proved that the probability that random testing is right is not the probability of having tested every fault, but the probability of having tested the fault which is most difficult to detect. If p_d is the detection probability of the fault most difficult to detect, and N is the length of the random test, and e_i the escape probability, then $N = \lceil (\ln e_i) \, / \, \ln(1 - p_d) \rceil$ (Bardell (1983). Unfortunately, determining p_d or a good approximation to it is very difficult. Savir (1984) gave an alternate specification. Given a combinational circuit that has to be tested with N random patterns, either prove that $100-\varepsilon$ percent of the population's single stuck-faults would be detected with probability $1-\delta$ or modify the logic to satisfy this. Typically, we would like to have $\varepsilon \leq 2$, $\delta \leq 0.001$. To do this, identify all the random pattern-resistant faults, namely those faults whose detection probability falls below a given threshold. Then increase the observability of those 'hard' faults. The threshold value is determined by the affordable test time and is roughly 10^{-6} for a random pattern test of ten million patterns. Savir showed that there is a relationship between signal probability (Parker, 1975) and detection probability, and uses a cutting algorithm to compute a lower bound of the detection probability. If this lower bound is larger than the threshold it may be marked off as an 'easy' fault. Otherwise it will be marked as a 'hard' fault, whose detection probability would have to be upgraded. The random testing technique seems efficient for testing sequential circuits, but similar bounds have not been determined.

Using reference circuits, which may fail, for testing is somewhat risky. An alternative is to record the correct outputs for each test pattern and compare them with the outputs for the circuit under test. This raises many of the same problems of test simulation and storage that random testing tries to avoid. Thus the idea of compressing the output data and comparing this single datum with the correct answer was developed (Benowitz, 1975). This data was popularised under the name *signature testing* by Frohwerk (1977), and has been analysed by many people (David, 1984; Bardell, 1983). Signature testing methods will be seen to have several advantages, but they run the risk that masking will occur. Masking is said to occur if a faulty circuit and a good circuit behave differently during testing, but the signatures are identical. Carter (1982) proves that if the generated input patterns are sufficiently random, according to a mathematical definition, then the probability that error masking will occur is small for reasonably large modified feedback shift registers.

Another technique for test pattern generation is *exhaustive testing* (McCluskey, 1982). A complete test set for a n-input combinational network can be obtained by applying all 2^n Boolean logic combinations to the circuit inputs. Most combinational networks have multiple outputs, and usually each of the outputs depends upon only some of the inputs. Methods for generating such sets of inputs are given by McCluskey (1982) and Tang (1984). Applying such a test may require too much time, but no test analysis is needed other than determining the correct output.

As discussed earlier, processor controllers are used to apply, observe, and analyse detection and diagnostic tests. For efficient test application, the processor controllers for such systems must be able to partition and control the clocks for the main system (Reilly *et al.*, 1982), so the unaffected processor units can continue operation. Since for any VLSI scan design system the tests must be applied by shift registers, this results in the circuits being tested operating at speeds well below those specified for them when the tests are externally applied. Unfortunately, any of numerous kinds of random manufacturing or wear-out defects, although allowing correct d.c. operation, can cause a device to perform at a speed below that specified for it. There are two current solutions: extend test generation algorithms and programs to cover such faults (Hsieh, 1977) or add circuitry to the LSI or VLSI chip so that the chip can test itself at full a.c. speed without recourse to external logic signals (Konemann, 1979). Adding circuitry for independently controlled self-test is called *built-in self-test* (BIST) and is described by Bardell (1983). BIST often uses random testing techniques for input pattern generation and output data compression. A BIST scheme using signature analysis with a 16-bit LFSR has been developed for the MC6804P2 Motorola microprocessor. The signature is updated on a cycle-by-cycle basis during the execution of a test program stored in an on-chip ROM. An additional ROM verify mode also utilises the same circuitry to test both the storage containing the customer program and the ROM containing the test. Test pins are provided so that the BIST can be used for both logic and parametric testing. The coverage for the BIST and ROM test is approximately 96% of the total single stuck-at faults.

Classical fault detection methods are not efficient for generating tests for many VLSI circuits such as PLAs, memories, and microprocessors which contain a very large number of gates, flip-flops and interconnections and which therefore require an enormous amount of computation to generate complete test sets. In addition, since a self-contained unit is often purchased, the required gate and flip-flop level description is usually not available to microprocessor test designers working in a user environment. Efficient methods have been devised for testing such self-contained units and these will now be described.

PLAs are being increasingly used as a cost effective way to use VLSI (Logue *et al.* 1975). Converting a PLA to an equivalent logic model and then applying standard test pattern generation techniques is inadequate since the model does not represent the PLA's defects. A typical PLA structure has three kinds of fault behaviour: the usual *s-a-v*; shorts between neighbouring lines; or cross-point defects (missing or excess devices on the cross points of a search or read array). Ostapko and Hong (1980) and Fujiwara and Kinoshita (1980) show how to add a small amount of circuitry so that a conventional PLA is transformed into an easily testable PLA which can be thoroughly tested by a fixed test set which is independent of the logic function implemented in the PLA personality. These augmented PLAs have the following features: (a) for a PLA with n inputs, m columns (product terms) and k outputs, there exists a 'universal' test set such that the test patterns and responses do not depend on the function of the PLA but depend only on the size of the PLA (the values n, m, and k); (b) the number of tests is of order $m + n$. Universal test sets are derived which detect single and multiple stuck faults and cross-point faults in these augmented PLAs. For multi-chip systems, the ability to broadcast a uniform test to all chips should considerably simplify the system testing problem. Agarwal (1980) showed that if all single contact faults in a PLA are tested, then 98% of all multiple contact faults of size 8 or less are covered. Min (1984) gave design rules which allow a PLA to be designed for which it is easy to generate a test set which detects all stuck-at faults, bridging faults, missing/extra cross-point defects, and any combination of these.

Efficient algorithms are necessary for testing semiconductor RAMs and the usual stuck-at theory has been shown to be inadequate. A memory can be defined to be functional if it is possible to change every cell from a 0 to 1 and conversely, and to read every cell correctly, independently of the state of the remaining cells. Breuer and Friedman (1976) list the tests usually used, *walking ones* and *GALPAT*, which are quite comprehensive but of complexity $o(n^2)$.

Nair, Thatte, and Abraham (1978), have devised a new test of complexity $o(n)$, extending the usual techniques. The errors considered are produced by the combinations of the following faults: one or more cells *s-a-v*, incorrect decoder logic, read or write logic *s-a-v*, or one or more pairs of cells coupled. A cell is coupled to another when a transition of values in that cell causes a transition of values in the other. They show that these faults include the usually tested memory faults. There are three test requirements. The first condition is that each cell must undergo a 0–1 and a 1–0 transition, and must be read after each transition before undergoing any subsequent forced transitions. A forced transition of a cell is initiated by the testing algorithm writing into the cell. The second condition is that for every pair of cells (i,j), cell i must be read after cell j makes a forced transition and before cells i and j make any further forced transitions, in all four possible cases. Finally, for every cell triple (i,j,k), if the test makes a transition in cell j from y to $-y$ after cell i makes a transition from x to $-x$ and before cell k in state z is read, then the test must possess another sequence where either (a) cell k in state z is read after an x to $-x$ transition in cell i and before a y to $-y$ transition in cell j and before an x to $-x$ transition in cell i. They prove that this set of conditions is necessary and and sufficient for a test to detect all faults in their fault model, and give an algorithm which can be implemented by a program of complexity $o(n)$.

Nair (1979) later showed how to improve slightly an efficient memory test (Knaizak, 1977) so that a test of length $13n/3$ will detect all multiple stuck-at faults in a memory with n words, if the address decoder has a special design; otherwise a test of length $5n-2$ is needed. You and Hayes (1984) have designed a self-testing dynamic RAM chip to achieve a reduction in testing time. Self-testing is achieved through the introduction of a special shift operation to generate neighbourhood data patterns and on-chip logic to generate test sequences. The use of identical cell partitions in the self-testing RAM allows test response verification to be implemented by comparing the responses of partitions. Kinoshita and Saluja (1984) have developed simple circuitry for a self-contained test circuit to test a random access memory for pattern sensitive and weight sensitive faults in neighbourhoods of a base cell.

To test a microprocessor, Thatte and Abraham (1980) used a graph model to introduce equivalent registers with respect to information transfer. There exists a directed edge from node A to node B if and only if there exists an instruction which causes transformation of data or information from node A to node B. Instructions are represented by a set of functions such as (i) register decoding, (ii) data transfer paths, (iii) data manipulation functions, and (iv) instruction sequencing. A functional fault model is then developed for each of these functions, and tests are generated to detect all the faults in the fault model. While this method can be used to generate efficient tests for faults in the relatively simple functions such as the register decoding and data transfer paths, it fails to provide a systematic way to generate tests for faults in the more complex instruction sequencing function. In Brahme and Abraham (1984) a more detailed view of the instruction execution process is developed by classifying the faults into three categories. Tests are generated to detect faults in each of these three categories. The fault model is general and can be used for any microprocessor and the process of test generation can be easily automated.

Thevenode-Fosse (1981, 1983) developed random tests for a microprocessor. The basic test principle was to execute random instructions on random data. When the microprocessor reads data, it finds a random pattern. When n cycles are completed, a new instruction is randomly drawn and the process is repeated. Experiments have been run by Fedi and David (1984) with different sets of M6800 microprocessors supplied by different French companies. From a field of 3000 microprocessors, already tested for faulty circuits by a French specialised company, 60 were selected for further testing, by random testing. The original testing, performed with a Fairchild tester using a deterministic sequence of 1024 instructions, found that, of these 60 selected, 30 were 'good' and 30 were 'bad'. Using random testing, the following results were found: (1) of the original 30 'bad' circuits, the testing confirmed all to be faulty using a random test of less than 25 000 instructions; (2) of the original 30 'good' circuits, the testing found, to the contrary, that all were faulty according to a random test of less than 80 000 instructions (equivalent to 0.3 s approximately).

DESIGN TO OVERCOME THE EFFECTS OF ANTICIPATED FAULTS

The traditional approaches for achieving reliable systems are fault avoidance and fault tolerance. Fault avoidance attempts to assure reliability by a prior elimination of the causes of faults. The principal fault avoidance technique is to develop reliable modules, then ensure that these modules are fault free. Fault tolerance attempts to overcome the effects of faults. Faults are expected to occur, but their effects are counteracted by the protective action of additional components or programs which provide alternative independent methods for valid computation. The key to successful design of protective redundancy is the systematic and balanced selection of fault tolerance techniques which complement and reinforce the best selection of fault avoidance techniques. In designing to counteract the effects of faults, we are changing from planning a static machine structure to considering the dynamic structure of a running computer: we must understand the effect of errors and how (or whether) the system tolerates the associated changes. This is the basic problem of redundancy management, the most important aspect of fault tolerance.

The errors resulting from faults are counteracted by recovery, defined as the continuation of system operation with data integrity after an error occurs. The basic hardware design specification for dynamic recovery requires the following. All hardware errors should be detected, contamination of information restricted, and the existence of the errors signalled. Critical status information must be reconstructed from saved syndromes for damage assessments; the faults causing the error located; and the severity of the damage determined. Intermittent faults must be handled so as to preserve the system redundancy, usually by a system timeout followed by hardware retry or forward error recovery. If this is unsuccessful, the system is reconfigured, if possible, and program operation is restarted from previously saved valid data, while on-line repair proceeds. If this is not possible the system must be interrupted for maintenance and then validated.

In this section we shall consider methods for designing systems so that the integrity of their information is preserved during normal operation, and preparation is made to mitigate the inevitable appearance of errors. In order to preserve system integrity, error occurrence must be detected. Error detection is implemented by using assertions which indicate the correct functioning of the system by monitoring the functioning of subsystems. The choice of assertions depends upon the specifications of the subsystem whose operation is being monitored, the causal relationship assumed to hold between faults and errors, and the assumed probability of such faults and errors occurring in a period of time. Several such causal relationships have been assumed between faults and errors. The oldest is the temporal theory: estimate the time needed for process completion, and stop the process if the time is exceeded. This assumes some fault has caused some error, but gives no aid in finding either. This was followed by the functional theory: examine the function or algorithm, then determine the error(s) in the function output caused by the presence of various types of faults. Next came the structural theory: determine the effect of faults on the directly affected part of the system structure, and determine the resulting errors. Then modify the system structure so that such faults can be detected (usually encode part of the original structure). The most recent theory states that no relationship will be assumed between faults and errors (Lee *et al.*, 1981). In this case some system outputs must be tested to show that the system functioning is valid. Implicit in many designs is the assumption that only n faults or m errors will occur at a given time, not that this is the most likely situation. Planning only for the most likely situation is known as the n fault trap, and has embarrassing (catastrophic) consequences (Hopkins, 1975). The possibilities of correlated faults, undetected latent faults, the inadequacy of the fault model because of environment or fidelity of modelling have all been discussed before.

Hardware redundancy is divided into two types, static and dynamic, based upon the terminal activity of the redundant modules. Both techniques frequently explicitly or implicitly use coding to construct the assertion functions for the error monitoring circuits, so coding will be briefly surveyed.

The elements in the codes surveyed in this chapter are n-dimensional vectors over an integral domain, as these are the type most frequently used in computers. For more complete surveys see Chen and Hsiao, 1984; Langdon, 1984. First consider codes which use digits from a finite field of characteristic two with two elements. The codes consist of sets of n digit words, with k information and r check digits. The Hamming distance between two words is defined to be the number of positions in which the words differ (Hamming, 1950). Thus, a single error results in a Hamming distance 1 between a transmitted and a received word. If a code is used only for error detection and must detect all patterns of $d-1$ or fewer errors, it is necessary and sufficient for the minimum Hamming distance between code words to be d. If the minimum distance is d, no pattern of $d-1$ errors can change one code word into another. If the minimum distance is $d-1$ or less, there exists some pair of words at distance less than d apart, and a pattern of fewer than d errors which will carry one into the other. It is possible to decode in such a way as to correct all patterns of t or fewer errors if and only if the minimum distance is at least $2t + 1$, since after t errors the closest code word is the original word. Finally, if it is desired to correct t errors and detect d errors ($d>t$) then the minimum distance between code words is $2t + d + 1$.

Following Peterson and Weldon (1972), any set of basis vectors for such a linear block code V can be considered as the rows of a matrix G, called a generator matrix of V. A vector is a code vector if and only if it is a linear combination of the rows of G. If code vectors v have k information digits and r check digits, then $G = (I_k P_{kr})$, where I is a k by k identity matrix and P is a k by r matrix. If a vector u has k information digits $a_1,..., a_k$, then

$v = uG = u(I_kP_{kr}) = (u, c_1,..., c_r)$, written (u,c) is a code vector if and only if $(u,c) (P'_{kr}I_r)' = 0$, where P'_{kr} is the transpose of P_{kr} , I_r is the r by r identity matrix, and 0 stands for the r dimensional 0 vector. The matrix $H = (P'_{kr}I_r)$ is called the parity check matrix.

If there are w erroneous digits in a word v_e, then the digits in these positions can be represented by $v_j + e_j$, where j ranges over the indices of the w erroneous digits. The e_j may independently assume any digit value. Writing the erroneous word v_e as $v + e$, where e stands for the vector with e_j in the erroneous positions and 0 elsewhere, $v_eH = vH + eHj = eH = s$ where s is the r dimensional vector called the syndrome vector. It is clear that the code has Hamming distance d if and only if all r by d submatrices of H have rank d. For correction, let y represent the vector with t digits $x_1,..., x_t$ in any t positions, and 0s elsewhere. Correction can occur if and only if there is a vector y such that the equation $yH' = s$ has a solution or $(v_e + y)H' = 0$. This equation has a solution if and only if the submatrix A of H' determined by the indices of y has the same rank as (A,s). For t error correction and d error detection, it must be shown that if d errors occur, then the resulting syndrome is such that any submatrix with t columns will have rank less than that submatrix augmented by the syndrome.

The simplest error detection code is parity. The parity check matrix is $(1,..., 1)$. Clearly any submatrix has rank 1, so any single error is detected. Over the field of characteristic two with two elements, errors affecting an odd number of bits are detected, and all errors affecting an even number are missed. Over any other integral domain, all single erroneous characters are detected, and the probability of detecting multiple errors is nonzero. Over other fields of characteristic two, the check digit is usually called the cyclic redundancy check digit, and the process is referred to as CRC; sometimes the check digit is called the signature by analogy with the testing procedure. For integers, the check digit is called a check sum, and overflow must be handled correctly. The original Single Error Correcting (SEC) code was devised by Hamming (1950) for vectors whose elements are in the field of characteristic two with two elements. If a code of length n greater than or equal to $2^{(j-1)}$ and less than 2^j is desired, the code will have j check bits and $(n-j)$ information bits. In the parity check matrix, each column corresponding to a check bit must represent a power of 2, and each other column must be chosen to have at least two nonzero bits and to represent a distinct number between 2 and $2^j - 1$. Clearly the syndrome for any single error will be one of the columns, so the submatrix represented by this column has the property that the rank of this submatrix is equal to the rank of the augmented submatrix. This submatrix is unique because any other column will be different from the syndrome, so the augmented matrix will have rank 2. A double error will be detected if the sum of the two columns is different from any column in the original matrix, otherwise a miscorrection will occur. Hamming also devised a Single Error Correcting/Double Error Detecting (SEC/DED) code by adding another bit to every column of the parity check matrix and adding one more check bit. Hsiao

(1970) devised an improved parity check matrix by using a selection of columns with each column having an odd number of bits. A double error results in an even number of bits in the syndrome, and so is detected. Implementations of codes using such parity check matrices use the least decoding and encoding circuitry.

Codes were devised and analysed originally to detect with certainty a specific class of errors. However, in addition to a particular class of errors, such codes detect some elements of other classes of errors. For example, the popular SEC/DED code for 64 data bits is a SEC/DED code for any data between 57 and 120 bits long. The shortened code for 64 bits will detect additional classes of errors depending upon the generator matrix and the decoder design, and will detect elements from other classes (triple errors for example) with a probability which can be calculated. Since (when these codes are used in computers) the occurrence of faults and their resulting error patterns is a probabilistic process, estimating both the certain and probabilistic detection of errors allows the fault coverage of a code to be estimated more accurately for a given physical situation. Such estimations can be used to tailor codes and implementations to fit specific physical situations. Once again the simplest example is checking byte parity in registers. As was seen, all single bit errors will be detected. However, in addition to bit storage, the clock circuits, gating circuits, power distribution circuits, and chip pads may fail. Bossen and Hsiao (1982) show that for two or more bytes controlled by the same clock, gating and power distributions, a considerably higher probability of error detection is obtained if the bits are interleaved in distinct registers. Reliable memories are usually built so that only one bit in a word is read from a chip. The chip contains the addressing and storage logic, but often the power and other supporting modules at the card level serve b chips. Thus errors in these support modules will cause error patterns over b bits. Chen and Hsiao (1984) show that the generating matrices for the SEC/DED code mentioned earlier can be reorganised to detect such errors. The resulting code is called SEC/DED/DbED, where DbED indicates error detection for any set of errors in one byte, for byte width 3 or 4.

Coding for high speed channels presents difficult problems because of intersymbol interference, literally the interference of adjacent 1s or adjacent 0s (Franaszek, 1972). In transmission channels there is an analogous problem called *spectral shaping*. In addition the internal clock of the system is disrupted by such sequences. Constrained coding places a restriction on the maximum and minimum number of 0s which can occur between consecutive 1s. These codes require at least d but no more than k 0s between consecutive 1s. Thus for magnetic recording, the binary information to be saved begins as a data sequence of 1s and 0s. This sequence undergoes a second-level encoding process based on a finite state description, taking into account the code, the incoming bit stream, and neighbouring segments of information. The (2,7) code is used very successfully in the IBM high capacity disk drives.

The error statistics of some recently developed VLSI circuits show that errors are unidirectional, i.e. both 1→0 and 0→1 are possible in data, but in any particular word all errors are of the same type (Cook, 1973; Anderson, 1973). Berger codes and constant weight k-out-of-n codes detect such errors. In Berger codes (Berger, 1961) the information and check bits are separated, so encoding/decoding and data manipulation can be done in parallel, while in constant weight codes the information and check bits are not separated, so parallel operations are not possible. The k check bits for the $n-k$ bits of a Berger code are formed by taking the binary number corresponding to the number of 1s in the information bits and forming the complement of each bit. This code detects all unidirectional errors, all single errors, and a large proportion of multiple errors of any type. These codes have recently been generalised by Bose and Lin (1984).

In static hardware redundancy the effect of a fault is masked instantaneously by permanently connected and concurrently operating circuits, and codes are used implicitly. The level at which replication occurs has ranged from individual circuit components to entire processing systems, and the number of replicated elements from two to four, although n-way redundancy has been theoretically discussed. Clearly, two-way redundancy (duplication and comparison or pairing) can only detect the presence of errors, and processing can continue only with sequential (program) aid (see Ramamoorthy and Han (1975) for a basic survey). Similarly, Hamming 1 bit SED, called two-rail logic, has been used. A logic one is encoded as the twin signals 1 0, a logic 0 becomes 0 1, and the signals 0 0 and 1 1 represent errors. Each line in the original design is replaced by two lines and the original logic by new logic. AND gates are replaced by an AND gate and an OR gate, the dual applies for OR gates, and NOT becomes line interchange (the main advantage of this method). For some applications this is preferable to ordinary duplication and the S/360 Model 40 ALU was built using this code.

von Neumann (1956) developed and analysed a scheme employing triplication of logic elements with majority voting at selected interfaces to perform correction, called *triple modular redundancy* (TMR, equivalent to a 1 bit Hamming SEC). He proved that if the voters are sufficiently more reliable than the logic elements, and are properly placed, then arbitrarily high reliability can be obtained from unreliable components. Replication of relays, introduced by Moore and Shannon (1956) was improved to quadded logic by Tryone (1962). Quadded logic corrects single errors in basic circuit elements. Schwab and Yau (1983) have studied an algebraic model of fault-masking logic circuits, assuming bit-wise logical operations and a separate single-valued coding system. Methods of constructing such circuits, their error-propagating and error-correcting properties, capabilities and limitations are analysed. When TMR is used at the unit level, as in the Saturn V Launch Vehicle, the problems of voter design and placement (Anderson and Randell, 1979), and unit testing and validation must be considered. In the Saturn V Launch Vehicle, the configuration used was called TMR/Simplex (Dickinson *et al.*, 1964). In this case, in addition to voting, each pair of lines used as inputs to the voters was compared. This allowed testing each module, so it could be shown that before launch all modules were working. If one module were consistently in error, it and another module would be disconnected and the remaining module used as long as possible. This improved the expected reliability. When any voting scheme is proposed the methods of unit testing, the effect of the voters, the specific configuration, and the types of faults expected must be analysed to determine the expected dependability.

As pointed out by Wakerly (1975a), transient faults and errors cause a problem for microcomputer systems using TMR. A transient may have an arbitrary effect upon the state of a microprocessor, and after the transient disappears the affected processor may continue to have an incorrect state. If a second fault (permanent or transient) affects a corresponding line in another processor before the correct state of the first is restored, then the TMR system will fail. Wakerly showed that frequently using a synchronising sequence of length one will overcome the effect of such transients, if a design very similar to LSSD is used.

Meyer (1971) showed that von Neumann had implicitly assumed synchronisation in his system, and if synchronisation were not present, then single errors could corrupt the TMR system. The very practical problem of clock synchronisation (Daly *et al.*, 1973) showed that for synchronisation with arbitrary drift four clocks are necessary. Pease *et al.* (1980) generalised the idea of synchronisation, and reading data serially from external units, to the ideas of source congruency and synchronisation. While making no assumptions about the behaviour of faulty components, they showed that in general $3t + 1$ units, with several interchanges of data, are needed to overcome the effects of t faulty units.

The old Airforce technique of four-way redundancy (dual/dual) is being employed by the Stratus Computer (Serlin, 1984). Each subsystem (a printed circuitboard) has an identical counterpart, its hot backup unit. Each subsystem consists of sets of pairs of identical units which receive identical inputs. The pairs use two-way redundancy. The subsystems are tightly synchronised. After an error is detected that pair stops, and indicates that an on-line repair is necessary. The other subsystem continues.

The use of static hardware redundancy is based upon the assumption that failures of the redundant components are independent. This is no longer true with VLSI, or even LSI. Other difficulties are the difficulty of ascertaining that the components are initially operating correctly, synchronisation, source congruency, and the frequent absence of warning when the redundant module finally fails. The cost of the redundant hardware modules was a disadvantage before VLSI units and the rising cost of programming. Now the relative cost is a design decision.

In the dynamic redundancy approach, redundant operations and algorithms are carried out by several modules, and the set of modules in use varies depending upon the number of detected faults. The first plans for dynamic redundancy concentrated on the replacement of the faulty element or module by a standby spare (often called self-repair). The SAGE system (Everett *et al.*, 1957) used two computers with one operating and the other monitoring the operation of the first. The operating computer periodically sent signals indicating correct functioning and checkpoint data as necessary to the monitoring computer. The monitoring computer kept checkpoint data, did secondary processing, and was ready to assume primary control. Some of these systems are still in use. The next step was to use the redundant units in multiprocessing. After a failure, processing continued in a degraded mode. Connecting similar processors as multiprocessors instead of units and continuing processing while faulty processors are being repaired is another old idea.

Fundamental to the way hardware aids to recovery are implemented is the selection of the individual modules, their design, the interconnection paths between the modules and the operational set of programs and procedures which control the recovery process. In addition, preparation for recovery during normal operation must include plans for the following: error detection, containment of erroneous information, capture of the error environment, signalling for proper program flow modification, and controls for initiating the recovery process. Since information integrity ends after an error is detected, the error detection function is the most important function for dynamic redundancy implementations.

Since the first computers, information integrity has been assured by devising circuits which should detect the errors (hardware or software) which would corrupt the information during computer operation. Techniques similar to test generation are used to determine the effect of the occurrence of faults in a particular class. If the errors caused by such faults affect the information being protected, these errors should be detected. Error detection functions (commonly called *checking circuits* or *checkers*) are the implementation of assertions which indicate that, during the monitored period of activity of a module, there has been no occurrence of an error attributable to the occurrence in the module of a fault in the class of faults modelled. Many commercial systems have used checkers based upon the causal relationships between faults and errors listed earlier. *Watchdog timers* are implemented using processor timers, which can be set by program. The timer monitoring interval is application dependent, and is a frequently used method of final protection against the n-fault trap. *Function checks* indicate that the output of the function implemented by the module is correct. Module duplication with output comparison (ALUs for example) has been widely used since UNIVAC days (1952). Alternatively, the format of the output (instruction code, decimal digit, or data address) is checked for validity. The assertions for *structural checks* are determined by using coding information (parity, SEC/DED). Usually the information and codes are processed independently, and in parallel. The code for the new information is determined (implicitly or explicitly), and the two code representations are matched for equality. The fault classes classically considered have been either the Boolean single stuck-at fault class or the unidirectional fault class for VLSI. *Assertions of validity* usually are implemented by operating either two modules with diverse implementations of the same function or two modules implementing equivalent functions, then comparing the output values.

To study error checking in general, some definitions are needed. A computer is called *self-checking* if its operation is constantly checked by the information processing invoked by normally occurring input sequences. A digital system is *fault secure* if during operation any modelled fault (hardware or software) either does not affect the system's output or its presence is indicated no later than when the first erroneous output appears. A system is *partially fault secure* if a fault in a specified subset of the modelled faults either does not affect the system's output or its presence is indicated no later than when the first erroneous output appears. A system is *totally self-testing* if any modelled fault eventually results in an error being detected during normal system operation. A system is *partially self-testing* if a subset of the modelled faults will eventually result in an error being detected during normal operation. A system is *totally self-checking* if it is both totally self-testing and fault secure. (See Smith and Lam (1983) for formal definitions.) Clearly a self-checking system is partially self-testing and partially fault secure. If a system is self-checking, then it contains a *hardcore* which is that part of the system which must be correct in order for the system to function correctly when no error is detected. Self-checking systems will be considered to consist of processing, control, storage, and software modules, and the data and control transmission paths between modules. The techniques to be described usually depend upon synchronous circuits. Usas (1975) showed how to design totally self-checked clock signal checkers.

Module selection is a system problem. Clearly the modules should perform atomic actions (Lomet, 1977). Actions are atomic if, after receiving inputs, the processes performing the action are not aware of the existence of any other active processes, and no other process is aware of the activity of the atomic action until its outputs (data and control) are available. Examples are the transfer of data between computer registers or the data storing transaction in a database system. In order to specify other rules for module selection, the properties of such modules must be studied.

The first step in the design of a fault tolerant module is determining the assertions for the checking functions at the interfaces of the atomic actions, using the specifications of the module and the fault classes whose effects are to be detected. In early work design techniques were devised for particular types of units, e.g. counters, adders and memories, assuming single stuck-at faults. Sellers *et al.* (1968b) reviewed these techniques. They also gave very general guidelines for checker placement: the error should be detectable before it corrupts other information; errors should be locatable to a replaceable unit; and the cost should be minimised. Carter and Schneider (1968) began the study of general models and design methods, made more formal by Anderson and Metze (1973). In addition to clear definitions of fault secure and self-testing, they defined a circuit G to be a code disjoint circuit if it maps noncode inputs into noncode outputs. Requiring a circuit to be code disjoint imposes severe restrictions on its implementation, but they showed that if all faults from a particular class are to be detected, then a code disjoint implementation of the checking circuit must be used. Carter and Schneider had pointed out that checkers should be placed on the inputs of non-code-disjoint units, and if code disjoint units are used, the placement of checkers can be deferred. For good detection, Chang and Scanlon (1969) stated that the functions of each subunit should be carefully specified, and the subunit interfaces should be simple. Wakerly (1975b) added the rule that there should be a checker in every data path loop.

In most computers, data transmission between units in the central processor is checked by byte parity, or other coding, assuming that the data and addresses are synchronous. Levitt *et al.* (1968) carefully studied the interconnection problem for computers and devised some ingenious fault tolerant switches. Ko and Breuer (1978) show how to extend conventional parity techniques so that any number of errors may be detected. Fault tolerant networks are widely used in distributed systems, and are considered in Chapter 4. The interaction between units must be considered, in addition to data and control paths and networks. Smith and Metze (1978) gave some general design rules for units, then generalised these ideas to strongly fault secure logic networks by considering interactions between units. Smith and Lam (1983) formalised and improved this work, studying unit interactions at length.

Data being transferred between units can be checked by BCH or Fire codes (Peterson and Weldon, 1972), or by rectangular codes, in which both dimensions of the data block are coded. Using a parity check in both directions results in a SEC/DED code. Combining a parity check and a cyclic redundancy check byte, or a generalisation of this process (Patel and Hong, 1974) is widely used. In this case, if errors exist in a single column, they can all be corrected. If instead of the CRC, integer addition is used, and there is no overflow, Wakerly (1975c) proved that all unidirectional errors are detected.

Parity checks have been superseded for use in storage by SEC/DED/DbED codes (Chen and Hsiao, 1984). Recently SEC/DED codes, when used for storage in the IBM S/370 larger models (Bossen and Hsiao, 1980) and in spacecraft (Carter and McCarthy, 1976), have been modified to use sequential decoding to detect errors caused by alpha particles. Bossen (1970) devised an excellent implementation for single byte error correction for storage which is built with basic storage arrays of width b, i.e. b bits are returned for each storage access to the basic array. This use of Reed-Solomon codes is now called b-adjacent error correction (SbEC). Various SbEC/DbED codes, as well as the probabilistic detection of multiple errors, have been considered by Carter and Wadia (1980) and Kanada and Fujiwara (1980).

It is more difficult to find general methods for checking processing units. Residue codes can be used to check or correct arithmetic units and counters (Block *et al.*, 1948, Avizienis, 1971). Checking Boolean logic operations requires sequential manipulations or duplication (Peterson and Weldon, 1972). An old error detection technique that continues to appear is duplication and comparison, implemented in either hardware or software. Recovery after such error detection usually involves other units. The recovery process is simplified by using the TMR operation of three units with n standby spares called *hybrid redundancy*. Such a unit was built for the NASA Self Testing and Repair processor (STAR) (Avizienis *et al.*, 1971) and extensively tested (Avizienis and Rennels, 1972). Clearly it is possible to use $k + 1$ out of $2k + 1$ instead of 2 out of 3. This has been called NMR. NMR has been extensively analysed by Ingle and Siewiorek (1976), who included the reliability of various switching and status register designs.

Experimental distributed systems (Wensley *et al.*, 1976, Hopkins and Smith, 1977) used computers in TMR sets with hybrid redundancy as a basis for their fault tolerant systems. They discovered all the problems of source congruency and synchronisation (Pease *et al.*, 1980), and solved them by a mixture of hardware (Hopkins) and programming (Wensley).

Because hybrid redundancy simplifies the recovery process, its use is becoming popular (Frison and Wensley, 1982). Each such basic system (called a channel when connected in n-way static redundancy) consists of processing, storage, timing and synchronisation, and I/O devices. The advantages of static redundancy are understood to be conceptual simplicity and its instant action, entirely transparent to the user. Unless repair is planned, it needs no diagnosis during operation, and converting a non-redundant design to such a design should be relatively straightforward. If the constraints of interactive consistency are considered, the main design difficulties arise from synchronisation, the processing of analog data, and the handling of interrupts. All too frequently in practice the system design either has single points of failure, negating the redundancy, or requires very complicated programs requiring much time for execution, not at all like the simple programming for non-redundant system design. Wensley and Frison (1982) studied all three problems, showed that simplistic methods previously used are invalid, and proposed improved approaches. Smith (1981) identified the unique operations required of such redundant systems, and devised instructions which would allow them to be performed with efficiency, and would also be syntactically equivalent to the corresponding simplex instructions, so that the same instruction streams could be used in each channel after a simple substitution. Systems using such instructions have been built and tested for conformity to source congruency and synchronisation requirements while handling serial I/O and external interrupts and maintaining synchronisation (Smith, 1984).

Checking computer controls is even more difficult. Diaz (1974) proposed checking computer controls using m-out-of-n codes and state table transformations. Toy (1978, 1981; Cook *et al.*, 1973) in designing ESS systems checked the action of controls by reconstructing the microprogram control inputs from the transmitted control signals. During data transfer, computer control signals are asynchronous with data and must be encoded separately. Pollard and Patel (1984) show that control errors can be detected by modifying the usual protocol, and control line errors can be tolerated by duplicating the control lines. Wong *et al.* (1983) designed a microprogram control unit using the more general unidirectional error fault class.

As the complexity of programs increases, and program errors become more numerous and serious, the use of hardware checking to help detect program errors is increasing. As in hardware, atomic actions can be ensured only if the control flow within a process and data flow between processes are controlled. Older systems are relying upon format checking of data, instruction, and addresses (illegal operation code checking for example), some address bound checking, and paging or virtual memories. Paging allows the definition of virtual machines and some addressability control.

Modern systems (Needham, 1974; Berstis, 1980) are using capabilities and protection domains to achieve: first, addressability control for system closure (Denning, 1976), second, object protection, including a form of abstract data types, and third, process isolation. For capabilities, addresses are composed of two segments, the identifier and the offset. Segment identifiers control data access and sharing by authorisation rights which are checked. Objects, which are high level constructs (simple abstract data types) are protected by capabilities. Machine instructions are of two types, byte oriented (as usual) or instructions which perform high level functions on objects. A program consists of both types of instructions, and is translated into machine executable code immediately before execution. The running protected program consists of machine (often micro) instructions, the input and output data, and storage for the intermediate data. Note that this means that the operating implementation of objects is independent of but derived from their original protected abstract definition. Processes are isolated unless there is planned data sharing, since for data to be shared the sharing program must provide access to itself.

For totally self-checking unit design, an important consideration is that the set of inputs to each subunit contain enough patterns to test the subunit (Carter *et al.*, 1970; Anderson, 1973). Jha and Abraham (1984) show how to design totally self-checking checkers for the unidirectional fault hypothesis. Smith and Lam (1983) consider this problem for systems, and give necessary conditions for some possible solutions to this problem.

Compared to the cycle time of a computer, many faults seem static, while errors are produced in a dynamic environment only after the occurrence of the proper circuit input pattern. Thus there is an interval between the occurrence of a fault and its manifestation as an error. This period is defined to be the fault latency (Shedletsky, 1975). The latency interval, the minimum number of input patterns necessary to achieve a probability c of observing an error due to a fault, is more easily estimated. This latency interval for a fault f' can be shown to be ($\log(1-c)$ / $\log(1-$ (probability f' causes an error))), an obvious exponential function. For a combinational circuit with m inputs a lower bound for the probability of an input pattern causing a fault is $1/2^m$. Assuming an input rate of 10^7 input vectors a second with 40 inputs, the mean upper bound error latency is 1.27 days and the latency interval for 0.9 probability of error occurrence is 2.92 days. If there are 50 inputs the mean is 3.58 years and the latency interval for 0.9 probability is 8.24 years. In such cases the latency interval is of the same order of magnitude as the mean time between hardware faults, and the possible presence of latent faults must be considered in defining and using fault classes. As usual, the error latency is even more significant for sequential circuits (Shedletsky, 1978). Clearly if the single fault hypothesis is used for checking assertion specification, then measures must be taken to test periodically for latent faults.

In addition to physical circuit characteristics, system design influences the choice of checking procedures. Memories again provide good examples. If a chip fails, the disabled unit is a card, so a substantial amount of memory may be lost. It is common practice to divide such a memory card into domains, and have one spare chip available per domain. Now after the error has been signalled, the system can proceed with full capacity while waiting for repair. Finally, a word is stored across several chips. Single bit storage errors are the most prevalent, and can be corrected until two of them are aligned by the addressing planes. Bossen *et al.* (1984) show how to permute the bits used in addressing memory so that one of several physical configurations may correspond to a single address. When a double error occurs the address bits may be permuted so that the two bits which have failed are now part of two different physical configurations for words, and processing may continue. In paged virtual memory systems, the unit for protection is really a page (4K bytes) or in a cache where the unit for protection is a block (32 to 256 bytes). In these cases an uncorrectable error in a word will result in the loss of a page, or a block. Matick (1982) proposed using a page per chip organisation for such memories, and proved that substantial reliability improvements can be achieved in some cases. In the design of a current supercomputer architecture, the processors and memories are connected by an Omega-type network. If an error occurs in a switching node of this network, a pattern of four errors will result (Arlat and Carter, 1984). To combat this, a 9-bit shortened code was used. This code will perform error correction for any of the 15 possible group errors in the data, and error detection of 49% of the possible double group errors in the data. In addition, all single group errors and 49% of the double group errors will be detected in the 24-bit address (also transmitted through the switch).

The advent of VLSI and the parallel operation of many processors without individual checking circuitry has resulted in new uses for checking assertions. Good old duplication is of course widely used, in spite of its problems. The old method which has found most new uses is parity checking over domains other than the field with two elements. Huang and Abraham (1982) propose the application specific idea of forming banded matrices by appending to each row and column the sum of the elements in the row or column. Such matrices, if the negative of the sum is used, form an algebra with an identity element, under the usual matrix operations. The result of matrix operations is checked by comparing the computed parities of the banded matrices with the newly computed parities of the standard matrix results. As a very different application, the run-time behaviour of re-entrant programs can be monitored by this technique. At compile time each program is partitioned into a sequence of branchless blocks, and for each block a parity check sum is formed (called the signature by Namjoo, 1982, and Eifert and Shen, 1984). At program execution time, the parity check is formed as the instructions are executed, and at the end of each block the computed and stored parities are compared. Errors affecting a single instruction are always detected, and there is probabilistic detection of other errors. Mahmood *et al.* (1983) show that with modern circuitry it is feasible to use more complicated assertions for important problems. To adapt Berger codes for wider use in VLSI computers, assuming that the unidirectional fault hypothesis is necessary, Bose and Lin (1984) have generalised Berger codes to systematic t-unidirectional codes. They have developed optimal systematic codes capable of detecting 2, 3 and 6 unidirectional errors using 2, 3 and 4 check bits respectively.

Once a set of assertions appropriate to the system design and class of faults whose effects are to be detected has been chosen, a good choice must be made of the method of monitoring the actions of the assertions while the system is running. The basic monitoring function is to determine if the current values of the inputs to the assertions chosen are such that the assertion is true and repeat this step for every period of activity that is to be monitored. In addition, if an assertion is false (an error has occurred) the monitoring function must contain the spread of contaminated information, capture the erroneous environment, and signal recovery control that an error has occurred. As always, the operating overhead in time, hardware and software must be reasonable. Three major methods are used to perform this task: concurrently operating independent special circuits, programmed test routines operating in the same computer, and independently operating processor controllers.

SPECIAL CIRCUITS

As the use of circuits is most traditional, it will be considered first. The data to be checked is easily available, and the observation period is short. The implemented assertions are usually checked in data or control registers after a computer minor cycle, or in module interfaces after an input information transfer or before an output transfer. Techniques for implementing the standard assertions are well known. As always there is one more problem: for a totally self-checking system how will it be determined that the error checking circuits have failed? Clearly they will fail, and to attain high values for the coverage their failure must be detected. Carter and Schneider (1968) showed that a totally self-checking checking circuit must have at least two outputs, and no output may take on a constant value for code inputs. Two check outputs are sufficient for most fault classes, so usually check circuits are chosen which map code outputs to (0,1) or (1,0). Noncode inputs must be mapped to either (0,0) or (1,1). For example, an odd parity checking circuit G can be made self-checking by dividing the q input lines into two disjoint subsets q_1 and q_2 ($q_1 + q_2 = q$), and checking each set q_1 and q_2 by disjoint parity check circuits. It is clear that this two-output circuit is self-checking, that it maps code words into (1,0) or (0,1), and noncode words into (0,0) or (1,1). In Carter and Schneider, the matching circuit is derived from the important self-checking circuit which allows two (or more) error line pairs to be combined into a single error line pair. Anderson and Metze (1973) and Smith and Metze (1978) also designed self-checking check circuits for m out of n codes except for the case of $m = 1, n = 3, m = 1, n = 7$. Marauf and Friedman (1977) gave more economical designs for the class of m out of n codes which can be made self-checking under the gate input and output s-a-v assumption. Nanya and Tohma (1983) devised a systematic procedure for obtaining a 3-level design of totally self-checking checkers for any m-out-of-n code for $n \geq 4$. If $n = 2m$ these reduce to the usual 2-level circuits. Fujiwara (1983) generalised Ko's 1978 technique so that the generalised parity circuits are totally self-checking. Carter *et al.* (1970) devised techniques for building self-checking SEC/DED translators. An experimental self-checking SEC/DED to parity translator for a memory with spare planes and soft error sequential decoding was built (Carter and McCarthy, 1976). Ashjaee and Reddy (1977) have designed totally self-checking checkers for many codes.

TEST ROUTINES

To help attain high system dependability, self checking using test routines can be used to replace or supplement hardware detection and diagnosis. Checking by software has the advantage that the amount of checking used at a particular time is easy to vary. Thus frequently hardware checking is augmented by periodic software checking of equipment which is expensive to check by hardware. Such software testing is frequently used to test for the possible existence of latent faults, especially in maintenance logic, non-critical functions, or redundant hardware present for fault tolerance. In order to use software routines to check detection and exception handling circuits, extra circuitry and extra control lines used only during software checking are added. Reconfigurable units can be tested for latent faults to ensure their protection is not diminished (Murray *et al.*, 1977). If a unit is found to be faulty it can be immediately treated, avoiding many complications in the recovery process. Chang *et al.* (1973) supplemented hardware checking by software testing for a telephone switching exchange. Gay (1977) studied how frequently test routines should be run. He used a Markov model, and showed that the optimum routine exercise frequency for a simplex unit is a function of the execution time of the test programs. The optimum frequency for redundant units is more a function of the unit switching time from standby to active. If faults affecting operation can be identified, the techniques of interleaved testing and operational testing can be used to reduce downtime to close to the theoretical minimum for a totally self-checked simplex unit. However, as discussed previously, the disadvantages of addressing resolution, timing resolution, and using a unit which is unreliable remain. With the advent of practical processor controllers, self-checking systems using software tests is much less widely practised, except for very small systems.

PROCESSOR CONTROLLERS

In the design of STAR, Avizienis *et al.* (1971) included a Test And Repair Processor (TARP) to serve as a monitor and diagnosis unit. TARP initiated all recovery and replacement actions on the basis of the unit status signals. Ayache *et al.* (1982) proposed monitoring the progress of several industrial control processors by simulating the Petri net specification of the program being used in the processors. This system is now in operation (Ayache *et al.*, 1982). Liu (1984) surveyed several commercially used processor controllers. While monitoring normal operation, processor controllers can scan processor internal states, run audit programs to check assertions, and monitor the error detection signals from units. Reilly *et al.* (1982) designed the monitoring of the power and thermal conditions of a processor, and methods to assist it to recover from transient conditions. This processor controller could selectively stop the system clocks, so that only the failing component is disabled. Dahbura and Masson (1983) studied standard hardware checking techniques used to check for program correctness, and found that to improve efficiency program control flow monitoring should be improved. Namjoo (1982) did this with a processor controller, while Eifert and Shen (1984) used linear feedback shift registers. Both monitored programs using flowcharts as specifications. Lu (1982) monitored the structure of Pascal programs. Such monitoring techniques have the advantages of programs on the same computer, i.e. using complicated assertions and easily variable test procedures, without the disadvantages of not running independently. However, they suffer the disadvantage of being only able to monitor actions which occur relatively infrequently.

An important advantage of using circuits for concurrent detection is that the circuit error signals can be used to limit the spread of information contamination. The usual technique is to halt the clock cycle temporarily.

However, if an error is not detected, then the contamination will spread. Delayed detection can pollute a system. Even if the system is not polluted, there is no way of determining that it is *not* polluted, so, for valid recovery, the assumption of widespread information pollution must be made if delayed error detection is probable. Clearly program checking is ineffective in halting the dissemination of erroneous information. The independent processor is better, but is still in the relative position of the watchdog timer.

It is much easier for a checking system based on concurrently operating circuitry in a computer to capture the environment in which an error is detected. Halting the clock to prevent the spread of contamination freezes all latched information. Now the difficulty is to ensure that the correct data is available, and that it is accessible to independently operating circuits. Computers designed with the equivalent of LSSD (Carter *et al.*, 1964; Eichelberger and Williams, 1977) or HEALS (Scola, 1972) have some information easily available, especially if hardware retry is planned. After environment capture, the data must be stored so as to be available for later analysis. Reilly *et al.* (1982) give a good description of current techniques. This technique uses a combination of local circuit checking and independent processor controller action. The information must be designed so that it is easy to analyse, since time for diagnosis is the largest part of maintenance time. Bossen and Hsiao (1982) introduced the idea of saving *syndromes* which can be used for easier analysis of the captured state after an error signal.

The final step is signalling that an error has been detected. Initiating a signal is simple, but making its use effective is more difficult. In a fault tolerant system, the atomic modules operate at hierarchical levels, passing input and output data, procedure initiation signals, and information about the progress of operations to each other. Error signals are the most important exception signals (Cristian, 1982). Each level will initiate error signals. There are different types of such signals. In the first case, the error can be dealt with locally, e.g. SEC in memory. However the information that this has occurred should be available to the main system control. This may be achieved by an informational exception signal, or by keeping the relevant information locally but having it accessible to other levels. In the second case, the exception can not be handled locally. Now this signal must be passed to another level, together with information indicating whether the signal originated at this level or at another level. Clearly several priorities and types of exception signalling are very useful. As a complicating factor, there are events which occur occasionally and asynchronously during correct operation. These events are not currently incorrect and usually occur because of restrictions such as finite register length (arithmetic over/under flow). However, if ignored they could cause the procedure output to be erroneous even though no error in hardware had occurred. Such events should be monitored and be indicated by signals indicating their priority and type.

In totally self-checking systems the exception and event signalling lines, and the lines determining protection control must be treated differently. In most of the modules considered previously, all lines were considered to be active, i.e. they change from 0 to 1, or conversely, frequently while the computer is running, or were coded so that they did, i.e. the checker outputs. However, lines which in normal operation have a single value (called semipassive lines in Carter *et al.* (1971)) occur frequently in the event and exception handling portions of a computer. Examples are syndrome lines in memory protection circuitry, ALU or I/O exceptional condition lines, or inter-unit error control signal lines. A set of semipassive lines have little useful application as individual lines but are normally interconnected by logic operators to result in semipassive Boolean functions; e.g. the OR function that takes the outputs of several checkers and produces one output as an error signal or the function which detects and signals a double error in a Hamming SEC/DED code. In these logic functions, all input, internal and output lines are semipassive and thus susceptible to undetected failure. Such failures can mask errors, allowing them to go undetected with resulting data contamination and lack of fault tolerance for the computer system. Carter, Wadia and Jessep (1971) showed that after replacing each semipassive line by a pair of lines, like the checking circuit outputs, the corresponding semipassive logic functions can be designed to be self-testing, and easily checked.

Operating large computer installations is an interactive monitoring and problem solving activity, which must be conducted in real time, and which is becoming increasingly more complex, particularly when system failures occur. Some of the new knowledge-based expert systems have been successfully used to aid such operations and shorten the time necessary for computer maintenance, and thus improve computer system availability. The Yorktown Expert System/MVS Manager (YES/MVS), a prototype expert system (Griesmer *et al.*, 1984), aids the operators of an IBM computer that runs under the MVS operating system. The following task categories have been implemented. Very large batch jobs are scheduled outside of prime shift, so as to adequately balance consideration of system throughput and individual user satisfaction. During prime shift, the job entry queue space is monitored and controlled. The networking of computers at the same site and systems performance are monitored in real time. Software incident reports and summary service reports are generated.

This section has shown that modules can be designed so that they will detect predictable faults, prevent the propagation of erroneous information, capture the erroneous environment, and signal that an exception has occurred. A choice of error monitoring techniques is available, and a combination of circuits and independent processors has many advantages. It has also been shown that all necessary logic for computer hardware can be modified so that it can be made totally self-checking. The problems of analysing costs and benefits still remain. The next step is to consider the interconnection of modules to form a system in which the problems of diagnosis and recovery are easily manageable.

DESIGN TO FACILITATE RECOVERY ACTIONS

In this section we shall consider methods for designing systems so that recovery actions may be effectively performed. During normal operation preparation should be made for the recovery procedures which will begin after the error indication signal has been received. The priority and type of the signal indicate whether an exception or an event has occurred, and possibly other information. The error environment is available, and contains information about the containment of erroneous data. Recovery procedures begin by determining a consistent state at some module level, then hardware controlled recovery will be attempted. If this is not successful, then the proximate fault, which will be the adjudged cause of the error, must be located. This fault, and the records of recent error environments, will allow the damage to data to be assessed. If automatic system reconfiguration is possible, it will be performed in accordance with current priorities, and program operation initiated from previously saved valid data. If this is not possible, manual reconfiguration, followed by restart, may be attempted. If necessary, a subsystem will be allocated so that online repair and validation may begin. If these procedures fail, system operation must be interrupted for maintenance. Almost all systems use a subset of these procedures, except in the rare case of computers which are in environments in which periodic repair and validation is not possible. The urgency of detection has been considered. The next methods are concerned with the necessity for accurate diagnosis and the required speed of initiating process continuation. While delayed detection can pollute the system, inaccurate diagnosis can eliminate the protection of redundancy too rapidly. Slow continuation can produce catastrophic instability in a real-time system, or result in unacceptable losses.

In many cases, program continuation may be achieved most rapidly by hardware controlled recovery. Such procedures are initiated by exception signals which indicate in which module the error occurred, and whether either forward error recovery or retry is possible. Forward error recovery is well illustrated by the actions necessary to apply SEC/DED in main storage. The local module signal indicates that an error has occurred, and whether single error recovery may be performed, or if it is not possible since a double error is indicated. The response to a double error signal depends upon the existence of a microprogrammed routine to recover from soft errors or to perform address permutation (Bossen, 1980, 1984). The frequency of, and location indicated by, single and double error signals is analysed to estimate the possibility of erroneous correction of data which could result from a triple error. Retry, a backward error recovery method implemented in hardware, is used to recover from CPU errors. It may be implemented at small cost at either the micro-instruction or instruction level (Carter *et al.*, 1977; Maestri, 1972). During the operation of an instruction (micro-instruction) the state of the beginning of the previous instruction is saved until the propagation of error signals from the checking circuits indicates no error. If an error is detected, after contamination containment the computer executes a time out for several cycles to achieve a stable state, saves the appropriate state information for later analysis, then attempts to re-execute the previous instruction. If successful, the computer operation proceeds; if unsuccessful the above process is usually repeated N times before diagnosis begins. If retry is successful, an event signal is sent to the supervisor; if unsuccessful an exception signal is necessary. In the first case, analysis of the number and location of errors can proceed while operational processing continues. Unless the system performance is hampered by an excessive number of such retries, fault diagnosis may be deferred. In the second case, immediate action is necessary in order to preserve a consistent state for the system. This simple procedure must be generalised for modern computer systems, which usually consist of several programmed units operating as a federated system (one main control). For example, in the IBM 3081 the central storage, system controller, external data controller, and two CPUs operate relatively asynchronously. Retry now is microprogram controlled, and a variable number of instructions in a stream may be retried.

After retry fails, damage assessment begins. If the error environment data indicates a relatively innocuous fault whose effects can be easily ignored, the supervisor may refresh the local state and try to execute the same instruction(s) again. If this fails, system diagnosis must begin. In a single hardware system being multiprogrammed, the simplest diagnosis is to determine the task containing the offending instruction, and attempt task retry. If this fails, it is necessary to notify the operator, since if priorities warrant, the operator may signal the system to perform a graceful stop (saving pertinent information) and then manual restarting procedures can be used. The necessary hardware system control features must be available. Damage assessment begins with fault isolation; locating a set of units, one of which contains the fault. Because of the necessity for repair, the units chosen are field replaceable units (FRUs). The FRUs in larger units can be listed and the lists used during system reconfiguration. Fault isolation effectiveness is the average number of units in the sets of units to which a fault is isolated. All automated techniques for fault isolation begin by determining (implicitly or explicitly) a fault dictionary. This is a list of error environment characteristics (often called syndromes) and for each syndrome an expected set of units which will contain the faulty component. The fault isolation problem is to determine a list of simple syndromes such that the fault isolation effectiveness is satisfactory. One way is to have the set of units corresponding to each syndrome be as small as possible and essentially disjoint from the other sets.

For fault isolation controlled by a single subunit, two methods of diagnosis are used. The oldest is error recreation, in which the state which caused the error is recreated. From this state the error environment characteristics and the unit(s) in error are determined. For solid faults, error recreation is very hard; for the others, impossible. The newer method is environment analysis (Lancto and Rockefeller, 1967; Bossen and Hsiao, 1982). In this method the environment captured when the error was detected, together with previous environments, is analysed to determine a list of entries to the fault dictionary. This technique is preferable, since, except for catastrophic errors, all errors are intermittent whether caused by solid, intermittent or externally caused faults. With modern circuitry more and more often the faults appear not to be solid, since the physical conditions which cause faults are not well understood and thus are not controlled during error recreation. The effectiveness of this technique depends upon capturing the error environment, determining the set of suspected faults, and the fault isolation effectiveness. For effective design, the fault isolation effectiveness must be calculated as the design proceeds (Bossen and Hsiao, 1982).

Fault analysis begins with the detection of an error signal, which indicates that the assertion defining a checking function has not been satisfied, followed by error environment capture (logout). Find the inputs to the checking function (usually a set of registers). From these inputs, which are functional circuit outputs, trace back to values which are available in logout. Analyse the network consisting of these circuits to determine if a fault in this network would cause the error signal, using the single fault hypothesis. The techniques are much the same as those used in finding tests for faults. If other single faults in a circuit could cause this error, add this circuit to the network. Continue until the inputs to this network are a checked interface. If a set of inputs to the network is error-free (no detected error) and the output checking circuit indicates an error, the fault causing the error must be in the network. The size of the network is usually too large. It can be reduced by finding state information which, when added to the syndrome, will divide the network into smaller pieces. If this is not feasible, choose observation points which will indicate transfer paths for data, and store information indicating which path was active at the time of error observation. In this way the FRU locating ability of syndromes can be improved. Tendolkar (1982) discusses analysis methods to isolate faults to units. The fault dictionary may be used for direct isolation of a fault from a given syndrome. More likely is the fact that several similar syndromes have occurred before fault isolation is started. If this is true, intersecting the sets of suspected FRUs will reduce their number. Two FRU replacement policies are possible. The first is replacement of all suspected units. The second is replacing the units most likely to have failed. As the design proceeds, fault isolation efficiency can be easily calculated from the probability of a fault occurring, the number of units corresponding to the syndrome indicating that this fault occurred and produced an error, and the analysis technique used.

Benowitz *et al.* (1975) showed that by using a linear feedback shift register and a cyclic redundancy check on state information a *signature* denoting proper operation of a functional unit could be determined. During operation such signatures are calculated and compared with the correct values. If the values do not agree the value of the shift register (the signature) is displayed, indicating the location of the unit containing the fault. Frohwerk (1977) discussed the efficiency of this technique in practical systems. The length of the random test for diagnosis is very important, and most work reported in the literature applies only to a detection test, not a diagnostic test. To locate the faults in a faulty circuit which might have more than one fault in it, a random pattern test of length suggested by the worst fault analysis is unacceptable. Each fault must be exposed at least once. In this way it would be possible to fix the faults, one by one, each time an error due to a different fault shows up. Savir (1983) showed that for the diagnostic problem, a random pattern test of length $11/p$ can detect as many as fifty hard faults having detection probability p, with 99.9% certainty. This analysis is clearly better performed on an independent processor, and is one of the tasks usually assigned to a processor controller. Although simply described, performing fault isolation efficiently is not easy, as shown by the following example.

In ESS-1, after an error indication, the good stand-by unit is used to test the other unit. Prell (1967) describes the circuits necessary for this testing. The two central controls are forced into step, the units synchronously execute the same test, and the matching circuits provide programmatic access to the microsteps within the unit operations. A judicious choice of the requirements for system diagnosis capability must be made if the matchers are not to be overly complex. Prell shows that the matching circuits must be able to perform both a directed match and a sampled match. In a direct match, the matchers are directed to look at match sources at specified time segments on a continuous basis. In the sampled match, the matchers are directed to look at specified sources, at a specified time segment, a given number of machine cycles from the point of initialisation.

The diagnostic analysis and synthesis problem has been studied in a general setting, assuming multiple units capable of diagnosis. The first formal model for the self-diagnosis of a system with multiple subunits was proposed and studied by Forbes *et al.* (1965) and Preparata, Metze and Chien (1967). They assumed that each subunit could be tested by some other subunit, and when one subunit tests another the result is reliable only if the testing unit is fault free. The system is modelled by a weighted directed graph, the nodes u_i represent units, the directed arcs b_{ij} between nodes i and j represent testing links (and physical connections and control), and the weights w_{ij} associated with the arcs are 0 if the test shows no fault, 1 if it does. The cyclic set of test outcomes w_{ij} represents the syndrome of the system; obviously w_{ij} can be assigned if and only if the corresponding testing link b_{ij} exists.

The next question is whether an existing system is capable of diagnosing two faults. Is this the capability of locating (a) up to two faults instantly, or (b) at least one fault unit if the number of faulty units present does not exceed two? A system of n units is one-step t-fault diagnosable if all faulty units within the system can be identified without replacement provided the number of faulty units present does not exceed t. A system of n units is sequentially t-fault diagnosable, or t-fault diagnosable with repair, if at least one faulty unit can be identified without replacement provided the number of faulty units present does not exceed t. As shown in Preparata, Metze and Chien, there are systems that are sequentially t-fault diagnosable, but not one-step t-fault diagnosable. They also proved that if a system S with n units is to be one step t-fault diagnosable, then $n \geq 2t + 1$ and each unit must be tested by at least t other units. They also give methods of designing n unit one step t-diagnosable systems in which $n = 2t + 1$ and each unit is tested by exactly t units. Hakimi (1977) proves the more complicated necessary and sufficient conditions for one-step t-fault diagnosability. However, if no two units test each other, then the necessary and sufficient condition is that each unit is tested by at least t other units. If the cost c_{ij} for unit i to test unit j is considered, there is a graph theoretic polynomially bounded algorithm to determine the connections for t-diagnosability if no pairs of units test each other. Sequential t-fault diagnosis requires fewer tests. Hakimi (1977) proves that for n units if $n > 2t$ there exists a sequentially t-diagnosable system with $n + t + 1$ tests.

Russell and Kime (1975a, b) have devised a more abstract model which applies to both hardware and software (if levels of invisibility (Parnas, 1972) are enforced). Rather than speaking of certain subsystems testing others, the model is formulated in terms of faults, tests, and the relationships between them. A broad interpretation is given to 'fault' and 'test'. For example, a fault may be defined as any condition that causes the malfunction of a particular part of the system such as a computer in a multicomputer complex or the arithmetic unit of a computer. A test can be any combination of hardware and software procedures used to determine if a fault has occurred. In particular each test has an associated set of invalidating units, generally a subset of the set of units cooperating for the test. When at least one unit of the invalidating set is faulty, the test outcome is unreliable. Barsi *et al.* (1976) considered the diagnosability of systems partitioned into complex units in which any unit has the potential to test any other. The diagnostic routines are complete for a given class of faults in each unit, and at least one mismatch occurs between actual and expected reaction to the test stimuli even if the testing unit itself is faulty. This hypothesis assumes that a self-checking design (Carter and Schneider, 1968) is adopted for the critical parts of the testing unit. As a result of these hypotheses they are able to prove the one step diagnosability of a system with n units now becomes bounded by $t < n-2$, not $2t < n-1$.

Friedman (1975) made the assumption that sometimes good as well as faulty modules may be replaced, depending upon the diagnostic strategy used. A system is k-step t/s diagnosable without repair if by k applications of the diagnostic test any multiple fault consisting of at most t single faults can be diagnosed to within s faults. The concept of k-step t/s diagnosability can also be applied to system diagnosability with repair. Apply the test, replace S_1 modules. After the replacement, apply the test again, assuming that the S_1 modules are good, and replace S_2 modules. Repeat until $\Sigma_1^n S_i \geq t > s$ so all faulty models have been replaced and the tests are all passed. A repair strategy may be defined for each value of k, determined by the testing facilities available, by the maximum number of faults which are assumed to exist, and by the number of incorrect responses received in a particular test. Karunanithi and Friedman (1977) derive necessary and sufficient conditions for units connected in a single loop to be one-step t/s diagnosable. Maheshwari and Hakimi (1976) have assumed that some faults are more easily diagnosed than others, and used this as a basis for replacing units. Nair (1978) considered the problem of finding at least one good unit from n units. This turns out to be as difficult as finding the faulty module in the single loop case. Chwa and Hakimi (1981) compare the fault tolerance and efficiency of modularly redundant and t-diagnosable systems. They present evidence showing that the average performance (error-free computational throughput) of t-diagnosable systems is greater than that of similar modularly redundant systems.

Such algorithms give methods for performing diagnosis, but as pointed out by Dahbura and Masson (1984), to identify the set of faulty units from the test results of a system usually uses an algorithm of complexity $O(n^3)$. They have devised a practical implementation of an $O(n^{2.5})$ algorithm. These algorithms in general assume that the results of tests are unambiguous and complete, which is very unlikely. However, as guidelines for practical design they are useful. Hosseini et al. (1984) look at a more realistic case, in which responses to the tests are not necessarily forthcoming. In their distributed algorithm every fault-free node can correctly diagnose the conditions of other nodes. The algorithm allows units and communication facilities to be replaced or repaired. They also show sufficient conditions for designing a distributed fault tolerant system by employing this algorithm. Dahbura and Masson (1983) have also proposed an algorithm which will aid in the design of fault tolerant distributed systems. This algorithm, too, does not assume that the results of tests are always accurate and available.

After the faulty unit has been determined comes the problem of damage assessment. For hardware, since isolation has been to a small set of field replaceable units, deciding upon the larger unit which must be isolated for reconfiguration is easy for routines in the processor controller. The real difficulty comes in determining what information has been damaged. A basic necessity is hardware help in providing levels of protection, even as little as two program states (supervisor and problem). If the system has been designed with capabilities available, the probability that data is protected by a capability currently in use can be determined (Denning, 1976; Berstis, 1980). Other possible hardware configurations which help with problem determination are the ability to easily provide duplicate files, and, to a lesser degree, virtual memory and separate virtual machines.

Hardware and program reconfiguration may be necessary if diagnosis and damage assessment warrant it. Reconfiguration will be discussed for four common types of systems. The first is distributed systems in which programs run on units consisting of three (or more) channels with a set of spare channels. Since standby redundancy is being used, the faulty channel must be replaced by a spare. The processor controller changes the system status information and gives a reconfiguration signal. The newly connected spare is rapidly tested. If the tests are passed, the hardware interfaces are correctly reconfigured. Next, its control information, program and data are updated. Supplemental periodic testing of spares makes it likely that the spare is good. If the test fails, another spare is tried, or more complicated application-dependent recovery routines are called. In all cases, the disconnected unit is marked for repair, which will begin according to schedule. During this processing the unit is running with one less channel than usual, so, while still protected, its recovery facilities are reduced. The second configuration is dual/dual. In this case, if the pair of spares has been ready to begin processing (hot standby), then the procedure is as above. In this case a second failure before the first repair is completed will cause system failure unless provision is made for this case. If the second pair of spares has been doing independent work while only keeping checkpoints for the programs in the first pair, the supervisor now must decide which programs will run, restart the programs which were being monitored by checkpointing, and inform the operator of the current status. The third case is redundancy with unit removal and degraded performance. Now the unit is disconnected and checkpoint/restart procedures are begun as above. Finally, if the reconfiguration is to bypass the fault by replacing the faulty function by an alternate function, then this reconfiguration is made and the new function is tested. Processing proceeds after the system state for the replaced function has been restored with its original information.

In order correctly to restart a program, the last valid program state must be available. This is easily available when two (or more) independent processors are executing exactly the same program. Otherwise this information must be saved, be available from an external source on a cyclic basis, or the system reinitialised and the program begun with its original data (which again must be available). Chandy (1975) and Gelenbe (1977) use the hardware failure rate to determine an optimum checkpoint interval but do not concern themselves with the probability of error detection. Shedletsky (1978) pointed out that the rollback interval depended upon the checking coverage and the component failure rate. Successful data restoration will occur only if the rollback is beyond the point of the first error occurrence. If the error detection is poor so the error latency is large, and the rollback interval must be very long. Such checkpoint data can be saved on any reasonably permanent storage device (depending upon the degree of security desired). However, this often results in the unnecessary storage of much data, slowing an overhead process. To speed this up, Horning *et al.* (1974) proposed the use of a recovery cache, and Lee *et al.* (1980) described the construction of an experimental system. The basic functioning of a recovery cache is that when a process is restarted with a new checkpoint, and an object is about to be written to (for the first time), the original value of that object is retrieved and stored away, together with its address, in the recovery cache. The object is then updated. In this way a minimum of recovery data is stored. Concurrent operation of the cache and the processor demands the addition of some instructions to the processor (and to the program). However, in many cases the overhead of checkpointing or backward error recovery is reduced. Many computers used for the control of processes read data from external sources on a regular basis, and, depending upon the application, missing a few iterations is not too important. Restart is easy in such cases, unless control signals have been sent to external devices. The status of external devices must be determined, since frequently such signals must not be repeated, e.g., rocket firing (Avizienis *et al.*, 1969). After the control signals have been reconstituted – and this clearly depends upon the application – hardware reconstitution can begin. Restarting processes from the beginning sounds easy, but if hardware failures have occurred the initial conditions must be carefully reconstructed and checked. Ossfeldt and Jonsson (1980) discuss hardware features, the most important of which are the structuring of the AXE system into functional blocks with signal interfaces so that it is possible to remove, add, or exchange individual blocks as long as the signal interface with the rest of the system is not affected.

Diagnosis is the most time consuming part of repair actions (Carter *et al.*, 1964). If a diagnostic routine assumes only a single error exists, it follows the ESS-1 idea of combinational testing. All tests are run, failure information is stored, and the fault is located by analysis of the failure data. Such routines run rapidly. If multiple errors are likely, the diagnostic routines use the sequential testing method. The first test starts with the smallest amount of circuitry possible. Each additional test adds a small increment to the circuitry tested. The sophistication of this approach is in the design and sequencing of the individual tests. The first failure found in the test sequence is repaired by reconfiguration, graceful degradation or physical repair before proceeding past that point. After a catastrophic failure, bring-up tests which expect multiple component faults are used. Bring-up tests first verify that the necessary basic machine properties operate correctly. Next other routines may be applied, and the search for complete integrity can begin. A very important but often overlooked design need is for standard methods of communication between the field engineer (FE) fixing the system and the faulty system. It is important that each command to the system be checked so that human errors do not further pollute the faulty system, as some of the normal defences may be inoperative because of the faults present. A diagnostic control program with standard console commands was used for the Honeywell D-1000 beginning in 1957. For IBM System/360 the program was expanded so that maintenance could be integrated with the rest of the system functions. Special diagnostic hardware was added (Carter *et al.*, 1964). Some examples are storage, channel and I/O control unit state latches accessible to CPU interrogation and *channel wraparound*. Maintenance analysis procedures (MAPS) were introduced in 1966 (Burnstein and Eppard) to aid the FE. These MAPS provided a step-by-step process to isolate the cause of a failure and tended to reduce the need to teach FEs how a product worked, permitting emphasis on a how-to-fix philosophy. Portable maintenance devices, introduced about 1979 (Hsiao *et al.*, 1981) contain a microprocessor, file, keyboard/display, communications port for remote support, and ports to connect to various devices. A file containing MAPS diagnostic procedures is used after the device is connected. Some of the new knowledge-based expert systems have been successfully used to aid maintenance, and thus improve computer system availability. An example is IDT (Shubin, 1982), an intelligent tool for diagnosing hardware faults that has been successfully used to locate field replaceable units (FRUs) in PDP 11/03 computers. The program runs on a VAX 11/780 at a site remote from the broken equipment. IDT selects and executes tests, and interprets the results. It is able to modify its test selection strategy on the basis of results of previous tests as well as opinions offered to it by the user. In addition to reasoning about test results, IDT can select and initiate new tests; IDT uses statistical information that predicts the likelihood that a particular FRU will be broken, opinions offered to it by the user, and results of previous tests. The prototype Yorktown Expert System/MVS Manager (YES/MVS) (Griesmer *et al.*, 1984) performs simple diagnostic analysis and suggests corrective actions to the operator.

If the problem can not be resolved locally, then help must be located. A method of connecting maintenance devices to a central system is used for maintenance for the Amdahl 470 and for the IBM S/370 using RETAIN/370 (Fitzsimons, 1972). The faulty computer is connected to a communications network. Then the faulty computer and a good computer at the network centre run the same diagnostic test. The good computer receives the results of the faulty computer and analyses them against its own. The analysis results are used as an entry to a diagnostic dictionary to locate the failing part.

In order physically to repair a computer, the unit in error must be determined, and then the Field Replaceable Unit (FRU) located. Electrical isolation of the appropriate unit is necessary, similar to that described for the AXE. If independent analysis has been performed (as discussed earlier, by signature or processor controller) and the FRUs to be replaced have been located, then only the larger modules containing the FRUs must be electrically isolated. Because of the possibility of system damage which may occur during repair if sufficient isolation is not available, this is a difficult design problem. If the FRU to be replaced has not been located, then the subsystem to be isolated must contain the suspected module, and a unit to provide, control and analyse the tests. After FRU replacement, the module must be tested to ensure that the fault is no longer in the module. If the tests are run by the system controller, the controller must be part of the subsystem which is isolated. If the tests are run by a mobile maintenance device, this must be available and have the correct tests available. Such tests begin with verification tests to ensure that the faulty unit has been correctly repaired (Reilly *et al.*, 1982). The next step is module architectural validation tests, which are programs and micro-programs designed using the techniques discussed above.

The partitioning of a system into modules can now be discussed. The first guidelines must concern the selection of the modules with atomic actions and the passing of data and control information between them. These modules will be used for maintenance, and the partitioning will result in unacceptable loss of performance unless planned early in the design process. The average number of FRUs to be replaced per call, and the number of calls, is of practical significance, and depends both upon the isolation effectiveness and the analysis routines used (Tendolkar, 1982).

Bernstein and Siegel (1975) discuss designing a level structured system with guidelines for module selection. The system is to be designed in stages. Stage definition can begin at a lowest level, level 0, of basic services. The other modules are defined using the concept of *uses the services of* (Anderson and Lee, 1981; Laprie, 1984). Initially, the designer selects one or more features not supplied by level 0 and designs a module using the services available from level 0. In the following steps another level may be designed using the services of the previous levels until the design satisfies the specifications. Clearly such modules can not be forced into an absolute level ordering until late in the design, and then several modules will be at the same virtual level. In this way module checking and testing is easier and diagnostic resolution is improved. Restriction of contamination of data and control and damage assessment are simplified. As pointed out by Bernstein and Siegel, such designs must have a convenient, fast method for switching levels. This is a search for the appropriate definition of services through successively lower levels until the desired module and entry point to its interface have been determined. Properly designed associative memories as well as stacks will aid such searching. The technique of using secure domains and translation of routines immediately before use (Berstis, 1980) will reduce the need for level changes. Returning to the original module must be rapid. Bernstein and Siegel discuss another method which must be available, passing the indication of a potential fault, detected by interface checking, from the requesting module to the calling module. Interrupts arising from external sources must be considered during the definition of each module, and local response or storage with masking determined. Such design, and its analysis, is still done heuristically. Designing such modules and connecting them to form a system must be done iteratively and with computer aids. Devising good procedures for error detection at module interfaces, control information passing, diagnosis and recovery are most difficult. Aids like the COMET program (Chang *et al.*, 1974) have been implemented to provide interactive help in partitioning systems into modules, and in determining content and methods for passing control information about the modules' internal states. After system modification, programs like LAMP (Chang *et al.*, 1974) may be used to evaluate the resulting system for fault tolerance features.

A second reasonable guideline is to try to have the unusual features introduced at a given virtual level made invisible at the earliest possible higher level. For example, it is desirable to have all error detection, diagnosis, reconfiguration and recovery invisible to applications programmers, e.g. rollback is more visible than fault masking. Special machine instructions should not impact higher level languages or operating system protocols. Microcode features for executing instruction retry should not impact machine code. Error checking should minimally impact the microcode. Associated with each level are possible configurations of fault tolerant and fault avoidance techniques. In making the choice of such features, the most critical mechanisms must be carefully identified and separated from similar but less critical mechanisms. Criticality depends on system specification and environment, and these concepts must be used to integrate the various views of criticality. As a general rule, the processes of greatest criticality themselves must be well structured and small enough to verify and control. The most important criticality constraint is recovery. The techniques of detection, diagnosis and continuation discussed in the previous section must be specified as processes and considered as part of the system design.

The third necessary step is that the fault avoidance techniques discussed earlier must be considered. Reliable components are selected, acceptable testing techniques and design techniques to allow the benefits of reliable components to be realised are devised, the best interconnection methods are analysed, packaging and shielding of the hardware to screen out expected forms of external interference are examined, and methods of validation of the logical structure are planned. The classes of faults that are to be tolerated by the design are identified, and for each, the extent of fault tolerance is specified. Cost-effective methods of protective redundancy are then chosen to cover every identified class of faults, using the techniques described in the second section of this chapter. As each technique is chosen, the processes already in the hierarchical system model must be modified to represent the change. The necessary paths for error control and analysis must be added. Remember that multiple faults can defeat replicated redundancy, but in the absence of correlation are not likely to. Induced faults, on the other hand, are apt to be multiple and correlated. Intermittent faults are hazardous because, if latent, they may not be detected, and if non-latent, they may not be isolated and repaired. In either case their effect may cause the system to fail. As an important part of the design, system bringup and checkout methods must be devised. If possible, all redundancy features should be tested. These methods may have to be used in case of unexpected errors – the *n*-fault trap – so the prospect of automatically applying a subset of them in an emergency must be possible.

The next step is to evaluate and analyse the system reliability. The evaluations will show the changes needed for the next iteration, and the design proceeds until the specifications are proven to be satisfactorily implemented. As stated earlier, complex designs of this type must be validated, and their resulting reliability, which rests upon the criticality of processes, must be determined as the design proceeds from initial specification to detailed specification to engineering implementation.

A hardware implementation which aids the type of system design just proposed is a hierarchical distributed structured system. This has a master processor controlling other dedicated processors. This has flexibility, is a short step from a digital bus structure, and lends itself to fault tolerance, especially if all processors are not of the same type and are each well self-checked. Ihara (1984) has designed systems composed of numerous autonomous subsystems. Some interconnection techniques are discussed in Chapter 4.

This chapter shows that careful design to produce a high checking coverage and efficient diagnostic procedures is necessary for the hardware upon which reliable recovery is based. All recovery procedures, hardware and software, must be specified at each design step. Careful modelling will allow the necessary evaluation to monitor the progress of the design, and ensure immediacy of detection, freedom from contamination, accuracy of diagnosis and speed of initiating continuation.

REFERENCES

Abramovici, M. *et al.* (1982). 'A Logic Simulation Machine'. *Proc. 19th DA Conf.*, 65–73.

Abrulhamid, M. E., and Carny, E. (1983). 'A Class of Test Generators for Built-In Testing'. *IEEE TC*, **C-32**, No. 10, 957–960.

Agarwal, V. K. (1980). 'Multiple Fault Detection in Programmable Logic Arrays'. *IEEE TC*, **C-29**, No. 6, 518–522.

Anderson, D. A. and Metze, G. (1973). 'Design of Totally Self-checking Check Circuits for m-out-of-n Codes'. *IEEE TC*, **C-22**, No. 3, 263–269.

Anderson, T. and Lee, P.A. (1981). *Fault Tolerance: Principles and Practice*. Prentice-Hall International.

Anderson, T. and Randell, B. (1979). *Computing Systems Reliability*, Chapter by W. C. Carter, 225–226.

Armstrong, D. B. (1966). 'On Finding a Nearly Minimal Set of Fault Detection Tests for Combinational Logic Nets'. *IEEE TEC*, **EC-15**, 66.

Arlat, J. and Carter, W. C. (1984). 'Implementation and Evaluation of a (b,k)-Adjacent Error-Correcting/Detecting Scheme for Supercomputer Systems'. *IBM J. R&D*, **28**, No. 2, 159–169.

Ashjaee, M. J. and Reddy, S. M. (1977). 'On Totally Self-Checking Checkers for Separable Codes'. *IEEE TC*, **C-26**, No. 8, 737–745.

Avizienis, A. (1971). 'Arithmetic Error Codes: Cost and Effectiveness Studies for Application in Digital System Design'. *IEEE TC*, **C-20**, No. 11, 1322–1331.

Avizienis, A. (1977). 'Fault-tolerant Computing – Progress, Problems and Prospects'. *IFIP Congress Proceedings*, Toronto, 405–418.

Avizienis, A. *et al.* (1977). 'The STAR (Self Testing and Repair) Computer: an Investigation of the Theory and Practice of Fault-tolerant Computer Design'. *IEEE TC*, **C-20**, No. 11, 1312.

Avizienis, A., Mathur, F. P., Rennels, D. A. and Rohr, J. A. (1969). 'Automatic Maintenance of Aerospace Computers and Spacecraft Information and Control Systems'. *AIAA Aerospace Computer Sys. Conf.*, paper no. 69–966, Los Angeles.

Avizienis, A. (1978). 'Fault-tolerance: The Survival Attribute of Digital Systems'. *Proc. IEEE*, **66**, No. 10, 1109–1123.

Avizienis, A. and Rennels, D. A. (1972). 'Fault-tolerance Experiments with the JPL STAR Computer. *Dig. COMPCON '72*, San Francisco, 321.

Avizienis, A. (1981). 'Fault Tolerance by Means of External Monitoring of Computer Systems'. *Proc. NCC*, 27–40.

Ayache, J. M., Courtiat, J. P. and Diaz, M. (1982). 'REBUS, A Fault-Tolerant Distributed System for Industrial Real-Time Control. *IEEE TC*, **C-31**, No. 7, 637–647.

Ball, M. and Hardie, F. (1969). 'Effect and Detection of Intermittent Failures in Digital Systems'. *Proc. FJCC*, **35**, Las Vegas, 329.

Banerjee, P. and Abraham, J. A. (1983). 'Generating Tests for Physical Failures in MOS Logic Circuits'. *IEEE Int. Test Conf.*, 554–559.

Bardell, P. H. *et al.* (1983). 'Built-In Test Concepts and Techniques'. *IEEE Test Tech. Comm. Tutorial.*

Bark, A. and Kinne, C. B. (1953). 'The Application of Pulse Position Modulation to Digital Computers'. *Proc. Nat. Elec. Conf.*, 656–664.

Barsi, F., Grandoni, F. and Maestrini, P. (1976). 'Diagnosability of Systems Partitioned into Complex Units'. *IEEE TC*, **C-25**, No. 6, 585–593.

Benowitz, N. *et al.* (1975). 'An Advanced Fault Isolation System for Digital Logic'. *IEEE TC*, **C-24**, No. 5, 489–497.

Berger, J. M. (1961). 'A Note on Error Detection Codes for Asymetric Channels'. *Info. and Control*, 68–73.

Bernstein, A. J. and Siegel, P. (1975). 'A Computer Architecture for Level Structured Systems'. *IEEE TC*, **C-24**, No. 8, 785–793.

Berstis, V. (1980). 'Security and Protection of Data in the IBM System/38'. *7th Ann. Symp. on Computer Architecture*, 245–252.

Block, R. M., Campbell, R. D. V., and Ellis, M. (1948). *The Logical Design of the Raytheon Computer*, MTAC.

Bose, B. and Lin, D. J. (1984). 'Systematic Unidirectional Error Detecting Codes'. *FTCS-14*, 94–99.

Bossen, D. C. and Hsiao, M. Y. (1980). 'A System Solution to the Memory Soft Error Problem'. *IBM J. R&D*, **24**, No. 3, 390–397, 656.

Bossen, D. C. and Hsiao, M. Y. (1982). 'Model for Transient and Permanent Error-detection and Fault-isolation Coverage'. *IBM J. R&D*, **26**, No. 1, 67–77.

Bossen, D. C. (1970). 'b-Adjacent Error Correction'. *IBM J. R&D*, **14**, No. 4, 402.

Bossen, D. C. and Hong, S. J. (1971). 'Cause Effect Analysis for Multiple Fault Detection in Combinational Networks'. *IEEE TC*, **C-20**, No. 11, 1252.

Brahme, D. and Abraham, J. A. (1984). 'Functional Testing of Microprocessors'.

IEEE TC, **C-33**, No. 6, 475–495.

Breuer, M. A. and Friedman, A. D. (1976). *Diagnosis and Reliable Design of Digital Systems*. Computer Science Press, Inc., Woodland Hills, California.

Carter, J. L. (1982). 'The Theory of Signature Testing for VLSI'. *Proc. 14th Symp. on Theory of Computing*.

Carter, W. C. *et al.* (1970). 'Error-free Decoding for Failure Tolerant Memories'. *Proc. IEEE Comp. Group Conference*, 25–30.

Carter, W. C. and Wadia, A. B. (1980). 'Design and Analysis of Codes and Their Self-checking Circuit Implementations for Correction and Detection of Multiple b-Adjacent Errors'. *Proc. FTCS-10*, 35–40.

Carter, W. C., Jessep, D. C., Wadia, A. B., Schneider, P. R. and Bouricius, W. G. (1971). 'Logic Design for Dynamic and Interactive Recovery'. *IEEE TC*, **C-20**, No. 11, 1300–1305.

Carter, W. C. and McCarthy, C. E. (1976). 'Implementation of an Experimental Fault-tolerant Memory System'. *IEEE TC*, **C-25**, No. 6, 557.

Carter, W. C., Montgomery, H. C., Preiss, R. J. and Reinheimer, H. J. (1964). 'Design of Serviceability Features for the IBM System/360'. *IBM J. R&D*, **8**, No. 2, 115–126.

Carter, W. C., Putzolu, G. R., Wadia, A. B., Bouricius, W. G., Jessep, D. C., Hsieh, E. P. and Tan, C. J. (1977). 'Cost Effectiveness of Self-checking Computer Design'. *Proc. FTCS-7*, Los Angeles, 117.

Carter, W. C. and Schneider, P. R. (1968). 'Design of Dynamically Checked Computers'. *Proc. IFIP 68*, 878–883.

Carter, W. C., Wadia, A. B. and Jessep, D. C. (1971). 'Implementation of Checkable Acyclic Automata by Morphic Boolean Functions'. *Proc. Symp. Computer and Automata*, Polytechnic Inst. of Brooklyn, 465–482.

Chandy, K. M. (1975). 'A Survey of Analytic Models of Roll-back and Recovery Strategies'. *Computer*, **8**, No. 5, 40–47.

Chang, H. Y. and Heimbigner, G. W. (1974). 'Controllability, Observability, and Maintenance Engineering Technique (COMET)'. *BSTJ*, **53**, 1505.

Chang, H. Y. and Scanlon, J. M. (1969). 'Design Principles for Processor Maintainability in Real-time Systems'. *Proc. FJCC*, **35**, Las Vegas, 319–328.

Chang, H. Y., Smith, G. W. and Walford, R. B. (1974). 'LAMP System Description'. *BSTJ*, **53**, 1431–1442.

Chang, H. Y. *et al.* (1973). 'The Design of a Microprogrammed Self-Checking Processor for an Electronic Switching System'. *IEEE TC*, **C-22**, 489–499.

Chen, C. L. and Hsiao, M. Y. (1984). 'Error-correction Codes for Semiconductor Memory Applications: A State-of-the-Art Review'. *IBM J. R&D*, **28**, No. 2, 124–134.

Chwa, K.-Y. and Hakimi, S. L. (1981). 'Schemes for Fault-tolerant Computing: A Comparison of Modularly Redundant and t-Diagnosable Systems'. *Info. & Control*, 212–238.

Cook, R. W. *et al.* (1973). 'Design of a Self-checking Microprogram Control Unit'. *IEEE TC*, **C-22**, 255–262.

Cristian, F. (1982). 'Exception Handling and System Fault Tolerance'. *IEEE TC*, **C-31**, 531–539.

Dahbura, A. T. and Masson, G. M. (1983). 'Greedy Diagnosis as the Basis of an Intermittent-fault/Transient-upset Tolerant System Design'. *IEEE TC*, **C-32**, No. 10, 953–957.

Dahbura, A. T. and Masson, G. M. (1984). 'A Practical Variation of the $O(n^{2.5})$

Fault Diagnosis Algorithm'. *Proc. FTCS-14*, 482–432.

Daly, W. F., Hopkins, A. L. Jr. and McKenna, J. F. (1973). 'A Fault-tolerant Digital Clocking System'. *Proc. FTCS-3*, 17–22.

Darringer, J. A. *et al.* (1981). 'Logic Synthesis Through Local Transformations'. *IBM J. R&D*, **25**, No. 4, 272–280.

David, R. and Blanchet, G. (1976). 'About Random Fault Detection of Combinational Networks'. *IEEE TC*, **C-25**, No. 6, 659–664.

David, R. (1984). 'Signature Analysis of Multi-output Circuits'. *Proc. FTCS-14*, 366–371.

David, R. (1980). 'Testing by Feedback Shift Register'. *IEEE TC*, **C-29**, No. 7, 668–673.

Davidson, E. E. (1982). 'Electrical Design of High-speed Computer Package'. *IBM J. R&D*, **26**, No. 3, 349–361.

Denning, P. J. (1976). 'Fault-tolerant Operating Systems'. *ACM Comp. Surveys*, **8**, No. 4, 359–389.

Diaz, M. (1974). 'Design of Totally Self-checking and Failsafe Sequential Machines'. *Proc. FTCS-4*, 3–19.

Dickinson, M. M. *et al.* (1964). 'Saturn V Launch Vehicle Digital Computer and Adapter'. *Proc. FJCC*, **26**, San Francisco, 501.

Eichelberger, E. B. (1965). 'Hazard Detection in Combinational and Sequential Switching Circuits'. *IBM J. R&D*, **9**, No. 2, 90.

Eichelberger, E. B. and Williams, T. W. (1977), 'A Logic Design Structure for LSI Testability'. *Proc. DA Conference*, 462–468.

Eifert, J. B. and Shen, J. P. (1984). 'Processor Monitoring Using Asynchronous Signatured Instruction Streams'. *Proc. FTCS-14*, 394–399.

Eldred, R. D. (1959). 'Test Routines Based on Symbolic Logic Statements'. *JACM* **6**, No. 1, 33.

El-ziq, Y. M. (1983). 'Classifying, Testing, and Eliminating VLSI MOS Failures'. *VLSI Design*, Sept., 30–35.

Evensen, A. J. and Troy, J. L. (1973). 'Intro. to the Architecture of a 288-element Parallel Element Processing Ensemble (PEPE)'. *Sagamore Comp. Conf. on Parallel Proc.*, 162–170.

Everett, R. R. *et al.* (1957). 'SAGE – A Data-processing System for Air Defense'. *Proc. EJCC*, 148–155.

Fedi, Xavier and David, R., (1984). 'Experimental Results from Random Testing of Microprocessors'. *Proc. FTCS-14*, 225–30.

Fitzsimons, R. M. (1972). 'TRIDENT – A New Maintenance Weapon'. *Proc. FJCC*, **41**, 255.

Forbes, R. E., Rutherford, D. H., Stieglitz, C. B. and Tung, L. H. (1965). 'A Self-diagnosable Computer'. *FJCC*, **27**, San Francisco, 1073–1087.

Fox, J. L. (1975). 'Availability Design of the System/370 Model 168 Multi-processor'. *Proc. 2nd. USA-Japan Comp. Conf.*, 52–57.

Franaszek, P. E. (1972). 'Run-length-limited Variable Length Coding with Error Propagation Limitation'. U.S. Patent 3 689 899 (Harker, J.M., *IBM J. R&D*, 1981 **25**, No. 5, 688).

Friedman, A. D. (1967). 'Fault Detection in Redundant Circuits'. *IEEE TC*, **C-16**, No. 2, 99.

Friedman, A. D. (1975). 'A New Measure of Digital System Diagnosis'. *Proc. FTCS-5*, Paris, 167–170.

Frison, S. G. and Wensley, J. H. (1982). 'Interactive Consistency and its Impact on the Design of TMR Systems'. *Proc. FTCS-12*, 228–233.

Frohwerk, R. A. (1977). 'Signature Analysis: A New Digital Field Service Method'. *H-P Jour.*, No. 5, 2–8.

Fujiwara, E. (1983). 'A Self-testing Group-parity Prediction Checker and its Use for Built-in Testing'. *Proc. FTCS-13*, 146–153.

Fujiwara, H. and Kinoshita, K. (1978). 'Testing Logic Circuits with Compressed Data'. *Proc. FTCS-8*, 108–113.

Fujiwara, H., Kinoshita, K. and Ozaki, H. (1980). 'Universal Test Sets for Programmable Logic Arrays'. *Proc. FTCS-10*, 137–142.

Gay, F. A. (1977). 'Reliability of Partially Self-checking Circuits'. *Proc. FTCS-7*, 135.

Gelenbe, E. (1977). *On the Optimum Checkpoint Interval. IRIA, Rapport de Recherche No. 232.*

Goel, P. (1980a). 'An Implicit Enumeration Algorithm to Generate Tests for Combinational Logic Circuits'. *Proc. FTCS-10*, 145–151.

Goel, P. (1980b). 'Test Generation Costs Analysis and Projections'. *Proc. 17th DA Conference*, 77–84.

Goldstein, L. H. and Thigpen, E. L. (1980). 'SCOAP: Controllability/Observability Analytic Program'. *Proc. 17th DA Conf.*, 190–196.

Goldstein, L. H. (1977). 'A Probabilistic Analysis of Multiple Faults in LSI Circuits'. *IEEE CS Repository*, R-77-304, IEEE CS, Long Beach, California.

Goldstein, L. H. (1979). 'Controllability/Observability Analysis of Digital Circuits'. *IEEE Trans. Circuits & Systems*, **CAS-26**, No. 9, 684–693.

Grason, J. (1979). 'TMEAS – a Testability Measurement Program'. *Proc. 16th DA Conf.*, 156–161.

Grason, J. and Nagle, A. W. (1980). 'Digital Test Generation and Design for Testability'. *Proc. 17th DA Conference*, 175–189.

Griesmer, J. H. *et al.* (1984). 'A Continuous Real Time Expert System to Assist Computer Operators'. *Proc. AAAI-84*.

Hackl, F. J. and Shirk, R. W. (1965). 'An Integrated Approach to Automated Computer Maintenance'. *IEEE Conf. Rec. on Switch Theory & Log. Des.*, 289–302.

Hakimi, S. L. (1977). 'Fault Analysis in Digital Systems – A Graph Theoretic Approach'. Chapter in *Rational Fault Analysis*, Saeks, R., and Liberty, S. R., eds., Marcel Dekker, Inc., New York, 1.

Hamming, R. W. (1950). 'Error Detecting and Error Correcting Codes'. *BSTJ*, **29**, 147–160.

Hayes, J. P. (1971). 'A NAND Model for Fault Diagnosis in Combinational Logic Networks'. *IEEE TC*, **C-20**, No. 12, 1496–1506.

Hayes, J. P. (1974). 'On Modifying Logic Networks to Improve their Diagnosability'. *IEEE TC*, **C-23**, No. 1, 56–62.

Hitchcock, R. B. Sr. *et al.* (1982). 'Timing Analysis of Computer Hardware'. *IBM J. R&D*, **26**, No. 1, 100–105.

Hitt, D. C. and Woessner, R. J. (1971). 'Universal System Service Adapter'. US. Patent 3 585 599.

Hong, S. J. and Ostapko, D. L. (1980). 'FITPLA: A Programmable Logic Array for Function Independent Testing'. *Proc. FTCS-10*, 131–136.

Hopkins, A. L. and Smith, T. B. (1975). 'The Architectural Elements of a Symmetric Fault-tolerant Multiprocessor'. *IEEE TC*, **C-24**, No. 5, 498–505.

Hopkins, A. L. and Smith, T. B. (1977). 'OSIRIS-A Distributed Fault-tolerant

Control System'. *Proc. COMPCON*, Spring, 279.

Horning, J. J. *et al.* (1974). 'A Program Structure for Error Detection and Recovery'. *Lecture Notes in Comp. Sci.*, **16**, Springer-Verlag, 171–187.

Hosseini, S. H., Kuhl, J. G. and Reddy, S. M. (1984). 'A Diagnosis Algorithm for Distributed Computing Systems with Dynamic Failure and Repair'. *IEEE TC*, **C-33**, 223–233.

Hsiao, M. Y. (1970). 'A Class of Optimal Minimum Odd-weight-column SEC/DED Codes'. *IBM J. R&D*, **14**, No. 4, 395.

Hsiao, M. Y. *et al.* (1981). 'Reliability, Availability, and Serviceability of IBM Computer Systems: A Quarter Century of Progress'. *IBM J. R&D*, **25**, No. 5, 453–465.

Hsieh, E. P. *et al.* (1977). 'Delay Test Generation'. *Proc. DA Workshop*, 486–494.

Huang, K-H. K. and Abraham, J. A. (1982). 'Low Cost Schemes for Fault Tolerance in Matrix Operations with Processor Arrays'. *Proc. FTCS-12*, 330–337.

Ibarra, O. H. and Sahni, S. J. (1975). 'Polynomially Complete Fault Detection Problems'. *IEEE TC*, **C-24**, No. 3, 242.

Ihara, H. and Mori, K. (1984). 'Autonomous Decentralized Computer Control Systems'. *Computer*, **17**, No. 8, 57–66.

Ingle, A. D. and Siewiorek, D. P. (1976). 'A Reliability Model for Various Switch Designs in Hybrid Redundancy'. *IEEE TC*, **C-25**, No. 2, 115–133.

Isaacson, P. (1980). Guest editorial: 'Window on the 80's'. *Computer*, **13**, 4–7.

Jha, H. K. and Abraham, J. A. (1984). 'The Design of Totally Self-checking Embedded Checkers'. *Proc. FTCS-14*, 265–271.

Kaneda, S. and Fujiwara, E. (1980). 'Single Byte Error Correcting Double Byte Error Detecting Codes for Memory Systems'. *Proc. FTCS-10*, 41–46.

Karunanithi, S. and Friedman, A. D. (1977). 'System Diagnosis with t/s Diagnosability'. *Proc. FTCS-7*, 65.

Kinoshita, K. and Saluja, K. K. (1984). 'Built-In Testing of Memory Chips'. *Tech. Rpt. EE8335*, Dept. of EE and Comp. E. Univ. of Newcastle, Australia.

Knaizak, J. Jr. and Hartmann, C. P. R. (1977). 'An Optimal Algorithm for Testing Random Access Memories'. *IEEE TC*, **C-26**, 1141–1144.

Ko, D. C. and Breuer, M. A. (1978). 'Self-checking of Multi-output Combinational Circuits Using Extended-parity Technique'. *J. DA&FT Comp.*, 29–62.

Konemann, B., Mucha, J. and Zweihoff, G. (1979). 'Built-in Logic Block Observation Techniques'. *Proc. IEEE Test Conf.*, 37–41.

Kraft, G. D. and Toy, W. N. (1981). *Microprogrammed Control and Reliable Design of Small Computers*, Prentice-Hall.

Kuban, J. and Bruce, W. (1983). 'The MC6804P2 Built-in Self-test'. *Proc. IEEE Test Conf.*, 295–300.

Lancto, D. C. and Rockefeller, R. L. (1967). 'The Operational Error Analysis Program'. *IBM Sys. J.*, **6**, No. 2, 103–149.

Langdon, G. G. Jr. (1984). 'An Introduction to Arithmetic Coding'. *IBM J. R&D*, **28**, No. 2, 135–149.

Laprie, J.-C. (1984). 'Proposal to IFIP WG 10.4, Reliable Computing and Fault Tolerance'. *Research Report No. 84.035*, LAAS-CNRS, Toulouse, France.

Larson, R. W. and Reed, I. S. (1972). 'Redundancy by Coding versus Redundancy by Replication for Failure-tolerant Sequential Circuits'. *IEEE TC*, **C-21**, No. 2, 130–137.

Lee, P. A. *et al.* (1980). 'A Recovery Cache for the PDP-11'. *IEEE TC*, **C-29**, No.

6, 546–549.

Levitt, K. N., Green, M. W. and Goldberg, J. (1968). 'A Study of the Data Communication Problems in a Self-repairable Multiprocessor'. *Proc. SJCC*, **32**, Atlantic City, 515–527.

Liu, T. S. (1984). 'The Role of a Maintenance Processor for a General-purpose Computer System'. *IEEE TC*, **C-33**, No. 6, 507–517.

Logue, J. L. *et al.* (1975). 'Hardware Implementation of a Small System in Programmable Logic Arrays'. *IBM J. R&D*, **19**, No. 2, 110–115.

Lomet, D. B. (1977). 'Process Structuring, Synchronization and Recovery Using Atomic Actions'. *SIGPLAN Notices*. **12**, No. 3, 128–137.

Lu, D. J. (1982). 'Watchdog Processors and Structural Integrity Checking'. *IEEE TC*, **C-31**, No. 7, 681–685.

Maestri, G. H. (1972). 'The Retryable Processor'. *AFIPS Conf. Proc. FJCC* **41**, Anaheim, Ca., 273–277.

Maheshwari, S. N. and Hakimi, S. L. (1976). 'On Models for Diagnosable Systems and Probabilistic Fault Diagnosis'. *IEEE TC*, **C-25**, No. 3, 228–237.

Mahmood, A., McCluskey, E. J. and Lu, D. J. (1983). 'Concurrent Fault Detection Using a Watchdog Processor and Assertions'. *IEEE Int. Test Conf.*, 622–628.

Marauf, M. A. and Friedman, A. D. (1977). 'Efficient Design of Self-checking Checkers for m out of n Codes'. *Proc. FTCS-7*, Los Angeles, 14.

Mathur, F. and Avizienis, A. (1970). 'Reliability Analysis and Architecture of a Hybrid-redundant Digital System: Generalized Triple Modular Redundancy with Self-repair'. *Proc. SJCC*, **36**, Atlantic City, 375–383.

Matick, R. E. (1982). 'Comparison of Memory Chip Organizations vs. Reliability in Virtual Memories'. *Proc. FTCS-12*, 223–227.

McCluskey, E. J. (1982). 'Built-in Verification Test'. *Proc. IEEE Test Conf.*, 183–190.

McCluskey, E. J. and Clegg, F. W. (1971). 'Fault Equivalence in Combinational Logic Networks'. *IEEE TC*, **C-20**, No. 11, 1286.

Meyer, J. F. (1971). 'Fault Tolerant Sequential Machines'. *IEEE TC*, **C-20**, No. 10, 1167–1177.

Min, Y. (1984). 'A PLA Design for Ease of Test Generation'. *Proc. FTCS-14*, 436–442.

Monachino, M. (1982). 'Design Verification System for Large-Scale LSI Designs'. *IBM J. R&D*, **26**, No. 1, 89–99.

Moore, E. F. and Shannon, C. E. (1956). 'Reliable Circuits Using Less Reliable Relays'. *J. Franklin Inst.*, **262**, 191–208 and 281.

Murray, N. D., Hopkins, A. L. and Wensley, J. H. (1977). 'Highly Reliable Multiprocessors'. AGARDograph No. 224, *Integrity in Electronic Flight Control Systems*, NATO.

Nair, R. (1979). 'Comments on "An Optimal Algorithm for Testing Stuck-at Faults in Random Access Memories"'. *IEEE TC*, **C-28**, No. 3, 258–261.

Nair, R. (1978). *Diagnosis, Self-diagnosis, and Roving Diagnosis in Distributed Digital Systems*. Ph.D. Thesis, Univ. Illinois. Al.

Nair, R., Thatte, S. M. and Abraham, J. A. (1978). 'Efficient Algorithms for Testing Semiconductor Random-access Memories'. *IEEE TC*, **C-27**, No. 6, 572–576.

Namjoo, M. (1982). 'Techniques for Concurrent Testing of VLSI Processor Operation'. *IEEE 1982 Int. Test Conf.*, 461–468.

Nanya, T. and Tohma, Y. (1983). 'A 3-Level Realization of Totally Self-Checking Checkers for m-out-of-n Codes'. *Proc. FTCS-13*, 173–177.

Needham, R. M. and Walker, R. D. H. (1974). 'Protection and Process Management of the CAP Computer'. *IRIA Int. Wkshp. on Protection in Operating Sys.*, 155.

Ossfeldt, B. E. and Jonsson, I. (1980). 'Recovery and Diagnostics in the Central Control of the AXE Switching System'. *IEEE TC*, **C-29**, No. 6, 482–491.

Ostapko, D. L. and Hong, S. J. (1978). 'Fault Analysis and Test Generation for Programmable Logic Arrays (PLA)'. *Proc. FTCS-8*, 83–90.

Parker, K. P. and McCluskey, E. J. (1975). 'Probabilistic Treatment of General Combinational Networks'. *IEEE TC*, **C-24**, No. 6, 668–670.

Parnas, D. L. (1972). 'A Technique for Module Specification with Examples'. *Comm. ACM* **15**, No. 5, 330.

Patel, A. M. and Hong, S. J. (1974). 'Optimal Rectangular Code for High Density Magnetic Tapes'. *IBM J. R&D*, 579–588.

Pease, M., Shostak, R. and Lamport, L. (1980). 'Reaching Agreement in the Presence of Faults'. *JACM*, **27**, No. 2, 228–234.

Peterson, W. W. and Weldon, E.J., Jr. (1972). *Error-detecting Codes*. MIT Press.

Pfister, G. F. *et al.* (1982). Papers on The Yorktown Simulation Engine, *Proc. 19th DA Conference*, 51–64.

Pollard, L. H. and Patel, J. H. (1984). 'Fault Tolerant Techniques for Control Signals in Bus Communication Protocols'. *Proc. FTCS-14*, 380–385.

Prell, E. M. (1967). 'Automatic Trouble Isolation in Duplex Central Controls Employing Matching'. *Proc. SJCC*, **30**, Atlantic City, 765–770.

Preparata, F. P., Metze, G. and Chien, R. T. (1967). 'On the Connection Assignment Problem of Diagnosable Systems'. *IEEE TC*, **C-16**, No. 6, 848–854.

Putzolu, G. R. and Roth, J. P. (1971). 'An Heuristic Algorithm for the Testing of Asynchronous Circuits'. *IEEE TC*, **C-20**, No. 6, 639.

Ramamoorthy, C. V. (1967). 'A Structural Theory of Machine Diagnosis'. *AFIPS Proc. SJCC*, **30**, Atlantic City, 743–756.

Ramamoorthy, C. V. and Han, Y. W. (1975). 'Reliability Analysis of Systems with Concurrent Error Detection'. *IEEE TC*, **C-20**, No. 9, 868–878.

Rault, J. C. (1971). 'A Graph Theoretic and Probabilistic Approach to the Fault Detection of Digital Circuits'. *Proc. FTCS-1*, Los Angeles, 26.

Reilly, J., Sutton, A., Nasser, R. and Griscom, R. (1982). 'Processor Controller for the IBM 3081'. *IBM J. R&D*, **26**, No. 1, 22–29.

Reynolds, D. and Metze, G. (1976). 'Fault Detection Capabilities of Alternating Logic'. *Proc. FTCS-6*, 157–163.

Roth, J. P. (1966). 'Diagnosis of Automata Failures; a Calculus and a Method'. *IBM J. R&D*, **10**, No. 4, 278–291.

Roth, J. P., Bouricius, W. G. and Schneider, P. R. (1967a). Programmed Algorithms to Compute Tests to Detect and Distinguish Between Failures in Logic Circuits'. *IEEE TEC*, **EC-16**, No. 5, 567.

Roth, J. P. (1977). 'Hardware Verification'. *IEEE TC*, **C-26**, No. 12, 1292.

Roth, J. P., Oklobdzija, V. G. and Beetem, J. F. (1984). 'Test Generation for FET Switching Circuits'. *Proc. IEEE Test Conf.*, 59–62.

Russell, J. D. and Kime, C. R. (1975a). 'System Fault Diagnosis: Closure and Diagnosability with Repair'. *IEEE TC*, **C-24**, No. 11, 1078–1088.

Russell, J. D. and Kime, C. R. (1975b). 'System Fault Diagnosis: Masking, Exposure and Diagnosability Without Repair'. *IEEE TC*, **C-24**, No. 12,

1155–1161.

Savir, J., Ditlow, G. S. and Bardell, P. H. (1984). 'Random Pattern Testability'. *IEEE TC*, **C-33**, No. 1, 79–90.

Savir, J. (1983). 'Good Controllability and Observability do not Guarantee Good Testability'. *IEEE TC*, **C-32**, No. 12, 1198–1200.

Savir, J. and Bardell, P. H. (1983). 'On Random Test Length'. *Proc. Int. Test Conf.*, 95–106.

Schertz, D. R. and Metze, G. (1972). 'A New Representation for Faults in Combinational Digital Circuits'. *IEEE TC*, **C-21**, No. 8, 858–866.

Schneider, P. R. (1967). 'On the Necessity to Examine D-chains in Diagnostic Test Generation – an Example'. *IBM J. R&D*, **11**, No. 1, 114.

Schwab, T. F. and Yau, S. S. (1983). 'An Algebraic Model of Fault-Masking Logic Circuits'. *IEEE TC*, **C-32**, No. 9, 809–825.

Scola, P. (1972). 'An Annotated Bibliography of Test and Diagnostics'. *The Honeywell Computer Journal*, **6**, 2, 97–104.

Sellers, F. F., Hsiao, M. Y., and Bearnson, L. W. (1968a). 'Analyzing Errors with the Boolean Difference'. *IEEE TC*, **C-17**, No. 7, 676.

Sellers, F. F., Hsiao, M. Y. and Bearnson, L. W. (1968b). *Error Detecting Logic for Digital Computers*. McGraw-Hill, New York.

Serlin, O. (1984). 'Fault-Tolerant Systems in Commercial Applications'. *IEEE Computer*, **17**, No. 8, 19–30.

Shedlestsky, J. J. (1978). 'A Rollback Interval for Networks with an Imperfect Self-checking Property'. *IEEE TC*, **C-27**, No. 6, 500–508.

Shedletsky, J. J. (1977). 'Random Testing; Verified Effectiveness vs. Practicality'. *Proc. FTCS-7*, 175.

Shedletsky, J. J. and McCluskey, E. J. (1975). 'The Error Latency of a Fault in a Combinational Digital Circuit'. *Proc. FTCS-5*, Paris, 21.

Shedletsky, J. J. and McCluskey, E. J. (1976). 'The Error Latency of a Fault in a Sequential Digital Circuit'. *IEEE TC*, **C-25**, No. 6, 655–659.

Shubin, H. and Ulrich, J. W. (1982). 'IDT: An Intelligent Diagnostic Tool'. *Proc. Conf. on Art. Intel.*, 290–295.

Siewiorek, D. P. and Swarz, R. (1981). *Theory and Practice of Reliable Systems Design*, Digital Press, Bedford, Ma.

Smith, G. L. *et al.* (1982). 'Boolean Comparison of Hardware and Flowcharts'. *IBM J. R&D*, **26**, No. 1, 106–116.

Smith, J. E. and Metze, G. (1978). 'Strongly Fault Secure Logic Networks'. *IEEE TC*, **C-27**, No. 6, 491–499.

Smith, J. E. and Lam, P. (1983). 'A Theory of Totally Self-checking System Design'. *IEEE TC*, **C-32**, No. 9, 831–844.

Smith, T. B. III (1981). 'Generic Data Manipulative Primitives of Synchronous Fault-tolerant Computer Systems'. *Proc. FTCS-13*, supplement.

Smith, T. B. III (1984). 'Fault Tolerant Processor Concepts and Operation'. *Proc. FTCS-14*, 158–163.

Szygenda, S. A. (1972). 'TEGSA2 – Anatomy of General Purpose Test Generation and Simulation System for Digital Logic'. *Proc. DA Workshop*, Dallas, 116.

Tang, D. T. (1984). *Exhaustive Logic Testing and Self Testing*. IBM Research Report RC 10341.

Tendolkar, N. N. and Swann, R. L. (1982). 'Automated Diagnostic Methodology for the IBM 3081 Processor Complex'. *IBM J. R&D*, **26**, No. 1, 78–88.

Thatte, S. M. and Abraham, J. A. (1980). 'Test Generation for Microprocessors'.

IEEE TC, **C-29**, No. 6, 429–441.

Thevenod-Fosse, P. and David, R. (1981). 'Random Testing of the Data Processing Section of a Microprocessor'. *Proc. FTCS-13*, 275–280.

Thevenod-Fosse, P. and David, R. (1983). 'Random Testing of the Control Section of a Microprocessor'. *Proc. FTCS-13*, 366–373.

Timoc, C. *et al.* (1983). 'Logical Models of Physical Failures'. *Proc. IEEE Int. Test Conference*, 546–553.

Toy, W. N. (1978). 'Fault-tolerant Design of Local ESS Processors'. *Proc. IEEE*, **66**, No. 10, 1126–1127, 1144.

Tryon, J. G. (1962). 'Quadded Logic' in *Redundancy Techniques for Computing Systems'*, Wilcox, R. H., and Mann, W. C. eds., Spartan, Washington, D.C., 205–228.

Usas, A. M. (1975) 'A Totally Self-checking Checker Design for the Detection of Errors in Periodic Signals'. *IEEE TC*, **C-24**, No. 5, 483–488.

von Neumann, J. (1956). 'Probabilistic Logics and the Synthesis of Reliable Organisms from Unreliable Components', in *Automata Studies*, Shannon, C. E. and McCarthy, J., eds., Princeton Univ. Press, 43–98.

Wadsack, R. L. (1978). 'Fault Modeling and Logic Simulation of CMOS and MOS Integrated Circuits'. *BSTJ*, 1449–1474.

Wakerly, J. F. (1974). 'Partially Self-checking Circuits and their Use in Performing Logical Operations'. *IEEE TC*, **C-23**, No. 7, 658.

Wakerly, J. F. (1975a). 'Transient Failures in Triple Modular Redundant Systems with Sequential Modules'. *IEEE TC*, **C-24**, No. 5, 570.

Wakerly, J. F. (1975b). *Principles of Self-checking Processor Design and an Example*. Tech. Rpt. 115, Digital Systems Lab, Stanford Univ.

Wakerly, J. F. (1975c). 'Detection of Unidirectional Multiple Errors using Low-cost Arithmetic Codes'. *IEEE TC*, **C-24**, 210–212.

Wensley, J. H. *et al.* (1978). 'SIFT: The Design and Analysis of a Fault-tolerant Computer for Aircraft Control'. *Proc. IEEE*, **66**, No. 10, 1240–1255.

Williams, M. J. Y. and Angell, J. B. (1973). 'Enhancing Testability of Large Scale Integrated Circuits via Test Points and Additional Logic'. *IEEE TC*, **C-22**, No. 1, 46–60.

Wong, C. Y. *et al.* (1983). 'The Design of a Microprogram Control Unit with Concurrent Error Detection'. *Proc. FTCS-13*, 476–483.

Yamamoto, H., Watanabe, T. and Urano, Y. (1970). 'Alternating Logic and its Application to Fault Detection'. *Proc. of IEEE Comp. Grp. Conf.*, Washington, D.C., 220–227.

You, Y. and Hayes, J. P. (1984). 'A Self-testing Dynamic RAM Chip'. *Proc. Conf. on Advanced Research in VLSI*, MIT, 159–168.

CHAPTER 3

Design fault tolerance

P. A. Lee

(*Resolution Systems, Massachusetts*)

and

T. Anderson

(*Computing Laboratory, University of Newcastle upon Tyne*)

Fault tolerance is becoming generally accepted as an important and integral part of many computing systems, as witnessed by the success of Tandem Computers Incorporated and the spate of start-up companies trying to emulate their success. Before Tandem showed that fault tolerance was cost effective and applicable even to commercial systems, the prime target for fault tolerance had been in specialised systems where the demand for reliability was paramount (e.g. telephone switching systems and defence systems).

The tolerance provided in present-day systems has largely been for 'traditional' hardware faults – by this is meant anticipated hardware faults whose occurrence and effects can be predicted. By making such predictions about faults and by assuming that hardware failures will be independent from each other, it has been possible to provide effective techniques to enable a system to continue to function in the face of hardware failures. Chapter 2 provides a detailed description of these techniques.

Obviously, hardware techniques will continue to play an important role in fault tolerant systems. However, as anyone who has worked with computer systems knows, software is often the major cause of unreliability. Many examples of the problems caused by software have been published (presumably, many, many more have not been published). *Software fault tolerance*, i.e. tolerance of software 'bugs', is rarely provided in fault tolerant systems, even though appropriate techniques exist and have been proved successful. These techniques will be described in this chapter.

Generalising, software fault tolerance is a particular instance of what may be termed *design fault tolerance*. Any system, hardware or software, can be considered to consist of a set of *components*, together with a *design* which permits those components to interact in a controlled and desired manner (Anderson and Lee, 1981). For example, regarding a circuit board as a system, the various integrated circuits can be regarded as the components of that system, while the tracks and wires on the board are the design that permits those components to interact to achieve the desired function. As another example, a CPU, memory and peripherals can be regarded as components of a payroll system which interact under the control of the payroll software – the software is the design of the payroll system.

When regarded in this way, the design is a true and active part of the system, as opposed to a more abstract concept of the system's design as captured on circuit schematics or flowcharts. This view of the design as being an active part of the implemented system is slightly unusual; a design is conventionally thought of as a more abstract notion. However, some advantages do accrue from adopting this viewpoint. In particular, since the design is considered to form part of the system, it can be faulty just like any other component (in reality, the design *is* just another component, albeit with special properties); techniques which permit the tolerance of such *design faults* are the subject of this chapter. The abstract concept of design clearly plays a part during the conception and construction of a system, but can play no explicit role when a system is operational and attempting to provide fault tolerance. It is the run-time behaviour that is of vital importance, and hence it is important to consider the design as a part of the system that can malfunction. In the rest of this chapter the term 'design' will be used in this active sense.

How do design faults originate in a system? The primary cause is unmastered complexity which causes the human designer to make mistakes. For example, software bugs can be introduced because the designer failed to consider a special case; in a complex hardware system connections can easily be misrouted, or omitted altogether. Such design faults will be present in the system from the start of its operation, but will be *latent* in that their effects will not be seen until that 'special case' occurs (as it undoubtedly will!). Of course, if the design fault is in a part of the system which is frequently used, or dependent upon a set of circumstances which arise frequently, then its effects will most likely be seen when the system is being tested. This is the prime reason for debugging hardware and software – to remove faults before reliability is an issue.

However, there can be no guarantee that testing can reveal all the latent design faults in a system. What this implies is that those residual design faults which are not detected during debugging will only manifest themselves in relatively obscure situations and hence with abstruse effects – this is one of the properties of design faults which complicates techniques for tolerating them, as is discussed subsequently.

A system's design is normally fixed, and not intended to change as the system operates (e.g. it is not expected that the payroll system will turn into a stock control system by accident). Hence, it is usual for a design fault to be present in the system from the start of its operation. However, since the design is one of the components of a system, there will be lower level components implementing that design. For example, the memory storing a program, or a wire interconnecting two chips, are such components of a design. It is possible for one of these components to fail, the outcome of which is that the system's design changes and thus a design fault is introduced into the system. For example, a wire could become detached and cause a short, or bits in the memory could change state and transform one instruction into another. If such an event is not detected directly, then the observed effect will naturally be that of a design fault – a memory failure causing an instruction to be transformed will have the same effect as the programmer generating the wrong instruction in the first place. (Conceivably, such failures could result in an existing design fault being repaired, but events are rarely so fortuitous.) The end effect of these undetected component failures is that the system will subsequently contain a design fault.

An alternative way of defining the presence of a design fault in a system is to consider the case when all of the components in a system are functioning correctly, but the system still fails. In this situation, the failure can only be attributable to a design fault.

So, the design fault tolerance approach is concerned with techniques for dealing with defects in the system's design. The difficulty of doing this stems from the nature of design faults. As discussed above, the design faults that remain in a system are usually rather obscure since otherwise (a) the mistake wouldn't have been made in the first place; or (b) system testing would have uncovered the problem. (Incompetence can override both of these considerations, however.) The exact nature of the design fault cannot be known or it would have been removed, and hence when the fault manifests itself its effects will be *unexpected*, *unpredicted* and *unanticipated*. The only prediction that can be made with confidence is that any complex system will contain residual design faults.

While the general principles on which fault tolerance is based are the same for design faults as for other faults, it is the implementation of those principles that requires different approaches to those currently employed for tolerating hardware problems. As noted earlier, most present-day hardware fault tolerance techniques rely on knowledge about the assumed failure modes of the components in question. Predictions can be made of when a physical component is likely to fail due to physical deterioration, and of precisely how that component will fail. Specific fault tolerance measures can then be implemented to detect and deal with the failure should it occur. For example, semiconductor memories usually provide efficient encoding schemes so that single-bit failures can be corrected and double-bit failures can be detected (Peterson and Weldon, 1972), these having been observed to be the most common modes of failure; multiple-bit failures are likely to overwhelm those fault tolerance techniques, as are design faults such as race conditions in the timing circuitry. It can be appreciated that techniques for predicted situations have little utility for the tolerance of design faults with their unexpected behaviour patterns.

The prime source of design faults affecting present-day systems is to be found in the software components. Hardware designs have usually been sufficiently simple for their residual design faults to be exposed and corrected during the testing phase and thus are not present in the operational system. (This is not to say that hardware design faults are unknown! Many of the 'glitches' in systems which cannot be tracked down may well be the consequence of unknown or unpublicised hardware design faults.) The proliferation of VLSI techniques is increasing the complexity of hardware to the extent that the prevalence of design faults in the hardware may well become a serious hardware reliability problem. If it does, the techniques discussed in this chapter, primarily in a software framework, will have equal applicability at the hardware levels.

In the next section the principles of fault tolerance and their application to design fault tolerance will be discussed. There then follows a description of *recovery blocks* and *N-version programming*, the two software fault tolerance schemes that have been proposed. The concluding section of the chapter reviews the current state of the adoption and recognition of design fault tolerance, and some of the experimental results that have been derived from practical applications of such techniques.

FUNDAMENTAL CONCEPTS OF DESIGN FAULT TOLERANCE

Discussion of these concepts will take place with respect to the simple system illustrated in Fig. 3.1, where a software or hardware module M takes inputs and generates outputs to be used elsewhere. The techniques to be discussed concern just how design fault tolerance can be added to make the outputs seen by the rest of the system tolerant of design faults in M.

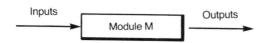

Fig. 3.1 Single module.

All fault tolerance techniques depend on redundancy being added to the system to detect the effects of a fault and to compensate for its presence. To be able to tolerate faults in the components from which a module M is constructed the designer essentially has two choices: either to add component redundancy within M (to make the components themselves more reliable), or to replicate M itself. However, the former option of adding internal redundancy to M is not appropriate if design faults within M are to be tolerated. In this case, it will be necessary to provide redundant versions of the module itself. Of course, direct copies of the module are also inappropriate for design fault tolerance; what is required is that *independently designed* alternative modules be provided. Without this independence of design, there is the obvious danger that all modules could suffer from the same design fault and hence all fail at the same time.

As well as the multiple alternative modules, it is also necessary to provide an *adjudication module* (Anderson, 1984), the purpose of which is to examine the outputs from the modules in order to detect and deal with the case when one or more outputs is erroneous. The success of the fault tolerance depends to a great extent on this adjudication module, and its operation will be considered in greater depth in following sections. However, it can be seen that the adjudication module has responsibility for detecting and rejecting erroneous outputs, while the availability of multiple modules provides the means by which the system can continue to provide its service in the face of design faults within the individual modules.

When a fault manifests itself in a system, i.e. has some effect on the system's operation, the outcome is that errors are generated in the state of the system. The fault is the cause, the errors are the effect. Both are likely to require action if fault tolerance is to be successful in preventing a system failure. Thus the main features of any implementation of design fault tolerance can be identified in the following two fundamental concepts:

(1) Detecting and dealing with errors, the effects of the fault.
(2) Locating and dealing with the cause, the fault itself.

(In this regard, the provision of design fault tolerance is no different to any other fault tolerance technique.)

For example, consider the presence of a bug in a program flying an aeroplane which causes the plane to dive towards the ground under a certain combination of events. If those events arise, correction of the currently erroneous (nose-down) state of the plane will certainly avert the most immediate potential failure, but this will be of little avail if the bug immediately recurs. Successful fault tolerance requires dealing with the bug as well as correcting the state.

DEALING WITH ERRORS

Before any fault tolerance techniques can be utilised, it is necessary to detect that something has gone wrong, i.e. to detect the presence of errors generated by the fault. The difficulty in doing this for design faults stems from the unpredictable nature of the errors. Unlike predicted faults, where a direct test for the expected erroneous results can be used, error detection for design faults has to adopt a different approach. Since the erroneous effects of a design fault are unpredictable, error detection must be based on checking the validity of the results produced rather than on checking to see whether specific erroneous states have arisen.

Ideally, what is required is that the detection mechanism within the adjudication module tests whether the results generated by M (or a version of M) are correct, and also checks that M has not changed anything else in the system of which it is a part. For example, if M was controlling an aircraft's attitude, the fact that the next set of control values calculated by M were correct would be somewhat irrelevant if M had somehow managed to switch off the engines. The need to confine the activity of a module will be returned to subsequently.

It must be recognised that, since error detection is performed by another component in series with the module it is checking, unreliability in the error detection component can have a dramatic impact on the overall system reliability. Hence, error detection mechanisms must themselves have high reliability. Note also that the need for a reliable error detection mechanism requires that the mechanism and the module being checked are as independent as possible, so that they cannot be affected by common faults which could otherwise destroy the effectiveness of the error detection.

As with many engineering situations, a conflicting set of requirements must be resolved. On the one hand, it is desirable that the error detection mechanisms completely check all aspects of the module they are monitoring and detect all errors; on the other hand the mechanisms themselves must be simple enough that their reliability can be guaranteed. Also, the check and the module must be independent and, for performance reasons, it is not usually acceptable to have a check that significantly degrades the overall performance of the system.

For some tasks it is relatively easy to formulate checks which satisfy these conditions. Many tasks perform a complex mapping from their inputs to their outputs, while the inverse mapping from outputs back to inputs remains fixed and simple. For these tasks, a *reversal check* can produce a suitable error detection mechanism satisfying the above conditions, where the check must calculate what the inputs should have been to produce the generated outputs. The calculated inputs can then be compared with the actual inputs to see if there is a discrepancy. Many mathematical control computations lend themselves to reversal checks. A reversal check was also employed in the hardware of an early fault tolerant computer, the JPL-STAR (Avizienis *et al.*, 1971), where the active gating signals in a hardware module were used to evaluate what function had been requested, which was then compared with the actual function requested to see whether any hardware malfunctions had occurred.

Of course, a reversal check is not appropriate for many tasks, and since it is rarely feasible to provide a simple reliable test for complete correctness, some lower standard of checking must be used. Such checks test for the *acceptability* of the results rather than checking their complete accuracy, so their coverage (i.e. the percentage of errors that they actually detect) is less than 100%. Of course, the aim in designing acceptability checks is to maximise coverage while maximising the simplicity (and therefore the reliability) of the check. The nature of acceptability checks is that they are system specific, and as such very little specific guidance can be given for their construction. Also, it is very difficult to obtain accurate estimates of their actual coverage. Another approach to error detection which can overcome some of these problems is based on the notion of a *replication check*. Replication checks, as their name suggests, entail calculating the outputs in a replicated fashion and then comparing the replicated results for discrepancies. For obvious performance reasons, the replicated calculations usually take place in parallel, as shown in Fig. 3.2. While duplication of the module M is sufficient for detecting errors, higher levels of replication can be deployed to aid the task of recovery and fault location, as will be discussed subsequently.

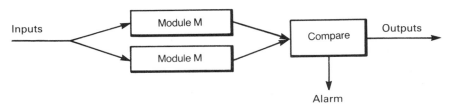

Fig. 3.2 Replicated module.

Replication checks with this structure have been, and continue to be, used in hardware systems for detecting component failures. For example, many systems check the operation of a microprocessor by running two in parallel and comparing output signals. But when using this structure for design fault tolerance, the approach of using exact copies of the module will not suffice – if both modules contain the same design fault they will clearly both produce the same wrong answers. Thus for design fault tolerance it is necessary for the replication to provide independently designed modules in the hope that they do not contain the same design faults.

At first glance, a replication check seems a much better mechanism for detecting errors than an acceptability check. In practice, though, some further complications have to be taken into account when considering the advantages and disadvantages of replication checks and acceptability checks.

Firstly, since it cannot be guaranteed that independently designed modules will produce their outputs at exactly the same time, the replication check has to take into account the different execution times of the modules, as well as the case where a module has crashed without sending any results, or is in an infinite loop. The overall execution time of the replicated module is thus constrained by the slowest module. In contrast, if the results of a replicated module are tested by an acceptability check then, in the absence of errors, the overall speed is governed by the speed of the fastest module.

Secondly, it may not be possible to ensure that independently designed modules produce the identical results that a simple comparison mechanism would require. If correct outputs could lie within a range of values then a simple bit-by-bit comparison would no longer suffice. For example, consider a software module containing floating point calculations. Different rounding errors resulting from different sequences of floating point operations in independently designed modules would produce results which were not identical. Another instance where different but correct results could be produced from multiple versions is when more than one distinct solution exists for a single set of inputs. For example, a sorting routine may be required to sort on only one key in a record; if multiple records with that key exist then differently designed modules could output those records in different orders, while still satisfying the requirement that the records be ordered on that particular key.

When complications such as these are taken into account, the replication check begins to lose much of its appeal, since dealing with these complications introduces many of the problems discussed earlier for acceptability checks. The complexity of the replication check is further exacerbated by techniques to cope with differences in the execution times of modules. Furthermore, when replication with more than two modules is implemented (for example, triple modular redundancy) the number of cases that have to be accounted for in the check can greatly increase its complexity. For example, to perform a range check between the answers from N modules is essentially combinatorial in nature. Nevertheless, when a simple comparison check can be formulated, a replication check comes close to the ideal for an error detection mechanism.

ERROR RECOVERY

Following error detection, the problem of *error recovery* must be considered. The detection of an error serves primarily to show the presence of a fault in a module, but does not necessarily identify all of the errors caused by that fault. For example, there may have been a delay between the manifestation of a fault and the subsequent detection of an error, during which time other corruptions of the state of the system could ensue. Thus the problem of confining the activity of a module must be considered before any error recovery can take place.

The simplest solution to this confinement problem is to attempt to guarantee at system design time that a module is completely isolated from the rest of the system (except for its input/output paths), and that the module can only affect the state of the rest of the system when the outputs are thought to be error free. The effects of any design faults in that module will then be limited to damage to the internal state of the module and corruption of the output values, which should be detected. This is a standard solution for replicated hardware systems, where physical separation often ensures the isolation required.

For software modules, this level of isolation can be harder to guarantee, except in capability-based systems (Levy, 1984) where a very fine grain of protection can be exploited, or in systems where the modules can be executed on physically separated computers. Without hardware mechanisms to enforce isolation, a program containing a design fault could easily corrupt a part of the system state to which it was not intended to have access.

If confinement of activity is achieved, then the use of replicated modules can obviate the need for error recovery. If three or more modules are available, the replication check can be extended to implement *majority voting* on the set of outputs it receives. Assuming that a majority of the outputs will be correct, any outputs which do not conform to that majority can be discarded as erroneous. Only voted-on results are permitted to affect the system's state.

An alternative approach is to provide a recovery technique powerful enough to deal with the effects of design faults. To reiterate, the problem is that of coping with the unexpected – the damage caused by a design fault cannot be known beforehand. Fortunately, *backward error recovery* is such a general recovery technique.

Backward error recovery is based on the notion of state restoration. If a copy of the system's state is saved just before a module is executed then restoration of that saved state *must eradicate all of the effects of that module's execution*. Hence, if a design fault affected the execution of a module then restoration of the state prior to that module's execution will remove *all* of the errors caused by the fault. It is exactly this characteristic which is needed for a recovery technique for design fault tolerance.

The principal advantage of backward error recovery over confining the activity of a module is in removing restrictions on the way in which modules are programmed. The main disadvantages are (a) the potential expense of having to save the system state; and (b) the fact that state restoration may not be applicable to all of the objects in the system (so-called 'unrecoverable' objects). However, mechanisms based on the approach of automatically saving only those portions of the state that are modified during the module's execution have been proposed and built (Lee *et al.*, 1980), and have been shown to provide effective solutions.

The problem of unrecoverable objects is typified by the example of printing a cheque on a lineprinter – it is difficult to recover from this event by state restoration. In practice, multi-level recovery techniques (Anderson *et al.*, 1978) can provide solutions, roughly categorisable into (a) providing actions to compensate for unrecoverable actions if recovery is invoked (e.g. send a message to the operator requesting destruction of the printed cheque – and send a message to the bank to stop payment of the cheque just in case the operator missed it); and (b) postponing unrecoverable actions until after the results have been accepted and recovery can no longer be invoked (e.g. spooling the print cheque request in a file which can be discarded if recovery is invoked). Note that the latter solution is essentially the same as constraining a module's execution to have no global effects, as discussed earlier.

DEALING WITH DESIGN FAULTS

When either an acceptability check or a replication check is applied to a software module's outputs and an error is detected then it is likely that that module is the one containing a design fault. However, there is little else that the running system can do to further locate the fault, since the nature of design faults means that human intervention is required. (Even humans are notoriously bad at locating and fixing design faults.) Since the redundancy provided is at the module level anyway, there would be little point in attempting, at run-time, to locate the fault more accurately. Of course, as many details as possible should be logged for off-line analysis.

The question arises as to whether, once identified as containing a design fault, a module should continue to be used. In hardware systems, a module with a permanent fault is usually removed from active service. While design faults are usually permanent, they normally behave as if they were transient, since it is generally an unusual set of circumstances which causes the latent fault to be manifest. Thus there may be some merit in merely avoiding the faulty module for the particular iteration which generated the errors. At the next iteration the faulty module could again be invoked in the hope that the next set of inputs will not cause the fault to manifest itself.

SCHEMES FOR SOFTWARE FAULT TOLERANCE

Schemes designed to provide software fault tolerance have been the subject of substantial research since 1973/4. Two main schemes have been proposed, namely the *Recovery Block Scheme* developed by a research team at the University of Newcastle upon Tyne, and the *N-Version Programming Scheme* which was devised by workers at the University of California at Los Angeles.

THE RECOVERY BLOCK SCHEME

The recovery block approach to software fault tolerance provides a notation which enables the designer of a sequential program to incorporate replicated modules (of independent design) together with a test for the acceptability of the outcome of a module (Horning *et al.*, 1974; Randell, 1975). The usual syntax is as follows:

ensure	*acceptance test*
by	*primary module*
else by	*alternate module 1*
	.
	.
	.
else by	*alternate module n*
else error	

A typical value of *n* would be 2 (or often, just 1).

The implementation of this construct must provide a mechanisation of state restoration since on entry to the recovery block the state of the system must, at least notionally, be saved to permit backward error recovery, should this prove necessary.

The primary module is executed first, and then the acceptance test (a logical expression with no side-effects) is evaluated to provide an adjudication on the outcome of the module. If the acceptance test holds (has value **true**) then the outcome is regarded as successful and the recovery block can be exited. However, if the test does not hold (has value **false**), or if any errors are detected by other means during execution, then an exception is raised and backward error recovery is invoked. This restores the state of the system to how it was on entry to the recovery block. After recovery, execution of the recovery block is repeated, but with the first alternate module instead of the primary module. Each alternate module can be used in turn until one succeeds in passing the acceptance test. If none of the modules pass the test then the recovery block itself has failed, and an appropriate exception must be signalled. Since recovery blocks can be nested, a higher level of recovery may still be available.

Although each of the modules within a recovery block endeavours to satisfy the same acceptance test there is no requirement that they all must produce the same results (Lee, 1978). The only constraint is that the results must be acceptable – as determined by the test. Thus, while the primary module should attempt to produce the desired outcome, the alternate modules may only attempt to provide an increasingly degraded service. In this form, a recovery block can be used to implement *gracefully degrading software*. As an example, Fig. 3.3 contains the outline of a program which is intended to enter a disk transfer request into a queue of outstanding requests.

ensure	*consistency of disk transfer queue*
by	*enter request in optimal queue position*
else by	*enter request at end of queue*
else by	*send warning 'Request ignored'*
else error	

Fig. 3.3 Gracefully degrading program.

THE N-VERSION PROGRAMMING SCHEME

A direct application of the hardware N-modular redundant (NMR) approach to software requires the utilisation of modules of diverse design. In the original proposals for N-version programming (Avizienis and Chen, 1977; Chen and Avizienis, 1978) these modules were all designed to satisfy a common specification. Recent work has examined the use of independently constructed formal specifications, to try to avoid the introduction of common source faults due to the use of a single specification (Avizienis and Kelly, 1984).

The semantics of the N-version approach are straightforward: each of N independently designed software modules is executed in parallel and their results (intermediate and final) are compared by a voting mechanism. Control of these N versions is provided by what is termed the *driver program*, which is responsible for:

(1) Invoking each of the versions.
(2) Waiting for the versions to complete their execution.
(3) Performing the replication check (majority voting) on the N sets of results.

To coordinate the versions, the driver program implements a synchronisation regime, based essentially on wait and send primitives, and incorporating a timeout mechanism.

Parallel execution is not essential, of course. What is essential (and may be harder to achieve if a sequential implementation is employed) is to ensure that versions do not interfere with each other. Each version must execute atomically with respect to the others. Physical separation of the versions, by executing each version on a separate processor, is one way to achieve this. Each version should receive an identical set of inputs, but should only be able to submit outputs to the voting check. Communication between versions, or direct outputs, or changes to the global system state, must all be precluded.

Finally, consideration must be given to the voting check itself. Only in certain applications can an exact comparison be used. In many situations minor discrepancies between valid sets of results could arise, such as 'cosmetic' changes in textual output. When this is the case it may be possible to provide 'inexact voting', i.e. a check which can identify a consensus despite the presence of limited discrepancies. One simple approach is to conduct a range check based on some prior estimate, or on a median value taken from all N results.

PRACTICAL EXPERIENCE

In software for critical applications some limited attempts have been made to provide design fault tolerance, usually in the form of 'redundant' tests, with emergency responses in the event of an error being detected. These measures are often referred to as *defensive programming* but are usually applied in a relatively *ad hoc* and unstructured way.

A few practical systems have employed replicated software, usually in response to pressure from the relevant regulatory authority. For example, the Airbus A310 slat and flap control system (Martin, 1982) has two independently developed versions of the software. The outputs from this software drive stepping motors via a comparator. In the event of a discrepancy the motors are halted, the control surfaces locked and the flight crew alerted. Similar approaches (see Anderson, 1984) have been adopted in systems for railway signalling, nuclear reactor shutdown, and in the 'space shuttle' – the NASA Space Transportation System. In the shuttle, a single back-up computer runs in parallel with four primary computers. Mission critical functions are supported by two completely independent versions of the software, one version in the primary computers and the other version in the back-up computer.

Experiments conducted at UCLA on the N-version programming approach have demonstrated that multiple versions can detect and mask design faults (Avizienis and Kelly, 1984). In one experiment, eighteen different versions of an airport scheduling program were written by students, each module containing about 400 PL/I statements. All 816 triad combinations were evaluated as 3-version programs. In 27% of the cases, two correct versions successfully masked the defective computation of a faulty version. Only 3% of the combinations generated an incorrect result.

Evaluation studies at Newcastle of the recovery block approach have also produced encouraging results (Anderson *et al.*, 1985). A major project applied an extension of recovery blocks in the implementation of a naval command and control system comprising about 8000 lines of CORAL programming. To maintain realism the system was constructed to commercial standards by experienced programmers. Analysis of experimental runs of this system showed that on 222 occasions the software would have failed in the absence of fault tolerance. But of these 222 potential failures, only 57 actually happened. Thus a failure coverage of 75% was achieved. Against this should be offset a total of eight failures which were actually *caused* by the provision of fault tolerance. Deducting these failures from the 165 successes reduces the notional coverage to 71%.

So, initial experience in research studies evaluating design fault tolerance techniques has certainly indicated their potential for enhancing software reliability. However, the real question to be posed is whether these techniques are cost effective, relative to approaches based on striving to preclude the presence of faults in design. Only when comparative studies have been undertaken will it be possible to answer this question, and thus enable reliability to be addressed as a topic within an engineering discipline of software construction.

REFERENCES

Anderson, T. (1984). 'Can Design Faults be Tolerated?' *Informatik-Fachberichte 84*, Fehlertolerierende Rechensystems, Springer-Verlag, 426–433.
Anderson, T. and Lee, P. A. (1981). *Fault Tolerance: Principles and Practice*, Prentice-Hall International, Englewood Cliffs.
Anderson, T. *et al.* (1978). 'A Model of Recoverability in Multilevel Systems'. *IEEE Trans. on Soft. Eng.*, **SE-4**, No. 6, 486–494.
Anderson, T. *et al.* (1985). 'An Evaluation of Software Fault Tolerance in a Practical System'. To appear in *Digest of FTCS-15*, Ann Arbor.
Avizienis, A. and Chen, L. (1977). 'On the Implementation of N-version Programming for Software Fault-Tolerance During Program Execution'. *Proc. COMPSAC 77*, Chicago, 149–155.
Avizienis, A. and Kelly, J. P. J. (1984). 'Fault Tolerance by Design Diversity: Concepts and Experiments'. *IEEE Computer*, **17**, No. 8, 67–80.
Avizienis, A. *et al.* (1971). 'The STAR Computer: An Investigation of the Theory

and Practice of Fault-Tolerant Computer Design'. *IEEE Trans. on Comp.*, **C-20**, No. 11, 1312–1321.

Chen, L. and Avizienis, A. (1978). 'N-version Programming: A Fault-Tolerance Approach to Reliability of Software Operation'. *Dig. of FTCS-8*, Toulouse, 3–9.

Horning, J. J. *et al.* (1974). 'A Program Structure for Error Detection and Recovery'. *Lecture Notes in Computer Science 16*, Springer-Verlag, 171–187.

Lee, P. A. (1980). 'A Reconsideration of the Recovery Block Scheme'. *Comp. J.*, **21**, No. 4, 306–310.

Lee, P. A. *et al.* (1980). 'A Recovery Cache for the PDP-11'. *IEEE Trans. on Comp.*, **C-29**, No. 6, 546–549.

Levy, H. M. (1984). *Capability Based Computer Systems*, Digital Press.

Martin, D. J. (1982). 'Dissimilar Software in High Integrity Applications in Flight Controls'. *AGARD Sym. on Software for Avionics*, The Hague, 36:1.

Peterson, W. W. and Weldon, E. J. (1972). *Error-Correcting Codes*, MIT Press.

Randell, B. (1975). 'System Structure for Software Fault Tolerance'. *IEEE Trans. on Soft. Eng.*, **SE-1**, No. 2, 220–232.

CHAPTER 4

Reliable communications

M. Morganti

(Italtel Sit, Italy)

The evolution of the basic computing model from a single sequential process to multiple concurrent processes has in just a few years radically changed the relative importance and the role of communications in computers. As a direct consequence of this evolution, large single processors are progressively being replaced by multiprocessors with networked architecture or by computer networks.

Similarly, at the logical level, the concepts of control flow and of information flow have definitely been separated and emphasis is now put on cooperation through communications rather than on common control (Fig. 4.1).

The reliability and integrity of large complex systems have become more and more dependent on the reliability and integrity of their communication mechanisms, and their fault-tolerant properties more and more dependent on their ability to cope with a wide variety of communication problems.

In this chapter we shall briefly analyse some of these problems and see how they can be prevented, or their consequences limited, through the adoption of appropriate protocols and recovery techniques based on different kinds of redundancy. As a reference model for this analysis we shall use a layered model consisting of several nested virtual machines. Although this is not the only model that could have been used for this purpose, it was chosen because it provides an intrinsic separation between the physical and the logical aspects of both communications and computing.

THE LAYERED MODEL

From the logical viewpoint, interprocess communication protocols can be grossly subdivided into two major classes:

  end-to-end protocols
  broadcast protocols.

It has to be emphasised, however, that this distinction has no implicit limitation on the number of parties, or processes, that can be simultaneously involved in any particular communication; broadcasting could in fact be well directed to only one potential destination whereas any end-to-end

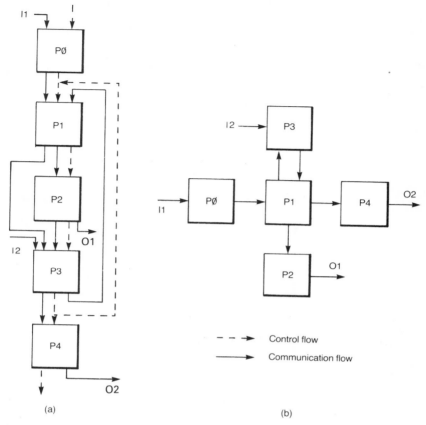

Fig. 4.1 Evolution of basic computing model from single sequential process (a) to multiple concurrent processes (b).

protocol can easily be extended in order to support all kinds of multiparty communications.

Instead, it is a theoretical distinction as to whether the originator of the communication is willing or not to identify any specific path to its destinations as an alternative to just starting to transmit in every possible direction. From the physical viewpoint, however, the distinction is somewhat more substantial, since every real communication channel or network will eventually be designed to support directly either one or the other of the two classes of protocols mentioned above.

Similar considerations obviously apply also to the topology of the network (bus, star, ring, linear, hierarchical, fully interconnected, etc.) or to its access protocols (collision or collision-free). Eventually, this should lead to a choice of the physical network that is consistent with the communication requirements of each specific system.

In practice, however, it is generally preferable to abstract from the physical network a virtual network that can support all kinds of protocols at the same time, in the same way in which virtual machines are abstracted from physical machines, i.e. by layering. However, the final result here is not just a series of nested virtual machines, but rather a lattice of fully interconnected virtual processors onto which any logical system designed on the multiple concurrent processes model could be mapped directly (Fig. 4.2).

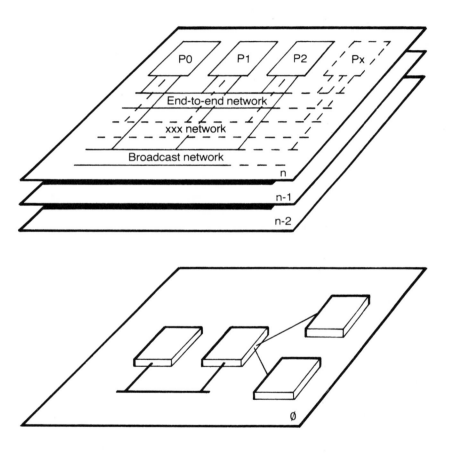

Fig. 4.2 The layered model.

Obviously, each layer in the abstract system will have to be characterised in terms of connectivity, functionality, performance, reliability, fault tolerance, etc., and a trade-off will have to be established at every step of abstraction in order to maintain an acceptable balance among these same parameters.

INCREASING THE RELIABILITY OF COMMUNICATIONS IN LOWER (PHYSICAL) LAYERS

POTENTIAL PROBLEMS IN COMMUNICATIONS

All problems affecting communications can be roughly partitioned into two major classes:

- data integrity problems, i.e. problems related to the reception of corrupted, incomplete, misrouted, or otherwise mishandled data; and
- time related problems, essentially deriving from transmission delays, but also including the apparently infinite delay that characterises the loss of data.

At the same time, all problems and the associated malfunctions can usually be referred to one of only three major causes:

- noise, typically associated with data corruption (although the corruption of addressing and routing information will usually show up as two problems, one for each class, at the same time);
- traffic, causing a higher average and, what is even more important, a higher variance in transmission delays; and
- faults, including design and engineering faults, causing both kind of malfunctions.

It is important to note at this point that all the malfunctions considered here, together with their causes, are indeed present in all kinds of communication networks, be they single lines, shared memory systems or satellite broadcast networks, although obviously their impact on the quality and reliability of communications themselves can vary widely depending on network size and topology.

Consequently, the identification and isolation of a specific cause for any given malfunction is not straightforward and may require substantial time and effort just to discriminate between physiological (noise and traffic) and pathological (faults) situations.

APPROACHING COMMUNICATION PROBLEMS THROUGH REDUNDANCY

By and large, two distinct strategies are used in practice, either as alternatives or in combination, to deal with communication problems:

prevention
detection and correction.

Both strategies are based on the availability, and therefore on the possible redundant use, of four basic resources:

power
information
time
space.

Power redundancy
As suggested by the name, this essentially consists of the use of more transmission energy than would normally be required by the physical characteristics of the transmission media itself; this is in order to increase further the signal-to-noise ratio, and therefore the signal immunity to such adverse environmental factors as thermal noise, gamma radiation, relative humidity, etc.

As an example, its closest equivalent in human communications is the common practice of speaking louder when the communication takes place in a noisy environment.

Information redundancy
The major part of this is also referred to as *redundant coding*, and it is based on the transmission of more information (bits) than would theoretically be required by the informative content of the communication itself.

Redundant codes are subdivided into two major classes:

● error detecting codes (such as parity, checksum, CRC, etc.);
● error detecting and correcting codes (such as Hamming codes).

Their equivalent in human communications is the limited number of phoneme and morpheme combinations used by each natural language.

As in natural languages, however, information redundancy is not necessarily limited to coding. Syntax, semantics, and pragmatics, too, intrinsically contribute to limit at every instant the number of possible choices, and can therefore be exploited to discriminate effectively between valid and invalid communications.

Further, not all codes are equally effective in all situations. Parity, for example, may well be applied in all parallel communications, including shared memory, but its effectiveness is almost zero in serial communications since noise bursts are typically longer than just one bit. Therefore the choice of code must always be closely linked to the physical characteristics of the environment in which it is applied.

Time redundancy
This essentially consists of transmitting the same information (be it redundantly coded or not) more than just once. When used unconditionally, it becomes substantially equivalent to a limited application of redundant coding.

Its most obvious equivalent in human communications is the repetition of single words or entire phrases that occurs in most real conversations both to correct errors and/or to further protect key information.

Space redundancy
This consists of providing several distinct transmission paths between each processor pair that needs to communicate.

Once more, an equivalent of space redundancy in human communications could be the fact of having two ears, or more simply the ability to move to another, less noisy, room to continue a disturbed conversation.

Obviously all kinds of redundancy have good points and bad points that should be carefully considered and balanced in order to avoid undesired side effects that could go far beyond a simple increase in costs. A naive use of power redundancy, for example, can significantly and unnecessarily increase the failure rate of physical components, while redundant coding has a direct impact on transmission efficiency and performance.

The major concern in applying any of the above techniques (with the possible exception of power redundancy) should be their direct or indirect impact on traffic, since its relation to the average value and to the variance of transmission delays is generally much more than linear, and often presents saturation phenomena that in turn can produce avalanche effects on system performance.

The possibility of even temporary overloads, due for example to the sudden activation of time and space redundancies, should therefore be accounted for at all stages in designing and/or sizing the capacity of the entire network and of each of its components.

IMPLEMENTATION OF PREVENTION STRATEGIES

Prevention-only approaches to communications problems are typical of unidirectional broadcast networks, since in this kind of network there is no possibility for the destination of the communication to inform the originator of any detected malfunction. Even in bidirectional and non-broadcast networks, however, this approach is often used in conjunction with the detection/correction approach in order to reduce the number of problems reported to the latter.

In summary, all prevention-only approaches eventually consist of some cocktail of the following ingredients:

- (Un)conditional power redundancy. (The 'un' of unconditional is between brackets because in most practical cases recourse is made to self-adaptive power regulation techniques based on either time-discrete or continuous measurements of the transmissive characteristics of the network as perceived by the originator.)
- Unconditional, and massive, use of error detecting and correcting codes, or even just error detecting codes when used in conjunction with other forms of redundancy (e.g. time and space).
- Unconditional use of time redundancy, usually in combination with error correcting codes, in order to increase the probability of having at least one copy of the information properly delivered to, and recognised as such, by the destination.
- Unconditional use of space redundancy, also usually in combination with error correcting codes and as an intrinsic feature of the concept of broadcasting.

Besides the general pitfalls indicated above, unconditional time and space redundancies in this approach also require special mechanisms for the destination to be able to discriminate between basic and redundant information in order to dispose of the latter. In principle this is easily achievable by attaching to each communication item (message, packet or other) a tag or a sequence number that immediately and unequivocally identifies it and all of its redundant copies.

In practice, however, this artifice will eventually result in the transmission of additional information, which also needs to be protected in order to be reliable and fault tolerant, and in the need for some further complication of the protocols in order to support resynchronisations and resets as required, for example, in the case of a major reinitialisation of the system.

IMPLEMENTATION OF DETECTION/CORRECTION STRATEGIES

To be successful, any specific implementation based on a detection/correction kind of strategy must, first of all, be supported by an adequate set of error detection mechanisms.

In the case of communications, two techniques have been found to be especially effective in detecting data integrity and time related problems. These are:

- consistency checking, exploiting all kinds of information redundancy that will eventually be available to the destination; and
- time checking on all transmission delays, based on watch-dogs and time-out counters.

The purposes and the limits of consistency checking are well understood.

Eventually its result will always be some sort of Boolean function that fails to detect malfunctions if and only if the elementary (single-bit) errors affecting a specific communication item are numerous enough, and malicious enough, to produce a consistent transformation of the information contained in the item rather than just its corruption or its loss.

Time checking is instead much more delicate and strongly dependent on both the physical (deterministic) and the traffic (probabilistic) characteristics of the network. In general, some careful, and possibly dynamic, tuning will be required, since otherwise:

- if the checking is too stringent, every traffic peak will activate it with the further risk of activating a sort of chain reaction that is sustained by the recovery actions initiated by the checking itself;
- if it is too loose, detection times will increase dramatically, and even common malfunctions, such as the misrouting or the loss of single data packets, will require significant amounts of time to be detected and eventually corrected.

In general, after a malfunction is detected, its correction requires at least one retransmission of the affected item, possibly accompanied by a temporary increase in transmission energy and/or by the activation of an alternative transmission channel or path. In brief, a well balanced cocktail of time, space and power redundancy, while information redundancy is generally used unconditionally, either for detection purposes only or also to minimise the number of detected malfunctions that require retransmission.

Here, too, special mechanisms and extensions of the transmission protocols are required in order to cope with such trivial problems as 'lost' items arriving after their retransmission has been requested, or broadcasted items that are received correctly by one destination and incorrectly by another. Additionally, formal connect and disconnect procedures will have to be agreed upon between originators and destinations in order to support the conditional activation of alternative or back-up channels.

Finally, detection and correction of communication errors do not necessarily imply a clear identification and isolation of their cause. This means that, if the cause is persistent (i.e. a fault) a good detection and recovery mechanism may have the unpleasant side effect of hiding the problem forever at the price of a substantial reduction of the overall performance. On the other hand, identification and isolation of faults in large networks can be extremely expensive and time consuming due to the large number of alternative paths provided by the network itself, and therefore it cannot be attempted indiscriminately at every detected malfunction.

To deal successfully with this problem, two more features must be added to the system:

- a logging function that by keeping trace (or just the count) of each specific malfunction will make it possible to discriminate (e.g. by comparison of the count with predetermined thresholds) between acceptable error rates and pathological situations;
- the possibility of de-activating upon request all sorts of recovery mechanisms in order for the isolation procedure to control each kind of redundancy independently of the others and hence avoid possible masking effects.

DEALING WITH RESIDUAL UNRELIABILITY IN THE UPPER (LOGICAL) LAYER

In the previous paragraphs we have seen how power, information, time and space redundancy can be combined at each layer of the layered model in order to increase the reliability and fault tolerance of processes and communications to the possible detriment of performance and cost.

Eventually this process must come to an end and converge to some realistic limit in order to maintain an acceptable balance between cost, performance and reliability. This implies that, even at the top of the layered model, processes and communications will continue to show a certain degree of unreliability.

At this point only three approaches are possible:

(1) Ignore the problem, i.e. decide that the residual unreliability is negligible with respect to the particular application and therefore accept the fact that the system may fail unpredictably if any of its components fail.
(2) Acknowledge the problem but choose fault intolerance.
(3) Design the logical system so that it can survive the failure of some of its components.

Approach (1), although very common and usually well justified in terms of probabilities *vs.* costs, is obviously of little interest here. Rather, both (2) and (3) deserve more comment and will therefore be examined in greater detail in the following paragraphs.

In either case, the recovery techniques that are available to achieve the specific objectives of each of the two approaches are basically:

backward recovery and
forward recovery

which can be used either as alternatives or in combination, and which, as suggested by their names, essentially differ in the direction (in time) in which the system is moved in order to be returned from an erroneous to a non-erroneous state.

In backward recovery each process in the system is rolled back to a previously recorded non-erroneous state (a recovery point), typically but not necessarily preceding the malfunction that caused the system to fail, and consistent with the states assumed by all the other processes (i.e. belonging to the same recovery line). In forward recovery, on the other hand, the system is forced to evolve to a new, non-erroneous state determined on the basis of the current state only, and therefore basically independent of the system history prior to reaching that state.

THE FAULT INTOLERANT APPROACH

The main difference between (1) and (2) above consists of the fact that, although in both cases the system is not required to be able to survive the failure of any of its components, the failure of the system is sure and predictable in (2) only.

With this precision, the main objectives that can be achieved by a fault intolerant approach are two:

fail-safe and
hot-restart.

The fail-safe objective mainly consists of ensuring that:

• the system will always fail detectably, and therefore no doubt will exist as to whether it has failed or not;

- there will be no harm to the system environment because of the failure or because of the associated recovery action;
- the failed state that is reached is stable and is not by itself potentially dangerous to the system environment.

These requirements make fail-safe a natural candidate for forward recovery techniques. Conversely, the hot-restart objective is naturally based on backward recovery techniques, since its basic requirements are that:

- the system must fail to a consistent state that will be used as an initial state when the system is restarted;
- the state must be such that a significant part of the useful work carried out by the system between its previous activation and its failure is preserved.

Communications are of the utmost importance, both as a means of achieving these objectives and as part of the objectives themselves.

In achieving the fail-safe objective, for example, external communication channels could be used by the boundary processes to shut the system down and isolate it from its environment. At the same time, however, the protocols used to communicate with this environment should be such that, if the failure occurs in one or more of the boundary processes and/or the external communication channels, the failure will still be detected unambiguously.

Also, it is easy to show that this second requirement also applies to internal protocols unless a separate, and failure-independent, communication network is provided to broadcast the failure condition to all the boundary processes and initiate the shut-down procedure.

In achieving the hot-restart objective, on the other hand, communications are the main obstacle to achieving a successful backward recovery.

However, they are necessary, and from this viewpoint the requirements are the same as those described above: all processes must agree on a specific recovery line and roll-back to it.

But they are also the source of the 'domino' effect which can cause roll-back to propagate indefinitely (Fig. 4.3a) unless the set-up of recovery lines is made explicit (Fig. 4.3b) or redundant (Fig. 4.3c).

Further, an explicit decision must be made on whether, in rolling a system back to a previous state, the external communications that occurred during the failure should be considered as lost or not, thus leading to a pre-emption or a pre-set of the relevant communications channels.

THE FAULT TOLERANT APPROACH

In spite of its name, the fault tolerant approach considered here is in fact in no way more complicated than the fault intolerant one. This statement becomes clear when we consider that explicit redundancy in the upper layer of the layered model is not, almost by definition, a logical necessity.

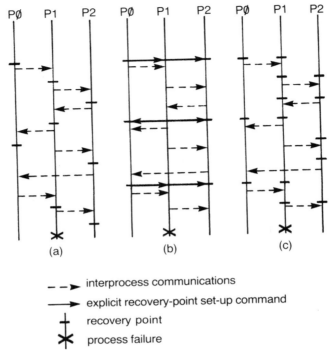

Fig. 4.3 Three interactive processes with (a) arbitrary recovery points leading to the 'domino' effect; (b) explicit set-up of recovery lines; (c) redundant set-up of recovery points.

Therefore, it can easily be embedded in a lower layer or at least handled in the same way.

Possible objectives of the fault tolerant approach are instead:

- the exploitation of the non-determinism that is typical of asynchronous distributed systems;
- the possibility of continuing operation with reduced capabilities (also called *partial fault tolerance* or *graceful degradation*).

In particular, the exploitation of non-determinism consists in rolling the system back, as for a hot-restart, and then in letting it re-process all the inputs that it received between the selected recovery line and its failure.

Since the recovery line itself is not built up of synchronous recovery points, since the system configuration is likely to have changed in the meanwhile, and since the arrival times of the inputs are no longer the same, the entire system is now likely to behave differently. It can then be a reasonable assumption that, if the failure was not caused by a single event, but rather by the malignant combination of several events at one time, then this combination will not reappear and the system will not fail.

Partial fault tolerance is instead essentially a matter of forward recovery,

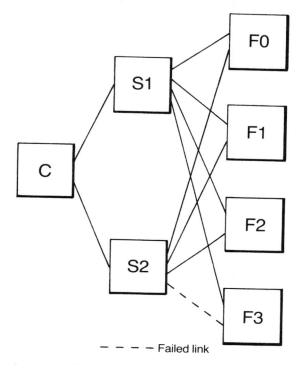

Fig. 4.4 Example of one-client/two-server system showing functional asymmetry after link failure.

aiming at isolating the faulty components while excluding the functionalities associated with them.

However, especially if the failed component is a communication channel, a distributed implementation of the strategy can easily cause unacceptable asymmetries in the system behaviour, such as two load-sharing processors with different capabilities (Fig. 4.4). Therefore, here too, a broadcast mechanism is required to ensure that local decisions will eventually be consistent in spite of the possible malignant behaviour of one or more system components.

CONCLUSIONS

Evolution of the basic computing model from a single sequential process to multiple concurrent processes has determined a significant change in the role and importance of communications in computer systems.

Once almost a dummy attribute of control, communications are now possibly the major single key factor in system performance, reliability, quality, and even functionality.

Communications and communication mechanisms have been briefly examined here with respect to both their characteristics and to their possible malfunctions. It was shown how their reliability, fault tolerance and functionalities could be steadily increased through the levels of a layered model and by an appropriate use of different kinds of redundancy.

The layered approach itself was chosen as a reference model essentially because, by separating logical problems from physical, it provides a natural guideline to the analysis of all communication issues, from thermal noise to high level protocols. Yet, the same model is general enough to ensure that the analysis is just driven and not influenced by the model itself and that therefore its results are of general application.

Although many issues were touched upon, the analysis made here is obviously far from being exhaustive. On the other hand, its major objective was to supply guidelines to a set of possible solutions rather than solutions themselves.

BIBLIOGRAPHY

Tanenbaum, A. S. (1981). *Computer Networks*, Prentice-Hall.

Edge, S. W. and Hinchley, A. J. (1978). 'A Survey of End-to-End Retransmission Techniques', *Computer Comm. Rev.*, **8**, No. 4, 1–18.

Schwartz, M. (1977). *Computer-Communication Network Design and Analysis*, Prentice-Hall.

Siewiorek, D. P. and Swarz, R. S. (1982). *The Theory and Practice of Reliable System Design*, Digital Press.

Randell, B., Lee, P. A. and Treleaven, P. C. (1978). 'Reliability Issues in Computing System Design', ACM *Comput. Surveys*, **10**, No. 2, 123–165, June.

CHAPTER 5

Resilient real-time systems

H. Kopetz

(*Technical University of Vienna, Austria*)

The requirement for fault tolerant operation is particularly urgent in real-time applications. In such an application there is normally no time available for human intervention in order to correct manually the consequences of a computer system failure.

After a description of the real-time environment the application of standard fault tolerance techniques to this environment is discussed in the first part of this chapter. It is shown that the introduction of active redundancy is the best choice in such an environment.

THE REAL-TIME ENVIRONMENT

A typical real-time system can be described in the following way (Franta *et al.*, 1981; LeLann, 1983). A control object ('the control environment') and the control system (the computer) are connected via sensor and actuator based interfaces. The control system accepts data from the sensors either at regular intervals or event driven, processes the data and outputs the results to the control object via the actuators. The output data influence the control object so that the effects can be observed via the sensors, thus closing the loop (Fig. 5.1).

The following properties are characteristic for the real-time environment:

- The control system must respond to a stimulus from the control object within an interval dictated by the environment (the *response time*). This response time must be guaranteed even under extreme load conditions and under anticipated fault conditions. Typical response times are in the order of 10 ms to 1 s and above.
- Many real-time systems have to operate for long periods of time (up to many years) without shutdown for maintenance or functional enhancements. Thus the requirements on reliability and ease of maintenance are very high.
- If a serious failure occurs, either in the control system or the control object, the system must shut down in a controlled predetermined manner (fail-safe operation).
- There can be a significant physical distance between the different sections of the control object and the control system, such that local

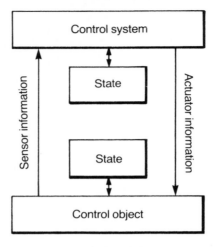

Fig. 5.1 A typical real-time system.

processing and multiplexing of signals can significantly reduce the installation (cabling) costs.

The real-time environment is thus a prime candidate for the application of fault tolerant distributed control systems, since in such an architecture it is possible to:

- provide the necessary processing capacity to guarantee the required response time;
- mask operational faults and support online maintenance and incremental extensions;
- place elements of the control system in close proximity to the control object to reduce the installation costs.

The behaviour of many real-time control systems is very regular, i.e. the same sequence of actions is performed periodically.

DUTY CYCLE

The *duty cycle* is the time period between two related sequences of actions.

Short duty cycles are typical for many real-time applications. If the duty cycle is considerably shorter than the required response time, even event driven actions can be processed within the regular duty cycle. This has the advantage of an intrinsic flow control and provides protection of the system from overload conditions which can have dramatic consequences for the behaviour of the system in the time domain.

In order to respond correctly to a stimulus of the environment, the real-time control system must contain a consistent image of the internal state of the control object (Fig. 5.1).

STATE CONSISTENCY

The internal state of a control system is consistent with the internal state of the environment if at time t:

(1) All external events which occurred in the environment before $t-\delta t$ are recorded in the internal state of the control system at the latest at time t.

(2) All output events which have been recorded in the internal state of the control system before $t-\delta t$ have been accepted by the environment at the latest at time t.

The interval δt must be significantly smaller than the duty cycle.

It is evident that this state consistency is time dependent. Delaying a system for a time period δt destroys this consistency between the internal state of the control system and the environment (and *vice versa*).

Example

Consider an 'automated car' before a traffic light. Waiting longer than δt on the traffic light information 'the light is green' will destroy the consistency between the car and the traffic light (and possibly much more).

Any response of a control system must be based on a consistent internal state. Every commitment of a result to the environment leads to a permanent change of the environment and the internal state of the control systems and cannot be undone (Davies, 1979). Thus at a point in time δt after the point of commitment the 'old' state information becomes invalid, i.e. any checkpoint information which has been recorded before a point of commitment has to be discarded. Consequently, backward recovery in real-time systems, which normally contain frequent points of commitment, is severely constrained.

FAULT TOLERANCE

Fault tolerance is concerned with the continuation of acceptable service of a system despite internal faults. It can only be achieved if there are enough 'redundant' resources in the system to detect and circumvent the consequences of a fault (Anderson and Lee, 1981).

In a real-time environment, a control system can fail in two domains, the value domain and the time domain. In the rest of this chapter we will use the following definitions.

Correct result

A result is correct if its values are consistent with the intentions of the user.

Timely result

A result is timely if it is produced within the intended interval of real time.

Valid result
A result is valid if it is correct and timely.

In the 'non-real-time world' we are only concerned with the value domain, i.e. with correctness. There is an abundance of literature concerned with the correctness problem (e.g. Boyer and Moore, 1981), which will not be discussed any further here. The inclusion of the domain of real time adds a new dimension to the problem in real-time systems, since the speed of processing in a given interval, i.e. the system performance, becomes an essential property. It is therefore necessary to examine if the fault handling techniques which have been successful in the 'non-real-time world' can be transferred to the real-time environment without modifications.

If we analyse the time characteristics of faults we can distinguish the following cases:

(1) *Transient faults.* A fault that starts at a particular point in time and remains in the system for some period after which it disappears again. Examples of transient faults are hardware deficiencies caused by external interference (e.g. electric, mechanical, radioactive, etc.). After the external disturbance disappears, the fault disappears as well.

(2) *Permanent faults.* Faults that start at a particular point in time and remain in the system until removed by some external action (i.e. the completion of a repair action). Examples of permanent faults are a broken wire in the hardware or a fault in a software program.

(3) *Intermittent faults.* Transient faults that occur repeatedly within some given interval. An example of an intermittent fault is a marginally working IC component, which operates some of the time but does not operate the rest of the time.

Fig. 5.2 shows the relationship between transient faults and permanent faults in computer systems (Kopetz, 1982). Although the 'original' transient fault has already disappeared the permanent effects of this fault remain in the system until they are removed by some action from the outside.

In the following we will distinguish between three different kinds of redundancy, *active redundancy*, *passive redundancy* and *time redundancy*.

Active redundancy
A system contains active redundancy if redundant subsystems operate in parallel, i.e. at the same time.

Passive redundancy
A system contain passive redundancy if a redundant subsystem is switched on after a failure of the primary system has been detected.

Time redundancy
A system contains time redundancy if, after detection of a failure, an

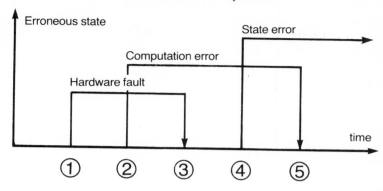

Fig. 5.2 Relationship between transient and permanent faults. (1) Start of hardware fault. (2) Interaction of hardware fault with computation. Start of computation error. (3) Termination of the hardware fault (transient). (4) Interaction of the computation with the internal state. Start of state error. (5) Termination of computation.

operation is repeated (at a later point in time) using the same physical resources as in the original operation.

Let us now examine how these different types of redundancy can be applied to handle the different error types and what effects they have on real-time behaviour (see table). Intermittent faults can be handled by active and passive redundancy only if it is possible to reuse the failed subsystem a short time after a transient fault has occurred.

Redundancy	*Errors*			*Effect on real-time behaviour*
	Transient	*Intermittent*	*Permanent*	
Active	yes	partially	yes	minimal
Passive	yes	partially	yes	significant
Time	yes	yes	no	significant

TIME REDUNDANCY AND PASSIVE REDUNDANCY

If the elapsed time is of no importance, time redundancy is the best technical and economical choice to handle transient and sporadic intermittent faults.

As is well known, many faults in communication systems are transient or intermittent, i.e. the fault condition lasts only for a short interval. In such a case a repetition of the transmission at some later time (the application of time redundancy), using the same transmission line, may lead to error-free results. Most error correction mechanisms in communication protocols rely on this application of time redundancy.

In many systems time redundancy is also applied to correct transient hardware errors, which are the most common source of failure in the computer hardware. After an error has been detected, the computation is restarted at the last checkpoint and a correct result will be provided at some later point in time.

As has been discussed in the previous section, time is a limited resource in the real-time environment. The uncontrolled application of time redundancy can lead to a delay of the information by more than δt and thus invalidate the information before it arrives at its destination. In most situations, invalid information is more dangerous than no information at all (refer to the previous example on the automated car before a traffic light).

Since the application of passive redundancy also requires some time for error detection and switchover, similar arguments apply to the application of passive redundancy.

It can be very difficult, if not impossible, to prove the timely behaviour of a real-time system under all anticipated fault conditions if time redundancy and passive redundancy are used for error correction throughout the system. This is particularly true for distributed real-time systems, which consist of a set of fairly autonomous nodes connected by a communication system (e.g. a local area network). If communication errors are masked by time redundancy in low level communication protocols and no global real-time base is available, then it is hopeless to try to prove that the system will provide a valid (i.e. timely) response under anticipated fault conditions.

ACTIVE REDUNDANCY

In the following we will concentrate on techniques to increase the fault tolerance of real-time systems without invalidating the time characteristics of the system. All these techniques are based on active redundancy. We will discuss two different techniques, the application of *triple modular redundancy* and *selfchecking components*. Both techniques require the specification of *smallest replaceable units* at the architectural level.

SMALLEST REPLACEABLE UNIT (SRU)
A unit with a given functionality which at any point in time is in either one of the two modes: operational or failed. The introduction of the SRU makes it possible to abstract from the complexity of the detailed inner structure and of the inner failure modes of such a subsystem.

A refinement of an SRU is the concept of a Selfchecking SRU.

Selfchecking SRU
An SRU which stops its operation immediately after the detection of an error.

The concept of a 'fail stop processor' (Schlichting and Schneider, 1983) is identical to the concept of a selfchecking SRU. The fundamental difference between an SRU and a selfchecking SRU is the behaviour under fault conditions. No assumptions are made about such behaviour for a normal SRU. Under fault conditions it may produce correct results at the wrong time or incorrect results at the right time or no results at all. A selfchecking SRU contains an error detection mechanism such that it will not produce any results under fault conditions.

An architecture based on selfchecking SRUs must contain mechanisms for error detection only in the time domain (since a faulty SRU will be quiescent). If the selfchecking assumption cannot be made, the architecture must provide additional mechanisms for error detection in the value domain and the suppression of the propagation of faulty information throughout the system.

It has been stated before that an SRU is a unit with a given functional and timing behaviour. If the SRU is a self-contained computer it must include the hardware and the application software. Any modification in the software to hardware assignment (logical to physical mapping) will change the SRU definition and result in severe consequences for the behaviour of the system under fault conditions.

In a fault tolerant architecture, the SRU is thus a fairly stable architectural element. Consequently it is reasonable to introduce the SRU also as a structural element in the design of a real-time application (software) system. This implies that the partitioning of the system into a set of SRUs is a basic design decision which has to be made at a relatively early stage in the design of a fault tolerant system.

In a distributed real-time system, an SRU can be defined at an abstract level by the messages it accepts, the operations it can perform, the messages it produces, its internal state space and its performance characteristics. In order to bridge the semantic gap between the design and the implementation of a distributed fault tolerant real-time system, such an SRU can be introduced as a basic element in the system design methodology.

TRIPLE MODULAR REDUNDANCY

Figure 5.3 shows the architecture of a triple modular redundant system. The sensor signals are triplicated to three independent SRUs which operate in parallel with identical software. The outputs of these three units are compared bit by bit in a two out of three voter before the results are released to the environment. Periodically the internal states of the control system are compared in order to maintain internal consistency.

The three units have to operate in close synchronism. If the results of one of the units is not received within a predetermined interval of real time or if the result of one of the units deviates from the result of the other two units, the voter outputs the majority result. In such an architecture error detection and correction are performed in a single step. An example of a

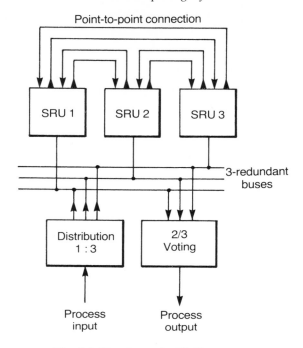

Fig. 5.3 Structure of a TMR system.

fault tolerant system based on TMR is the August system (Wensley, 1983) described in Chapter 13.

Experiments are under way (Avizienis and Kelly, 1984) to use different software versions in the three units in order to make the system tolerant to design faults in the software. In a real-time environment, such an approach is particularly difficult, since the three versions have to operate synchronously at every point of commitment. The achievable design diversity is thus limited.

SELFCHECKING COMPONENTS

If an architecture contains only selfchecking SRUs, it can be postulated that if a result is available it is a correct result (Schlichting and Schneider, 1983). In such an architecture, fault tolerance can be realised by duplicating the selfchecking SRUs and providing mechanisms for the dissemination of the required input information to the redundant SRUs as well as detecting and discarding redundant information from the redundant units. The system will continue to operate as long as any one of the redundant SRUs operates.

In our research project on fault tolerant distributed real-time systems MARS (Kopetz *et al.*, 1983) we implement fault tolerance by use of selfchecking components. Every component (a self-contained computer including the application software) has access to an approximate global time, i.e. a time reference which deviates from an 'abstract' global time by a fraction of a clock tick. Every message exchanged between components contains two time values, the time of sending the message and the validity time of the message. As soon as the global time passes the validity time of a message, this message is automatically discarded by the operating system, i.e. as long as a message exists it contains timely information. Since we assume that our components also have the selfchecking property, we can say that every message which exists is a valid message. The validity time has to be set according to the δt requirement of the given application.

The dissemination of the messages to an arbitrary number of redundant components is achieved through the proper design of the name spaces. The basic addressing mode in MARS is group addressing, i.e. any member of a group will receive a message. The sender does not know how many members there are in a group. Redundant components are thus members of the same receiver group.

The mechanism to detect and discard redundant input information is based on the time relation between redundant messages of the same semantic content. In MARS the message name refers to the semantic content of a message. When declaring a message, the system designer must specify an application dependent interval attribute. This interval attribute specifies the minimum time period between two semantically different messages of the same message class (i.e. the same name). As an example, consider a message which refers to the pressing of an elevator call button. The system designer has to define a period of time which identifies the redundant copies of this message, i.e. if a call button is pressed twice within this interval, the second message is a redundant copy of the first message. Whenever the first message arrives at the receiver, this time interval is opened. After the interval period, this time interval is closed. Any message of the same name (i.e. the same semantic content) which arrives after the first message during this interval is a redundant copy of this first message and will thus be discarded.

The fault tolerance properties of this architecture have been demonstrated in a prototype implementation. As long as any one of the redundant components operates, the user will not see the effect of a failed component. It is up to an independent maintenance component to detect failed components and call the repair man.

Since there is no need to compare the outputs of each redundant SRU bit by bit, this architecture is also suited to support design diversity. In one approach, time-outs at the receiver of the information are employed to distinguish between, let us say, a primary version and an alternate version of the design (Horning *et al.*, 1974). If the results of the primary version are not available on time, the system operates on the results of the alternate version.

In some real-time applications it is possible to fall back to a degraded mode of performance (e.g. operator control) if the computer system stops in a selfchecking mode. Examples are railway signalling systems or aircraft control systems with a manual backup operation. In such an environment the selfchecking property of the control system can be achieved by comparing the results calculated via two independent channels. In some safety critical applications the two channels execute diverse software in order to reduce the probability of a common mode design fault (e.g. see Martin 1982).

CONCLUSION

It has been shown that the application of time redundancy and passive redundancy in the real-time system environment is limited because of the real-time constraints and the frequent commitment of results to the environment. Active redundancy, which does not demand an additional time overhead, is thus the preferred solution for the implementation of fault tolerance in real-time systems. If the architecture is based on active redundancy with selfchecking components, design diversity for the tolerance of software faults can also be supported.

REFERENCES

Anderson, T. and Lee, P. A. (1981). *Fault Tolerance: Principles and Practice*, Prentice Hall International, Englewood Cliffs, 63–91.

Avizienis, A. and Kelly, J. P. J. (1984). 'Fault Tolerance by Design Diversity'. *Computer*, 7, No. 8, 67–89.

Boyer, R. S. and Moore, J. S., eds. (1981). *The Correctness Problem in Computer Science*, Academic Press.

Davies, C. T. Jr. (1979). 'Data Processing Integrity', in *Computing Systems Reliability*. Anderson, T., and Randell, B., eds. Cambridge University Press, 288–354.

Franta, W. R., Jensen, E. D. and Kain, R. Y. (1981). 'Real Time Distributed Computer Systems'. *Advances in Computers*, 20, 39–82, Academic Press.

Horning, J. J. *et al.* (1974). 'A Program Structure for Error Detection and Recovery', in *Lecture Notes in Computer Science 16*, Gelenbe, E. and Kaiser, C., eds. Springer-Verlag, Berlin, 171–187.

Kopetz, H. (1982). 'The Failure Fault Model'. *Proc. of the 12. Symp. on Fault Tolerant Computing*, Santa Monica, Ca. 14–17.

Kopetz, H., Lohnert, F., Merker, W. and Pauthner, G. (1983). 'A Message Based DCCS', *Proc. of IFAC Dist. Comp. Control Sys. Conf.*, Sabi Sabi, South Africa, Rodd, M. ed. Pergamon Press, 59–71.

LeLann, G. (1983). 'On Real Time Distributed Computing'. *Proc. IFIP Cong. 83*, Paris, 741–753.

Martin, D. J. (1982). 'Dissimilar Software in High Integrity Applications in Flight Controls'. *AGARD Symp. on Software for Avionics*, The Hague, 36.

Schlichting, R. D. and Schneider, F. B. (1983). 'Fail Stop Processors: An

Approach to Designing Fault-Tolerant Computing Systems'. *ACM Trans. on Comp. Sys.*, **1**, No. 3.

Serlin, O. (1984). 'Fault Tolerant Systems in Commercial Applications'. *Computer*, **17**, No. 8, 19–30.

Wensley, J. H. (1983). 'Industrial Control Systems'. *Electronics*, Jan. 27, 98–102.

CHAPTER 6

Robust distributed programs

S. K. Shrivastava

(*Computing Laboratory, University of Newcastle upon Tyne*)

Distributed systems pose reliability problems not frequently encountered in more traditional 'centralised' systems. A distributed system consisting of a number of computers (nodes) connected by some communication network is subject to independent failure modes of its components, such as nodes, links and operating systems. The lack of any centralised control can mean that part of the system can fail with other parts still functioning, thus leading to the possibility of abnormal behaviour of application programs in execution. We will consider a distributed system where the nodes provide various services (e.g. data storage, printing) which can be invoked by an application program. Such a program will be termed a *distributed program* whose execution will require a group of cooperating processes distributed over the system. It is natural to require that such a group of processes behave 'consistently' in the presence of failures. A very simple consistency requirement, expressed in terms of the behaviour of a distributed program, is that of *failure atomicity*: the program either terminates normally, producing the intended results, or is 'aborted', producing no results at all.

Ideally we would like programs to terminate normally in the presence of an arbitrarily large number of failures, but this may require so much redundancy in the system as to make it economically unattractive. Assume that a distributed program is subject to two kinds of failures: (i) lost messages (a message sent by a process does not reach its destination); and (ii) node crashes (a node stops functioning). We can then state the following range of reliability requirements for a distributed program.

(i) A program will terminate normally despite the loss of a (fixed) finite number of messages (but node crashes cause abortion as stated earlier).
(ii) A program will terminate normally despite the occurrence of a (fixed) finite number of lost messages and node crashes.

In either case, if the limitation on the number of lost messages or node crashes is exceeded, the program is aborted. The two types of requirements listed above represent a range from fairly to most reliable. Indeed, a very appealing technique for constructing type (ii) programs is to build them out of type (i) programs. In this chapter we will concentrate mainly on programs of type (i), which can be regarded as the basic building blocks of a software system, and then briefly discuss how the other type of program can be constructed.

So far we have discussed tolerance only to specified types of faults. If tolerance to unforeseen faults, such as software design faults, is required, then type (i) or type (ii) programs can be used, say, as alternates of recovery blocks. Since design fault tolerance has been discussed in an earlier chapter, we shall not discuss it further.

Having indicated the scope of the problem to be solved, let us investigate some structural properties of a distributed program. Most modern programming languages (e.g. Concurrent Euclid[1]) support the facility of data abstraction, enabling a programmer to associate a set of operations with data structures. The term *abstract objects* (or objects, for short) will be used to refer to instances of data abstractions. Abstract objects are structured entities that can only be manipulated by invoking the procedures associated with them. The term *object manager* will be used to refer to the provider of the corresponding abstract object. Programs constructed using abstract objects have a hierarchical structure in that higher level objects are constructed using lower level objects: making such a program reliable essentially involves making objects reliable (that is ensuring that objects remain consistent in the presence of failures of certain kinds). In other words, it will be the task of object managers to employ whatever fault tolerance techniques are necessary to provide (or maintain) reliable objects; such managers will be termed *robust object managers*. It is natural to assume that distributed programs will have a similar structure to that discussed above, the only difference being that objects may be distributed over the network. All that is then necessary is to provide network protocols enabling a program to invoke operations of a remote object. Such a protocol should provide the abstraction of invoking a procedure. Hence the term *remote procedure call* (RPC) is often used to refer to the services provided by the protocol. Our task is thus to investigate reliability techniques for constructing reliable distributed programs of type (i) and (ii), which in turn implies investigating reliability techniques for robust object managers whose operations can be invoked by making use of RPCs. We begin by investigating the notion of atomic actions.

ATOMIC ACTIONS

We will assume that objects can be shared between various programs. It is then necessary to ensure that concurrent executions of programs be free from interference, i.e. concurrent executions should be equivalent to some serial order of execution.[2,3] To understand this, consider the following two programs (where x, y and z are distinct variables):

P1: $z:=10; x:=x+1; y:=y+1$
P2: $w:=7; x:=x\times2; y:=y\times2$

Assume that $x=y=2$ initially. Then, a serial execution order 'P1;P2' will produce the result $z=10$, $w=7$, $x=y=6$, and execution 'P2;P1' will produce the results $z=10$, $w=7$, $x=y=5$. The partly concurrent execution order given below

$$(z:=10 \parallel w:=7); \; x:=x+1; \; y:=y+1; \; x:=x\times2; \; y:=y\times2$$

will be termed interference free, since it is equivalent to the serial order 'P1;P2'. However, an execution order such as

$$(z:=10 \parallel w:=7); \; x:=x+1; \; x:=x\times2; \; y:=y\times2; \; y:=y+1$$

is not free from interference since it cannot be shown to be equivalent to any serial order. Programs that possess the above mentioned 'serialisable' property are said to be *atomic with respect to concurrency* (or simply atomic), and the computations that are invoked by these programs are termed *atomic actions*. We will embellish such programs with the failure atomicity property mentioned earlier, thus ensuring that any computation progresses without interference from other computations and at the same time either terminates normally (producing intended results) or is aborted (terminated without producing any results). It is reasonable to assume that once a computation terminates normally, the results produced are not destroyed by subsequent failures (node crashes). Hence, we will also require that an atomic action be enriched with the permanence of effect property (i.e. the state changes produced should be stable or durable, with a high probability of surviving node crashes). An atomic action with the failure atomicity and permanence of effect properties will be termed a *robust atomic action*. In view of the discussion presented in the preceding section, we will investigate in subsequent sections the fault tolerance techniques that an object manager should employ to support robust atomic actions. We will begin this investigation by first considering local (non-distributed) computations and then discuss what extensions, if any, are required to support distributed computations.

We conclude this section by briefly dwelling on the topic of concurrency control for atomic actions. This subject has been and continues to be intensely researched,[4] and although the research has been largely confined to databases, the techniques proposed are applicable to other areas. A very simple and widely used approach is to regard all operations on objects to be of type 'read' or 'write', which must follow the well known synchronisation rule permitting 'concurrent reads but exclusive writes'. This rule is imposed by requiring that any computation intending to perform an operation that is of type read (write) on an object, must first acquire a 'read lock' ('write lock') associated with that object. A read lock on an object can be held concurrently by many computations provided no computation is holding a write lock on that object. A write lock on an object, on the other hand, can only be held by a computation provided no other computation is holding a read or a write lock. In a classic paper,[2] Eswaran *et al.* proved that all computations must follow a 'two-phase'

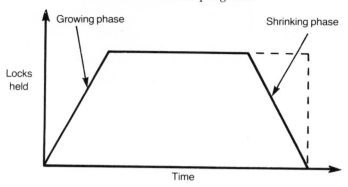

Fig. 6.1 Two-phase locking.

locking policy (see Fig. 6.1) to ensure the atomicity property (i.e. lack of interference).

During the first phase, termed the growing phase, a computation can acquire locks, but not release them. The tail end of the computation constitutes the shrinking phase, during which time held locks can be released but no locks can be acquired. Now suppose that a computation in its shrinking phase is to be aborted, and that some objects with write locks have already been released. If some of these objects have been locked by other computations, then abortion of the computation will require these computations to be aborted as well. To avoid this cascade roll back problem, it is necessary to make the shrinking phase 'instantaneous', as shown by the dotted lines. In effect this means that all the held locks are released simultaneously. For the sake of simplicity, in the rest of the chapter we will assume that some concurrency control technique, such as two-phase locking, is being employed and, further, that there is no danger of cascade roll back.

FAULT-MODELS AND EXCEPTION HANDLING

We assume that the communication system connecting all the nodes is faulty, as are the nodes themselves. Communication system faults are modelled as being responsible for the following types of failures: (i) a message sent by a node does not reach its destination; (ii) a message gets corrupted during its passage; (iii) messages çan arrive out of order at a destination; and (iv) a message can get replicated during its passage. We will assume that there is sufficient redundancy in a message (e.g. a checksum) to enable a receiver to detect corrupted messages with a very high probability of success. Thus, we need only concern ourselves with failures of types (i), (iii) and (iv). It will be the responsibility of the underlying RPC protocol to cope with these failures and to signal exceptions when failures cannot be masked (see section on Remote Procedure Calls, page 115).

We will model node faults in a very simple manner. We assume that a node either works perfectly or it simply stops working (crashes). After a crash, the node is repaired within a finite amount of time and made active again. A node can have two types of storage facilities: stable (crash proof) storage, and non-stable (volatile) storage. All the data stored on non-stable storage is lost when a crash happens. The data stored on stable storage, on the other hand, remains unaffected by a crash.

The reader may perhaps find our model of a faulty node less realistic than that of the communication system. The problem is that a malfunctioning node is capable of arbitrary behaviour (and not just remaining silent as assumed here). Designing systems under an arbitrary failure mode assumption is an extremely difficult task and is not within the scope of this chapter (but see Ref. 5 for further reading). If we assume that a malfunctioning node is quickly 'shut down' by some external agency, then our model can be said to approximate to reality. Alternatively, or in addition, it is also possible to introduce enough redundancy in a node for its behaviour to approximate more closely to that of the model.

We will adopt the exception handling strategy proposed in Ref. 6. We will say that an invocation of a procedure either completes successfully (a normal return is obtained) or abnormally (a specified exceptional return is obtained). Let C be a procedure that can **signal** two exceptions e1 and e2; then, we will adopt the following notation to indicate this fact:

> **procedure** C(...) **signals** e1, e2;
> **begin**
> ...
>   **assert** B<fail: ... ; **signal** e1>;
>   ...
>   D(...)<p1: ... ; **signal** e2>;
>   ...
> **end**<fail: ... ; **signal** fail>;

The body of the procedure also illustrates several further points: (i) angular brackets enclose exception handlers; (ii) a 'fail' exception is generated if the Boolean expression of the assert command evaluates to false; (iii) the handler for exception p1 causes C to signal e2; (iv) every procedure can signal a fail exception. The invoker of C can provide specific handlers for e1, e2 and fail:

> C(...)<e1: H1 | e2: H2 | fail: H3>;

where vertical bars separate handlers. The handler for a fail exception is intended to cope with the fail exception and all other exceptions generated for which no specific handler is available:

> C(...)<fail: H>;

In this case H will 'catch' e1, e2 or a fail exception.

ROBUST NON-DISTRIBUTED PROGRAMS

RECOVERY SEMANTICS

In this subsection we will present principles of backward error recovery. For the sake of simplicity, only local computations (non-distributed) will be considered. Using the terminology and concepts developed for an earlier paper,[7] for a computation or a process to have the abstraction of backward error recovery (henceforth termed *recovery*) requires the provision of the following three primitive facilities:

(1) *Establish a recovery point.* A process can establish a recovery point, thus indicating the start of a new recovery region (see Fig. 6.2). This implies that, if necessary, the states of any recoverable objects modified in that region can be restored automatically to those at the start of the region. We will assume that a primitive operation 'erp' is available for establishing a recovery point.

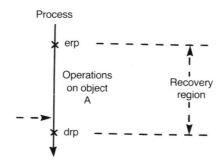

Fig. 6.2 A recovery region.

(2) *Discard a recovery point.* A process can discard a previously established recovery point by invoking the operation 'drp', thus indicating the end of a recovery region.

(3) *Restore.* This operation invokes (backward) recovery.

By definition, a recoverable object is an object with the property that if its operations are invoked from within a recovery region, then the invocation of recovery will see the object automatically restored to its abstract state prevailing at the start of the recovery region. Of course, this also means that if a recoverable object is modified when outside a recovery region, then no automatic recovery capability will be available. Let A be a recoverable object. From Fig. 6.2 we note that a number of operations have been performed on A. Suppose the flow of control has reached the point shown by the arrow when recovery is invoked. How is object A restored?

First of all, we note that it is the responsibility of the manager of A to perform state restoration. There can be several ways an object manager can mechanise the recovery. Here are two examples:

(1) When the executing process enters a recovery region, the manager records the current state of the object on some data structure (the manager takes a 'check point'). Recovery then involves the manager substituting the recorded state for the current state. (In general, a 'reverse' procedure is required to perform recovery.[8])

(2) The manager records enough information about the operations performed since the recovery region was entered so as to be able to sequentially 'undo', in reverse order, all these operations.

The recovery cache algorithm for recovery blocks (Chapter 3) employs an optimised version of the first approach. We will assume a similar approach for managers (see the next subsection).

As an example of the usage of these primitives, consider the following program, where S is any command.

```
        erp;
start:  S<fail: restore; goto start>
        drp;
```

What will happen if an exception is detected during the execution of S? (S is retried.) As an exercise, try modelling the behaviour of recovery blocks. (Answer is given in the appendix to this chapter.)

It is possible for recovery regions to be nested, as exemplified by, say, nested recovery blocks, but for the sake of simplicity we shall not consider nested recovery regions further. It is important, however, to understand what nesting of recovery regions implies. Consider the following recovery block program:

R1: **ensure** at1 **by** A.op(...) **else-by** B.op(...) **else** fail;

where A and B are two abstract recoverable objects, and the notation 'A.op( )' indicates the procedure 'op' exported by object A. Suppose that the body of this procedure contains a recovery block:

procedure op(...)
R2: **ensure** at2 **by** S1 **else-by** S2 **else** fail;

We ask the question: is R2 nested within R1? Irrespective of what the answer is, the semantics of program R1 remain the same: if the test at1 fails, the states of objects A and B will remain unchanged. The mechanisation of recovery required to support the above semantics will, however, crucially depend on whether R2 is regarded as nested within R1. These issues are discussed at length in the paper already cited (Ref. 7). Here we will adopt the view that R1 and R2 represent recovery regions at two different levels of abstraction; hence they are not nested (are *disjoint*[7]). The program given below, on the other hand, does contain nested recovery regions.

R3: **ensure** at1 **by**
        ensure at2 **by** S1 **else-by** S2 **else** fail
    else-by ...

NESTED ATOMIC ACTIONS AND ROBUST OBJECTS

Let us ignore for the moment any issues concerning recovery and consider actions that are atomic with respect to concurrency. We will use the notation 'action S end' to indicate that the execution of S will be atomic. Let A and B be two abstract objects:

A1: **action** ... ; A.op(...); ... ; B.op(...); ... **end**

We will adopt the view that any action, such as A1, is composed out of smaller actions (which are themselves composed out of yet smaller actions, and so on). This is illustrated in Fig. 6.3, which depicts the structure of the

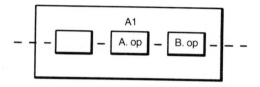

Fig. 6.3 Nested atomic actions.

computation invoked by A1, and indicates that the execution of program A1 gives rise to a computation with nested atomic action structure. Note that in program A1, the nesting of actions is *implicit*. If we permit concurrency within an action, then nesting of actions has to be indicated *explicitly*:

A2: **action**

   ...

    cobegin

      A3: **action** ... **end**

      A4: **action** ... **end**

    coend

   ...

   end

In the above program, concurrent actions (A3 and A4) are nested within A2. In this chapter we will primarily consider sequential programs. Nested concurrent actions provide a convenient means of constructing type (ii) programs, as we shall see in the final section of the chapter (page 119).

Any concurrency control technique employed must ensure that the execution of the entire program (e.g. A1) is free from interference. So, if two-phase locking is being utilised, then all the locks (including those acquired by internal actions such as A.op(...)) must be held till the outermost action terminates, so as to avoid the danger of a cascade roll back.[9]

Atomic actions provide a natural structure for introducing recoverability. We will now investigate the possibility of introducing failure atomicity and permanence of effect properties to obtain robust actions. We will assume that outermost atomic actions are to be embellished in this manner. Let Ci be the stable (crash resistant) state of a system (i.e. Ci is the aggregation of stable states of objects). Then the function of a robust atomic action (with write operations) is to change the state Ci to some new stable state Ci+1. Assuming that 'r-action S end' represents a robust action, we can visualise the implementation of 'r-action' and 'end' as depicted below (two-phase locking is assumed):

r-action →   erp →   record start of a
                         recovery region;

end   →   drp →   record new state on
                         stable storage;
                         release locks;

We assume the existence of a stable storage object that is used for storing state information of other objects. The exact details of how the recovery region data are managed need not concern us here but we will nevertheless briefly explain the basic principles involved.

To start with we will assume that every (recoverable) object is responsible for performing its own recovery. Assume that A1 (Fig. 6.3) is a robust action and some process P is executing it. Then the table given below summarises the recovery aspects. We assume that a data structure, referred to as the P-list, is created for the executing process to record recovery data, which includes the names of recoverable objects accessed so far and information regarding the locks acquired.

Operation	Actions of process P
erp	create a data structure for recording recovery data; (call this 'P-list')
A.op( )	if lock on A is not held then lock A; if name 'A' is not recorded in P-list then make an entry; call A.op( );
restore	for all object names in P-list do: call objectname.recover;
drp	for all object names in P-list do: call objectname.securestate; release locks on all objects whose names are in P-list; delete P-list.

We assume that every recoverable object provides a 'recover' procedure, the function of which is to adjust the internal variables of the object so that the abstract state of the object is restored to that at the start of the recovery region. In the simplest case, this will consist of reinitialising the objects to their latest stable states. Thus, whenever recovery is desired, process P executes 'restore' – this has the effect of restoring all the called objects to their stable states. Finally, when discarding the recovery point of A1, we must ensure that a new stable state has been created. Following our philosophy of letting object managers do the relevant work, the natural method is to invoke 'securestate' operation of all the objects recorded in the P-list so that each object stores its new state on stable storage. To summarise, a recoverable object has two special operations:

recover: restore the state of the object;
securestate: record the current object state on stable storage.

We can also add a third operation for coping with crashes; so crash recovery of a node involves calling the crash-recover operations of all the objects:

crash-recover: reinitialise the object to the current stable state.

Consider now the particular scenario depicted in Fig. 6.4, where A1 is an outermost robust action. Suppose that objects A and B are recoverable. Assume that the operation currently in execution (B.op2) terminates by signalling a fail exception and this calls for recovery of A1. The backward recovery of A1 will involve restoring objects A and B, and as we have seen, this is performed by automatically invoking the 'recover' operations of these two objects. So, a single call to 'A.recover' will undo state changes introduced by the two atomic actions (A.op1, A.op2). This illustrates a point not widely appreciated, and that is that recovery of an action (such as A1) need not involve individually recovering constituent atomic actions. It is certainly possible to adopt a recovery model in which recovery of an action is performed by recovering constituent actions (e.g. Refs. 9 and 10), i.e. recovery is performed on a call by call basis. However, we consider that the recovery model presented here is a more elegant way of mechanising object based recovery. Similarly, in order to make the state changes produced by A1 stable, it is not necessary that the state changes produced by each constituent action be made stable individually; rather, at the termination time all the recoverable objects used within A1 are asked to make their current states stable (see the table of recovery actions above).

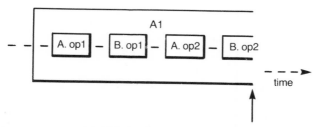

Fig. 6.4 Nested atomic actions.

As a consequence of the above observations, internal actions have no need for stable storage. In particular, if an operation such as B.op1 has recovery regions (the body of op1, for example, uses recovery blocks) then upon termination, all the recovery data is simply discarded. The details of managing recovery data at different levels of abstraction are somewhat involved and the reader is referred to Ref. 11 for further details.

A SECOND LOOK AT CRASH RESISTANCE

The framework for recovery presented above has one flaw which can be exposed by considering the following situation: a node crash occurs during the execution of the operation 'drp' of atomic action A1. Suppose object A has been secured to the new stable state but the same is not true for object B. Thus, after recovering from the crash, while object A will be in the new state, object B will be in the original state – an inconsistency. What is necessary is for the crash recovery algorithm of the node somehow or other either to restore A to the prior stable state or to bring B to the new stable state. Since the second option is not possible, we require that A be restored to the prior stable state. This suggests that the algorithm for 'drp' (for an outermost robust atomic action) be modified in such a manner that normal termination is performed only when *all* objects have made their states stable. The algorithm given below ensures this.

```
              The commit algorithm
              "implementation of drp"
              save process-state(cr); fate:=abort;
              [put 'process-state', 'fate' and 'P-list' on
                 stable storage];
              for all object names in P-list do
                    objectname. securestate;
              [fate:=commit];
     cr:      case fate of
        abort:    for all object names in P-list do
                       {objectname.recover; release lock}
        commit:   for all object names in P-list do
                       {objectname.commit; release lock}
              end "case"
              die "delete the process and the P-list"
```

Employing the terminology widely used, the termination of an action with the new state made stable will be referred to as *committing* the action, and the algorithm that determines whether an action is to be aborted or committed will be called the *commit algorithm*. The primitive drp (for an outermost robust action) implements the commit algorithm. We introduce a new operation for recoverable objects: 'commit' whose function is to make the most recent secured state the current state of the object. The operation 'securestate' is modified so that the object merely records the most recent object state on stable storage (which is not made the current state until the commit operation is executed). We assume that associated with the executing process, there is a variable named 'fate' which records the fate of the action (to be aborted or committed).

Looking at the algorithm, the process saves its state, ready to execute from label 'cr' and the variable 'fate' is initialised to the value 'abort'. A crash of the node at this point will result in the abortion of the action since all the objects will have been restored to the previous committed states, the recent states being discarded with locks released; at the same time, no state information about the process survives the crash. If there is no crash, the process executes the operations enclosed by brackets and makes itself crash proof (held locks also become stable). The execution of this set of operations itself must be failure atomic (this is indicated by the brackets), so that either all of the data regarding the process becomes stable or none is. Construction of stable storage which provides atomic update facilities is an interesting design exercise (see Ref. 12 for details). The fate of the process is changed to commit only when all the objects have secured their states. If a crash occurs during this process (some of the objects have yet to make their states stable), then after crash recovery the crashed process will be recreated, ready to execute the commit algorithm from point 'cr'. As can be seen, in this case all the objects will be restored. The operations 'recover', 'commit' and 'release a lock' must be idempotent – multiple executions are the same as a single execution. (Do you see why? Consider what will happen if a crash occurs during the execution of the case statement.)

ROBUST DISTRIBUTED PROGRAMS

Our next task is to extend the ideas developed in the previous section to distributed programs. We will do this in three stages. In the first subsection we will discuss a model of distributed computation, and follow this up with a discussion on issues concerned with design and use of remote procedure calls. In the last subsection we will discuss recoverability and commitment issues.

A MODEL OF DISTRIBUTED COMPUTATION

It was stated earlier that a distributed program will be executed by a group of processes. There can be several ways of structuring such a group. Here are three examples: (i) a new process is created to serve each remote call; (ii) each object manager has a few (internal) server processes that receive remote requests; (iii) a local process creates a server process on a remote node to execute all the calls directed at that node. We will adopt the last technique for our purposes, because it represents a very simple way of extending a non-distributed computation to a distributed one (the approach adopted in the ARGUS system[10] roughly corresponds to the first case).

Consider the following example: a distributed program makes use of three objects A (on the local node N1), B (on node N2) and C (on node

```
createworker (N3,...);
"returns W1 as the name of
the created process"
rpc (W1, C. op1,...);
createworker (N2,...);
rpc (W2, B. op1,...);
A. op1 (...);
rpc (W2, B. op2,...);
```

(a) A Distributed Program

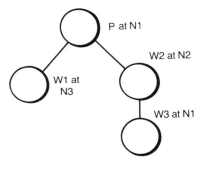

(b) Process Structure

Fig. 6.5 Distributed computation.

N3); further, object B itself accesses some object D on node N1. In Fig. 6.5, we have shown the program and the corresponding process structure. It is assumed that primitives 'rpc(workername, procedurename, . . .)' and 'createworker(nodename, . . .)' are available for invoking remote procedures and creating processes on remote nodes. The process executing this program creates a server process at a node before forwarding call requests to it. Thus process P will explicitly create processes W1 and W2. Object B is responsible for creating process W3 at N1 so that calls on object D can be made. We thus see that the execution of a distributed program can give rise to a hierarchy of processes.

This model of computation provides a straightforward means of incorporating the recovery and crash resistance properties discussed previously. So, for example, backward recovery involves each process calling the 'recover' operations of the objects it has directly manipulated: process P will invoke A.recover and also send 'restore' requests to processes W1 and W2. We will discuss these features in the section on Recovery and Crash Resistance, page 116.

REMOTE PROCEDURE CALLS

In this subsection we will briefly examine remote procedure calls, whereby a 'client' process (such as W1, Fig. 6.5) can invoke an operation of a 'server' process (such as W3, Fig. 6.5). Essentially, in this scheme a client's remote call is transformed into a request message to the named server who performs the requested work and sends the results back:

Client	*Server*
	cycle
send ( ) "call msg"	receive ( ) "get work"
	"work"
receive ( )	send ( ) "send results"
	end

Both the client and server will contain measures for dealing with failures such as lost messages. The design and implementation of remote procedure calls continues to be a subject of ongoing research, and the reader's attention is drawn to Refs. 13, 14 and 15. RPC protocols, in common with other types of protocol, typically employ time-out mechanisms to prevent indefinite (or long) waiting by a process expecting a message. Suppose that a server crashes in the middle of a call, in which case the client will not receive the result message and will eventually be 'timed out'. It is interesting to note that a time-out exception could indicate any of the following four possibilities: (a) the server crashed during the call; (b) the server did not receive the request (the client's call message got lost); (c) the server's reply did not reach the client; (d) the server is still performing the work (so the time-out interval was not long enough). We will assume that the client's time-out results in the call terminating abnormally with a fail exception. For the sake of simplicity, we will assume that this is the only exception a remote call can get (see Ref. 14 for other types of exceptions).

rpc (servername, procname, params)<fail: handler>;

We will assume the following semantics for the RPC: if the call terminates normally (no fail exception is generated) then exactly one execution for the call has taken place at the server; on the other hand, if the fail exception is generated then it is not known whether the server has performed the work. This will be termed *exactly once* semantics. What actions should be taken by the handler associated with 'fail'? A reasonable strategy is to retry the call a few times:

rpc(...)<fail: retry(n)<fail: handler>>;

The above notation indicates that the call is retried a maximum of n times. If the call succeeds, then as before we require that only one execution has been performed at the server. If all the retries fail then one possibility, assuming the call has been made from within a recovery region, is to invoke backward recovery:

rpc(...)<fail: retry(n)<fail: restore>>;

The implementation of 'restore' in a distributed environment will be discussed in the next subsection. It is also possible to select a 'stronger' semantics for RPCs, termed *at most once*: if a call fails then no side effects will have been produced. This requires the capability of undoing side effects of individual calls; not surprisingly, this call semantics has been chosen by the advocates of the 'call by call' recovery model.[10,16] As can be appreciated, one advantage of this approach is that, when a call fails, it is not necessary to recover the enclosing action (or more precisely, to the nearest recovery point) as is the case with the model adopted here.

With the exception handling strategy just mentioned in mind, a simple technique exists for creating a worker at a remote node:

procedure createworker(Ni,...)
    begin
       ...
       rpc(manager at Ni, create, params)
       <fail: retry(n)<fail: **signal** fail>>;
    end

This assumes that every node has a manager process that accepts calls for worker creation. The created worker enters the cycle for receiving calls (see the simplified RPC protocol at the beginning of this subsection) and sets a time out (the idle period). If the client's createworker call fails and a worker nevertheless is created, then this worker will never receive a request for work. Hence its time out will expire and the associated handler can simply kill the worker. (Modification to this strategy is required if the worker has become stable – see the next subsection.)

RECOVERY AND CRASH RESISTANCE
We will now extend the recovery model of the previous section so that: (i) if a process within the hierarchy of processes executes a 'restore' operation, then it and its siblings all perform backward recovery; (ii) commitment by the master process involves commitment by its siblings (which in turn will involve commitment of their siblings and so forth). We will consider all the five operations (erp, local call, rpc, restore, drp) and see what recovery management is implied.

(1) *Operation erp.* The executing process creates a data structure (P-list) to record recovery data.
(2) *Local call to an object.* If the object name is not on the P-list, then make an entry before the call.

(3) *Remote call*. If the name of the worker process is not on the P-list, then make an entry before making the call. The worker process will execute the call as a local call, i.e. the name of the object will be recorded in the P-list of the worker.

(4) *Operation restore*. The process performs the following operations: calls objectname.recover operations of all the local objects recorded in the P-list; sends restore commands to all the workers whose names are in the P-list. If a remote call fails then the process destroys itself (the outermost atomic action will eventually be aborted).

(5) *Operation drp*. The commit algorithm (for the outermost atomic action) to be executed by the master process, such as that shown in Fig. 6.5 is modified as shown below:

The commit algorithm of the master process
```
          "implementation of drp"
save process-state(cr); fate:=abort;
[put 'process-state', 'fate' and 'P-list'
    on stable storage];
for all local objects in P-list do
    objectname. securestate;
for all process names in P-list do
    rpc(processname, stable, ...)<fail: retry(n)
                            <fail: for all local object
                            names in P-list do
                            {objectname.recover;
                            release lock}; die>>;
[fate:=commit];
cr: case fate of
    abort:  for all local object names in P-list do
                {objectname.recover; release locks}
    commit: for all local object names in P-list do
                {objectname.commit; release lock}
            for all process names in P-list do
            rpc(...,commit,...)
            "retry till success"
    end "case"
die;
```

Comparing with the original commit algorithm, we notice a few differences. The process secures local objects first and then sends a 'stable' command to all the workers. This is a signal for a worker to make itself and its objects stable. If a remote call fails (after a few retries) then the master process performs local recovery and dies. We thus make it the responsibility of the workers to determine when to abort. A skeleton algorithm for a worker – modified from that given at the beginning of the section on Remote Procedure Calls, page 115 – is given below:

Life of a worker

```
fate:=abort; create an empty P-list;
cycle
    cr: get-work(...) "receive an rpc request"
            <fail: case fate of
                    abort: restore local objects; die;
                    heldup: checkifmasterup(...);
                            if up then goto cr else
                                    {restore local objects; die}
                    end "case">
        analyse-request;
        case command of
        restore: "see the description of command restore"
         stable: save process-state(cr);
            [put 'process-state', 'fate', 'P-list'
              on stable storage];
            for all local object names in P-list do
                objectname.securestate;
            for all process names in P-list do
                rpc(processname, stable,...)
                        <fail: retry(n)<fail:restore local
                                        objects; die>>;
            result:=done;
            [fate:=heldup]
        call: if lock on the named object not held then lock
            the object; if name not in P-list then make an
            entry; execute the call; prepare results;
     commit: "similar to the master"; result:=done;
        end "case";
        send-results(...);
    end "cycle"
```

A worker waits for requests, with an 'idle time-out'. If the time out expires (a fail exception is generated) and fate=abort, then the worker aborts, suspecting a crash of its master. On the other hand, if the fate is 'heldup' then the worker cannot abort unilaterally, and must check if its master has aborted. For this purpose, we assume the existence of a procedure 'checkifmasterup(...)' which returns **true** if the called node has the named process running and **false** otherwise. Looking at Fig. 6.5, when process P executes 'drp', the operation will terminate successfully only if P, W1, W2 and W3 all commit their objects.

The commit algorithm presented here is known as the two-phase commit algorithm.[17] There are several ways of optimising this algorithm, some of which are discussed in Ref. 18.

ANOTHER LOOK AT CRASH RESISTANCE

Robust actions described in the section on non-distributed programs have the property that a crash of the node causes all the actions in progress to be aborted (except those that are committing). Their distributed counterparts have a similar property in that a crash of any node belonging to the group of processes executing an action causes the abortion of that action. We will discuss how such type (i) programs can be utilised for constructing type (ii) programs, so that a computation can complete normally despite crashes. This is an attractive proposition for a distributed program if a distributed system contains redundancy in the form of services provided.

Assume that we wish to construct a program to run on node N1 that calls operations of some recoverable object, A, on node N2, and that there is another object, B, on node N3 which provides similar operations to A. We require the property that if N2 crashes in the middle of the computation in question (or becomes unavailable from N1 due to some communications breakdown), then rather than aborting the whole computation, only the side effects produced on A should be undone and the computation continue by accessing object B instead of A. We can make use of nested concurrent actions to achieve this property, as indicated below.

(1) The process (say P) running the main program as a robust action on N1 forks a process, Q, and waits.

(2) Process Q starts a new action and establishes a recovery point; it creates a server process, W1, on N2 to receive remote calls for A.

(3) If a call to A fails then Q performs local recovery and aborts; P now continues.

(4) There are two possibilities at node N2: either N2 has crashed, in which case there is no W2, or W2 is running. If the latter is true, then W2 will eventually abort (see the algorithm for a worker given in the previous subsection).

(5) Process P can fork another process to perform operations on object B.

We will gloss over the details of recovery data management for concurrent actions as they are not essential to understand the point that concurrent actions can be aborted independent of the enclosing action. Naturally, the above idea can be applied to any degree of nesting of actions.

Returning to our example, if the home node of the robust action (N1) crashes, then the entire action will be aborted. If this is not deemed desirable, then a distributed checkpointing facility will be required so that the intermediate state of the entire computation can be saved on stable storage. We will not pursue this topic further here.

This concludes our discussion on robust distributed computations. For further reading on this subject, the reader's attention is drawn to the already cited papers.[9,10,11,12,16,19]

CONCLUDING REMARKS

The approach adopted here was first to develop a framework for constructing robust non-distributed programs and then to extend that framework to encompass distributed programs. We have presented what may be termed an object based recovery approach, whereby objects are responsible for implementing backward recovery and crash resistance.

ACKNOWLEDGEMENTS

This chapter has benefited from critical comments from: Tom Anderson, Brian Randell, Josephine Anyanwu and Graham Parrington.

REFERENCES

1. Holt, R. C. (1983). *Concurrent Euclid, the Unix System and Tunis*, Addison Wesley.
2. Eswaran, K., Gray, J. N., Lorie, R. and Traiger, I. (1976). 'The Notions of Consistency and Predicate Locks in a Database System'. *CACM*, **19**, No. 11, 624–633.
3. Best, E. and Randell, B. (1981). 'A Formal Model of Atomicity in Asynchronous Systems'. *Acta Informatica*, **16**, 93–124.
4. Bernstein, P. A. and Goodman, N. (1981). 'Concurrency Control in Distributed Database Systems'. *ACM Computing Surveys*, **13**, No. 182, 185–221.
5. Lamport, L., Shostak, R. and Pease, M. (1982). 'The Byzantine Generals Problem'. *ACM TOPLAS*, **4**, No. 3, 382–401.
6. Cristian, F. (1982). 'Exception Handling and Software Fault Tolerance'. *IEEE Trans. on Computers*, **C-31**, No. 6, 531–540.
7. Anderson, T., Lee, P. A. and Shrivastava, S. K. (1978). 'A Model of Recoverability in Multilevel Systems'. *IEEE Trans. on Soft. Eng.*, **SE-4**, No. 6, 486–494.
8. Shrivastava, S. K. and Banatre, J.-P. (1978). 'Reliable Resource Allocation Between Unreliable Processes'. *IEEE Trans. on Soft. Eng.*, **SE-4**, No. 3, 230–241.
9. Moss, J. E. B. (1982). 'Nested Transactions and Reliable Distributed Computing'. *Proc. 2nd Sym. on Rel. in Dist. Soft. and Database Sys.*, 33–39, Pittsburgh.
10. Liskov, B. and Scheifler, R. (1983). 'Guardians and Actions: Linguistic Support for Robust, Distributed Programs'. *ACM TOPLAS*, **5**, No. 3, 381–404.
11. Shrivastava, S. K. (1981). 'Structuring Distributed Systems for Recoverability and Crash Resistance'. *IEEE Trans. on Soft. Eng.*, **SE-7**, No. 4, 436–447.
12. Lampson, B. and Sturgis, H. (1981). 'Atomic Transactions', *Lecture Notes in Comp. Sc.*, **105**, Springer-Verlag, 246–265.
13. Nelson, B. J. (1981). *Remote Procedure Call*, Ph.D. Thesis, CMU-CS-81-119, Department of Computer Science, Carnegie-Mellon University.
14. Shrivastava, S. K. and Panzieri, F. (1982). 'The Design of a Reliable Remote Procedure Call Mechanism'. *IEEE Trans. on Computers*, **C-31**, No. 7, 692–697.

15. Panzieri, F. and Shrivastava, S. K. (1982). 'Reliable Remote Calls for Distributed Unix: an Implementation Study'. *Proc. of 2nd Sym. on Rel. in Dist. Soft. and Database Sys.*, Pittsburgh, 127–133.
16. Svobodova, L. (1984). 'Resilient Distributed Computing'. *IEEE Trans. on Soft. Eng.*, **SE-10**, No. 3, 257–268.
17. Gray, J. N. (1978). 'Notes on Database Operating Systems'. *Lecture Notes in Comp. Sc.*, **60**, Springer-Verlag, 398–481.
18. Mohan, C. and Lindsay, B. G. (1983). 'Efficient Commit Protocols for the Tree of Processes Model of Distributed Transactions'. *Proc. of 2nd ACM Sym. on Princ. of Dist. Comp.*, Montreal, 76–88.
19. Jegado, M. (1983). 'Recoverability Aspects of a Distributed File System'. *Soft.: Prac. and Exp.*, **13**, No. 1, 33–44.

APPENDIX

Consider the following recovery block program:

ensure at1 **by** S1 **else-by** S2 **else** fail;

The program shown below utilises the three primitives (erp, drp, restore) to implement the recovery block.

```
     erp;
  A1: begin
         S1
         assert at1; goto B;
      end <fail: restore; goto A2>;
  A2: begin
         S2
         assert at1; goto B;
      end <fail: restore; drp; signal fail>;
  B: drp;
```

CHAPTER 7

Software safety

N. Leveson

(*Dept. of Information and Computer Science,
University of California at Irvine*)

A system or subsystem may be described as *safety critical* if a run-time failure can result in death, injury, loss of equipment or property, or environmental harm. Computers are not inherently unsafe, and until recently computers were not used to control complex, safety-critical systems. Thus although computers were used in such potentially unsafe systems as aircraft, air traffic control, nuclear power, defence and aerospace systems, a natural reluctance to add unknown and complex factors to these systems kept computers out of most safety-critical loops. But the potential advantages of using computers are now outweighing nervousness (some might say good sense), and both computer scientists and system engineers are finding themselves faced with some difficult and unsolved problems.

In safety-critical, real-time systems it is not unusual to have reliability requirements of 10^{-7} or 10^{-9} chance of failure over a short period of time. At a recent meeting of experienced researchers in the area of software reliability, the overriding group consensus was that these types of reliability requirements cannot be achieved or confirmed for software with current technology. In fact, available evidence indicates that current software reliability figures are orders of magnitude less than required (Dunham and Knight, 1981).

What can be done? One option is not to build these systems or not to use computers to control them. However, this is not realistic. There are too many good reasons why computers should be used and too few other alternatives. Therefore, other options need to be considered. One possibility is to consider reliability in a less absolute sense. That is, there are many failures of differing consequences that are possible in any complex system. The consequences may vary from minor annoyance up to death or injury. It seems reasonable to focus on the failures which have the most drastic consequences. That is, even if all failures cannot be prevented, it may be possible to ensure that the failures that do occur are of minor consequence or that even if a failure does occur, the system will 'fail-safe' in a manner which will not have catastrophic or serious results.

Another way of putting this is that the system should have an acceptable level of 'risk'.

It is useful to adopt this approach under the following circumstances: (a) not all failures are of equal cost and (b) there are a relatively small number of failures that can lead to catastrophic results. Under these circumstances, it is possible to augment traditional reliability techniques which attempt to eliminate all failures with techniques which concentrate on the high cost failures. These techniques often involve a 'backward' approach and start by determining what are the unacceptable or high cost failures and then ensure that these particular failures do not occur or at least minimise the probability of their occurrence. Another way of looking at this is that a 'forward' approach would ensure that all possible reachable states of the system are correct whereas a backward approach would ensure that incorrect states are not reachable. This is only practical under the above assumptions that there are a relatively small number of failures which are unacceptable and that these can be stated. In practice, this is usually the case even in complex systems. For example, this type of approach has been applied to nuclear power plants and missile defence systems.

When computers are used as components of larger systems, especially when they are a control component, considering the computer software in isolation will be of limited usefulness. The source of many of our problems in building real-time computer systems is a too narrow focus on the part of the computer scientist and especially the software engineer (Boebert, 1980). Most verification and validation efforts concentrate on proving the correspondence between the source code and the software specification, and much progress has been made in eliminating software implementation errors. Unfortunately, studies show that at least 60% of the failures in production systems stem from requirements and specification problems (Boehm *et al.*, 1975; Endres, 1975; Lipow, 1979). In addition, Iyer and Velardi (1983) examined software errors of a production operating system and found that 11% of all software errors and 40% of all software failures were hardware related.

These results are not surprising from a systems engineering viewpoint. Many, if not most, serious accidents are caused by complex unplanned and unfortunate interactions between components of the system and by multiple failures. That is, most accidents originate in subsystem interfaces (Frola and Miller, 1984). Therefore, any software safety techniques, especially analysis and verification, are going to have to consider the system as a whole (especially the interactions between the components of the system) and not just software alone.

Since much is already known about how to build safe electromechanical systems, it is instructive to take a brief look at system safety and then to see how these techniques can be extended to computers when they are used in safety-critical systems. By extending system safety techniques to include software, and *vice versa*, the necessary total systems approach can be achieved.

SYSTEM SAFETY

System safety is the part of system engineering that involves identifying hazards and eliminating them or reducing the associated risk to an acceptable level. Several terms have been defined which are useful for software safety. An *accident* or *mishap* is an unplanned event or series of events that result in death, injury, illness, damage to or loss of property, or environmental harm. *Damage* is a measure of the loss in a mishap.

Mishaps involve abnormal or unexpected releases of energy (Johnson, 1980). Conditions with the potential for causing or contributing to a mishap are called *hazards*. Hazards have a severity and a probability. *Hazard severity* is an assessment of the worst possible damage which could ultimately result, while *hazard probability* is the aggregate probability of the individual events which create a specific hazard.

An important element of safety is expected loss or *risk*. Risk is a function of both hazard severity and hazard probability. A risk assessment procedure is important in that it allows decision makers to evaluate properly the amount of risk involved relative to what it will 'cost' (in terms of resources and performance tradeoffs) to reduce the risk to an acceptable level.

Categorisation of risks may be based on severity alone early in the design phase. Severity is usually a qualitative measure of the worst credible mishap resulting from the hazard. Typical categories are negligible, marginal, critical and catastrophic. The actual definition of what constitutes each of these categories may differ for each system and may include such factors as injury to personnel, amount of system damage, dollar loss, man-hours lost, down-time, etc.

Along with severity, hazard categorization may also involve the determination of the likelihood of the hazardous event occurring. This may be stated in qualitative (non-numeric) terms such as frequent, probable, occasional, remote, improbable, or in quantitative (numeric) terms such as potential occurrences per unit of time, events, population, items or activity. In determining urgency of corrective action, it may also be important to consider the probability of occurrence of a mishap when a particular hazard exists.

The goal of system safety is to eliminate hazards if possible and, if not, to reduce their associated risk to an acceptable level. The level of risk which is considered acceptable for an activity or system will depend upon the cost of eliminating or reducing the risk, expected losses, the importance of functional or other conflicting requirements, and sometimes political or psychological factors. For example, people appear to be willing to accept a much higher level of risk on the roads than in the skies (i.e. in cars than in aircraft).

How is risk minimised? There are three aspects to risk: the probability of the hazard occurring (in most instances this involves some type of fault or failure), the probability of the hazard leading to a mishap, and the severity of the resulting mishap. Decreasing any of these three things will decrease risk. For example, to decrease the probability of a hazard occurring as a result of a software fault, fault tolerance techniques might be judiciously used. Note that the goal here is to detect the fault and to ensure that a safe state is maintained. However, this safe state need not be a correct state. In situations where the function being performed is not critical, switching to a degraded mode of processing or even switching to a fail-safe mode (e.g. shutting down the system completely) is equally effective, although perhaps less desirable from a total reliability standpoint.

Another way to minimise risk is to minimise the probability of a hazard, once it has occurred, leading to a mishap. An example of this might be a software monitoring program which detects an unsafe system state which may have occurred due to failure or environmental effect external to the computer (e.g. a rupture of cooling water pipes in a nuclear reactor, overheating, fire) or due to a computer software fault which is not detected before the system moves into the hazardous state. A reasonable software response to this situation might be to attempt to repair the state if possible or to minimise the risk of a mishap by sounding warnings, alerting human backup systems, etc.

In the worst case, i.e. a system failure is unavoidable, the goal is to minimise the severity of the effects of the failure. The controlling computer may be involved here by providing warnings or alarms, or taking other steps to mitigate potential damage (assuming the failure is in the controlled system and not the computer).

BUILDING SAFE SOFTWARE CONTROLLED SYSTEMS

When computers are used to control systems which are themselves inherently unsafe, system safety issues begin to impact the software and its development process.

The first step in building safety-critical systems involves identifying the hazardous states and establishing acceptable levels of risk. Safety requirements must be established early so that they can be weighed against contractual obligations, financial requirements, functional requirements and schedule restrictions. A successful safety programme requires specification and delegation of responsibility along with sound planning. For example, an independent group or person should be designated as responsible for overseeing safety and explicit safety requirements written into the software requirements. Past experience has shown that the degree of safety achieved in a system is directly dependent upon the emphasis given.

To achieve safe software, safety concerns and techniques must be integrated into all phases of the software life cycle. The first step in any large software program is the specification of requirements. The software specification normally includes the functional requirements of the system. In safety-critical systems, it must also include the safety requirements. That is, it is important that the software requirements specification include not only what the system shall do but what it shall *not* do. It should include means for eliminating and controlling hazards and for limiting damage in case of mishap. An important part of the safety requirements is the specification of the ways a system can fail safely and to what extent failure is tolerable. Thus the system specifier must determine (a) the hazardous states of the system which pose an unacceptable level of risk, (b) how the system can get into these hazardous states, and (c) what to do about it if it happens.

Determining the unsafe states of a system is called a *hazard analysis*. In general, a system can get into an unsafe state in several ways, including:

- hardware component failure
- interfacing (communication and timing) problems between components of the system
- human error in operation or maintenance where a human error is defined as a human action producing an unintended result
- environmental stress
- software control errors.

The safety requirements and design for a particular system under construction would need to consider all of these possible safety problems. In particular, software requirements must not only look at software control errors, but must also examine the interaction of the software with other components of the system. For example, a control action of the software may only be unsafe in the event of a separate failure of another component of the system or unusual environmental stress.

Interaction with humans must also be considered. For example, in a computer controlled aircraft landing system, the system performance must be up to the very high standards demanded by the pilot or safety may be compromised. One of the considerations in designing the auto landing system for the L1011 (Mineck *et al.*, 1972) was that unless the pilot has confidence in the system, there is a chance the pilot will disconnect it instead of allowing the landing to be completed automatically. System disconnection, however, is dangerous at altitudes below where safe manual take-overs can be assured. The system must, therefore, not only fly the aircraft safely, but must fly it in a manner that the pilot considers desirable. One way to maintain human confidence in an automatic system is to provide data so that the human can monitor the dynamic performance of the system.

There is also a problem in how much control should be given to the computer as opposed to the human controller, i.e. what is the ideal symbiosis between man and machine. When the human is merely in an overseeing capacity, there is a danger of inattention and erosion of skills due to lack of practice for the situations where the operator is required to take over. There is also a problem of complacency. For example, there have been instances where pilots have not intervened quickly enough to correct avionics computer errors because of overconfidence in the computer (Ternhem, 1981). This whole area of human factors in computer safety is an important one and needs more attention (Rouse, 1981).

The system safety engineer usually determines the potential hazards in a system and classifies them in a process called *preliminary hazard analysis* (PHA). The software hazards can be derived from the PHA in order to get the software safety requirements. This process is called *software hazard analysis*.

SOFTWARE HAZARD ANALYSIS

The problem of determining the requirements for software systems has proved very difficult to solve. However, at least in terms of safety, this may be one of the most important sources of problems. Consider the following examples of mishaps or near mishaps:

- In a fly-by-wire flight control system, a mechanical malfunction set up an accelerated environment for which the flight control computer was not programmed. The aircraft went out of control and crashed (Frola and Miller, 1984).
- A computer issued a close door command on an aircraft at the wrong time – luckily nobody was standing there at the time (Frola and Miller, 1984).
- Industrial robots have killed or injured humans who entered restricted areas to trouble-shoot or perform maintenance (Fuller, 1984).
- A wing-mounted missile failed to separate from the launcher after ignition because a computer program signalled the missile retaining mechanism to close before the rocket had built up sufficient thrust to clear the missile from the wing. The aircraft went violently out of control (Frola and Miller, 1984).
- In a computer controlled batch reactor, the programmers were told that if a fault occurred in the plant, all control variables should be left as they were and an alarm sounded. The computer received a signal that there was a low oil level in a gearbox when it had already added catalyst to the reactor but just as the computer had started to increase the cooling water flow to the reflux condenser. The computer program did as specified – the controls were left as they were and an alarm sounded. By the time the operators had responded to the alarm, the reactor had overheated (Kletz, 1983).

One common feature of the above is that the problems can be traced back to a fundamental misunderstanding about the desired operation of the software. These examples are not unusual. As noted above, many studies have shown that a majority of production software problems can be traced back to faults in the requirements or design. After studying actual mishaps where computers were involved, safety engineers have concluded that inadequate design foresight and specification errors are the greatest cause of software safety problems (Ericson, 1981; Griggs, 1981). These problems arise from many possible causes, including the difficulty of the problem intrinsically, a lack of emphasis on it in software engineering research (which has tended to concentrate on avoiding or removing implementation faults), and a certain cubbyhole attitude which has led computer scientists to concentrate on the computer aspects of the system and engineers to concentrate on the physical and mechanical parts of the system with few people dealing with the interaction between the two.

Given that requirements errors account for a large number of safety problems, then emphasis needs to be placed on this problem. One of the goals of software hazard analysis techniques is to determine the software safety requirements. Another is to extend verification and validation of software beyond showing consistency between the software specification and the implementation, to verifying that the software correctly implements the total system safety requirements. Several techniques have been proposed to accomplish this, including fault tree analysis, nuclear safety cross check analysis, and Petri net analysis techniques.

Fault tree analysis (FTA) is an analytical technique used in the safety analysis of electromechanical systems whereby an undesired system state is specified and the system is then analysed in the context of its environment and operation to find all credible sequences of events which can lead to the undesired state (Vesely *et al.*, 1981). The fault tree is a graphic model of the various parallel and sequential combinations of faults (or system states) that will result in the occurrence of the predefined undesired event. The faults can be events that are associated with component hardware failures, human errors, or any other pertinent events which can lead to the undesired event. A fault tree thus depicts the logical interrelationships of basic events that lead to the undesired event.

One advantage in using this technique is that all the different types of system components (including humans) can be considered. Although originally FTA did not include software, it has been extended to do so (Leveson and Harvey, 1983; McIntee, 1983; Taylor, 1982). Software fault tree analysis proceeds in a manner similar to the hardware counterpart. Consequently, the hardware and software trees can be linked together at their interfaces to allow the entire system to be analysed. This is extremely important since, for example, a particular software fault may cause a mishap only if there is a simultaneous human and/or hardware failure. Alternatively, the environmental failure may cause the software fault to manifest itself. In many previous mishaps, e.g. the nuclear power plant accident at Three Mile Island, the failure actually was the result of a sequence of interrelated failures in different parts of the system.

The analysis process starts with the categorised list of system hazards which have been identified by the PHA. The basic procedure involves assuming that the hazard has occurred and then working backward to determine the set of possible causes for the condition to occur. The root of the fault tree is the hazardous event to be analysed, called the 'loss event'.

Necessary preconditions are described at the next level of the tree with either an AND or an OR relationship. Each subnode is expanded in a similar fashion until all leaves describe events of calculable probability or are unable to be analysed for some reason. Figure 7.1 shows part of a fault tree for a hospital patient monitoring system.

Once the fault tree has been built down to the software interface (as in Fig. 7.1), the high level requirements for software safety have been determined. As the development of the software proceeds, fault tree analysis can be performed on the design and finally the actual code. Software control faults may involve:

- failure to perform a required function, i.e. the function is never executed or no answer is produced
- performing a function not required, i.e. getting the wrong answer or issuing the wrong control instruction or doing the right thing but under inappropriate conditions, for example, activating an actuator inadvertently, too early, too late, or failing to cease an operation at a prescribed time
- timing or sequencing problems, e.g. it may be necessary to ensure that two things happen at the same time, at different times, or in a particular order

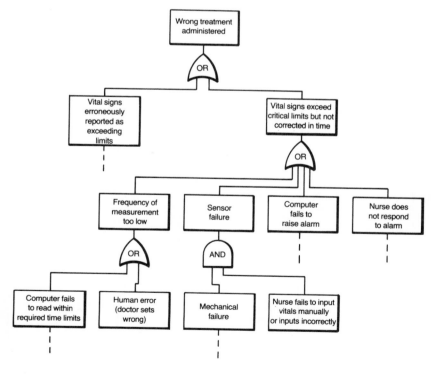

Fig. 7.1 Top levels of patient monitoring system fault tree.

```
(1) A := F(Y);
(2) B : = X−5.0;
(3) if A > B then
      Sub1;
    end if;
```

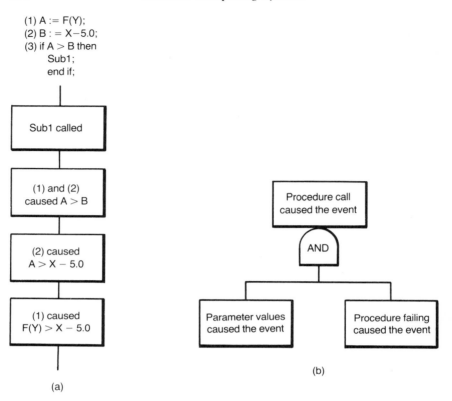

(a)

(b)

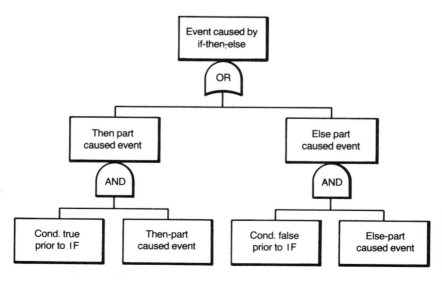

(c)

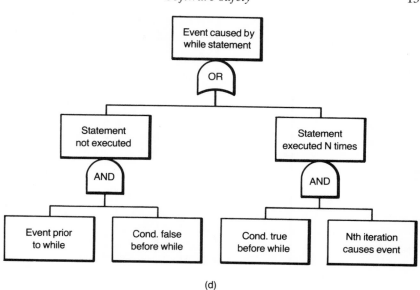

(d)

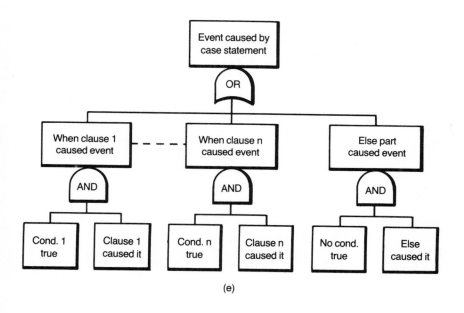

(e)

Fig. 7.2 (a) Fault tree for several assignment statements. (b) Fault tree for a procedure call. (c) Fault tree for an if-then-else statement. (d) Fault tree for a while statement. (e) Fault tree for a case statement.

- failure to recognise a hazardous condition requiring corrective action
- producing the wrong response to a hazardous condition.

Once the detailed design or code is completed, software fault tree analysis procedures can be used to work backward from these control faults through the program to determine whether the program can cause the top level event. The basic technique used is the same backward reasoning approach used in formal axiomatic verification (Hoare, 1969; Dijkstra, 1976). Constructs for some structured programming statements are shown in Fig. 7.2. In each, it is assumed that the statement caused the critical event. Then the tree is constructed considering how this might have occurred.

An example of the procedure (taken from Leveson and Stolzy (1983)) is shown in Fig. 7.3. An Ada program segment is shown which iteratively solves a fixed point equation. One possible top-level (loss event) for the segment is that no answer is produced in the required time period (and the answer is critical at this point). This loss event corresponds to the **while** loop executing too long (shown in Fig. 7.3(b) as 'Max' iterations).

In general, the software fault tree has one or both of the following patterns:

(1) A contradiction is found as shown in the left branch of Fig. 7.3(b). The building of the software fault tree, at least for this path, can stop at this point since the logic of the software cannot cause the event. This example does not deal with the problem of failures in the underlying implementation of the software, but this is possible and described below. There is of course a practical limit to how much analysis can and need be done, depending on individual factors associated with each project. It is always possible to insert assertions in the code to catch critical implementation errors at run-time. This is especially desirable if run-time software initiated or software controlled fail-safe procedures are possible. Note that the software fault tree provides the information necessary to determine just what assertions and run-time checks are the most critical and where they should be placed. Since checks at run-time are expensive in terms of time and other resources, this information is extremely useful.

(2) The fault tree runs through the code and out to the controlled system or its environment. In the example of Fig. 7.3(b), the fault tree shows one possible path to the loss event, and changes are necessary to eliminate the hazard. One appropriate action in this case may be to use run-time assertions to detect such conditions and simply to reject incorrect input or to initiate recovery techniques. Another possibility is to add redundant hardware, e.g. sensors, to eliminate incorrect input before it occurs.

Process control software often contains complex features such as concurrency and real-time constraints. Software fault tree procedures for analysing concurrency and synchronisation are described by Leveson and Stolzy (1983). Introducing timing information into the fault tree causes

```
get (X, Eps);                    while Err ≥ Eps loop

Err := Eps;                      NewX := F(X);
I := 0;                          Err := abs(X - NewX);
                                 I := I + 1;
                                 X := NewX;

                                 end loop;
```

(a)

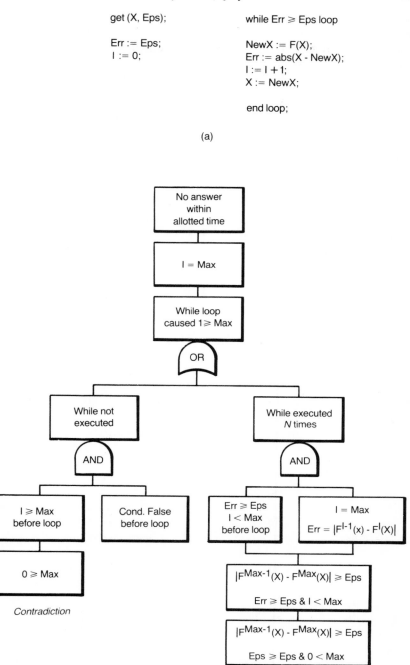

(b)

Fig. 7.3 (a) Example of Ada code. (b) Fault tree for example in Fig. 7.2(a).

serious problems. Fault tree analysis is essentially a static analysis technique while timing analysis involves dynamic aspects of the program. For example, analysing the effects of an Ada **delay** statement requires knowledge of the range of execution times of the code which in turn involves knowledge of the underlying hardware and software systems. Similar problems occur with multi-tasking since the programmer usually is not allowed to make any assumptions about the behaviour of the scheduler except that the task will eventually be run (and will have a particular priority if a priority specification is allowed in the programming language).

Taylor (1982) has added timing information to fault trees by making the assumption that information about the minimum and maximum execution time for sections of code is known. Each node in the fault tree then has an added component of execution time for the node. In view of the non-determinism inherent in a multi-tasking environment, it may not be practical to verify that timing problems cannot occur in all cases. However, information gained from the fault tree can be used to insert deadline mechanisms into the application program and the scheduler (Campbell *et al.*, 1979; Leveson and Shimeall, 1983).

The above high level language fault tree examples have focused on software logic problems. Fault trees at the assembly language level have been used to identify computer hardware fault modes (such as erroneous bits in the program counter, registers or memory) which will cause the software to act in an undesired manner (McIntee, 1983).

In summary, software fault tree analysis can be used to determine software safety requirements, to detect software logic errors, to determine multiple failure sequences involving different parts of the system (hardware, human and software faults) which can lead to hazards, and to guide in the selection of critical run-time checks. It can also be used to guide testing. The latter is especially useful if used in conjunction with a system simulator. The interfaces of the software parts of the fault tree can be examined to determine appropriate test input data and appropriate simulation states and events.

Experimental evidence of the practicality of SFTA is lacking. Examples of two small systems can be found in the literature (Leveson and Harvey, 1983; McIntee, 1983). But even if the software system is so large that complete generation of the software trees is not possible, partial trees may still be useful. For example, partially complete software fault trees may be used to identify critical modules and critical functions which can then be augmented with software fault tolerance procedures (Hecht and Hecht, 1982). They may also be used to determine appropriate run-time acceptance and safety tests. Although checking for complete correctness may not be practical, SFTA can provide information on minimal checks necessary at least to provide safe, if not totally correct, operation.

Other analysis methods have been developed or are currently being developed. Nuclear safety *cross check analysis* (NSCCA) is a rigorous methodology developed to satisfy US Air Force requirements for nuclear systems. The methodology employs a large selection of techniques to attempt to show, with a high degree of confidence, that the software will not contribute to a nuclear accident. The NSCCA process has two components: technical and procedural. The technical component evaluates the software by multiple analysis (including fault tree analysis) and test procedures to assure that it satisfies the system's nuclear safety requirements. The procedural component implements security and control measures to protect against sabotage, collusion, compromise or alteration of critical software components, tools and NSCCA results.

Another technique which has been proposed for hazard analysis involves the use of *Petri nets*. Petri nets (Peterson, 1981) allow mathematical modelling of discrete event systems in which a system is modelled in terms of conditions and events and the relationship between them. Analysis and simulation procedures have been developed to determine desirable and undesirable properties of the design, especially with respect to concurrent or parallel events. Leveson and Stolzy (1985) have developed analysis procedures to determine software safety requirements (including timing requirements) directly from the system design, to analyse a design for safety, recoverability and fault tolerance, and to guide in the use of failure detection and recovery procedures. Procedures are also being developed to measure the risk of individual hazards.

RUN-TIME SAFETY FACILITIES

Once the hazardous system states have been identified and the software safety requirements determined, the system must be built to minimise risk and to satisfy these requirements. Although verification can help to identify faults, the process is so complex as to be error prone itself and impractical to complete in very large systems. Thus, it must be assumed that faults will exist in the software. It may be possible to minimise the remaining critical faults by changing as many as possible into non-critical faults through careful software design. Any remaining potential critical faults must be handled through fault tolerance and fail-safe procedures.

DESIGN FEATURES

The goal of designing for safety is to minimise the number of potential logic or hardware induced software faults which can do serious damage to the system. Many of the design ideas to be described merely constitute good software engineering practice while others are specifically aimed at safety-critical software.

Software can cause problems through acts of omission (failing to do something required) or commission (doing something that should not be done, doing something at the wrong time or in the wrong sequence). Software is usually extensively tested to try to ensure that it does what it is specified to do. But due to its complexity, it may be able to do a lot more than the software designers specified (and intended). Design features can be used to limit the actions of software. For practical reasons, only a brief outline of some of these design concepts will be given.

One way to change potentially critical faults to non-critical ones is to design in such a way that non-critical functions are separated from critical functions and that failures of non-critical modules cannot put the system into an unsafe state, e.g. cannot impede the safety critical functions. To do this, strict modularisation and data access limitation strategies need to be employed. Since many faults originate in the interfaces between components, interfaces should be minimised. Critical functions should be concentrated in as few software modules as possible.

Since the goal is to limit hazards, a general design goal is to minimise the amount of time a potentially hazardous state exists. One way this can be accomplished is always to start out in a safe state and require a change to a higher risk state instead of the other way around. For example, multiple switches should be set close together, critical conditions should not be complementary (e.g. absence of 'arm' should not mean safe), and safety critical software decisions should be as close as possible to the output they protect.

Often in safety-critical systems, there are a few modules and/or data items which must be carefully protected because their execution (or in the case of data, their destruction or change) at the wrong time can be catastrophic, e.g. the insulin pump administers insulin when the blood sugar is low or the missile launch routine is erroneously activated. One standard method to limit access in software is the use of capabilities (Dennis and Van Horn, 1966). Essentially a capability is a permission to use certain objects or procedures. Capabilities can be implemented in the form of a list of permissible actions associated with each process where the default is to have no access. Each process is given no capability beyond that required to perform its task.

Often the sequence of events is critical. For example, a valve may need to be opened prior to filling a tank in order to relieve pressure. In electromechanical systems, an interlock is used to isolate two events in time. An example is a guard gate at a railway crossing which keeps people from crossing the track until the train has passed. Equivalent design features often need to be included in software. Concurrency and synchronisation features have been added to many programming languages (Ben-Ari, 1982) but care must be taken because some are so complex as to be error prone. These also do not necessarily protect against inadvertent branches caused by either a software or hardware fault (a serious issue, for example, in aerospace systems where hardware is subject to unusual environmental stress such as alpha or gamma particles). An example of a special software technique to deal with this is the use of a 'baton'. The baton variable is checked before the function is executed to ensure that the previously required routines have entered their 'signature'. Verification may also be required before a function is executed either by requiring human operator confirmation or an independent confirmation from another software routine. Another example of designing to protect against hardware failures is to ensure that bit patterns used to satisfy a conditional branch to a safety critical function do not use common failure patterns (e.g. all zeros). This is also true for any safety critical variables.

SAFETY-CRITICAL FAULT DETECTION AND RECOVERY

If a potentially safety-critical fault does occur, it needs to be detected and handled before damage occurs. Previous chapters of this book have described general software fault tolerance procedures, so the emphasis here will be on specific safety aspects. In general, there are two requirements: (1) monitoring facilities to detect hazards in both the computer and controlled system, and (2) recovery techniques to remain in or to return to a safe state.

Monitors can be employed to indicate whether or not a specific condition occurs or specific parameters are within normal ranges, whether the system is ready for operation or is operating satisfactorily as programmed (e.g. 'keep alive' signals), if required input is being provided, if required output is being provided and if it satisfies minimum safety requirements (e.g. is within the safety envelope), whether time limits are being met, etc.

There are some basic principles of monitoring. First, there may be a series of events leading to a mishap. Hence there may be an initiating fault along with contributory faults and finally a primary fault that actually causes the injury and damage. The longer that any fault effect or error remains undetected (the *exposure time* of the error), the more likely other contributory events are to occur. Therefore, there is a need to detect the hazardous condition, or its precursors, soon enough to minimise exposure time and to ensure there is still enough time to take action. Second, monitors themselves must be very reliable. Next, monitors should be independent so that a failure of a part of the program will not cause a failure in the monitor and *vice versa*. Finally, simplicity is the best way to achieve reliability. If the mechanisms supporting software safety and reliability are complex, then there is more chance that the use of the mechanism itself will introduce faults.

Figure 7.4 shows a high level view of the safety aspects of a software system. It is meant only as an example and does not imply that this is the only or necessarily best design. At the heart of the system is a safety executive. Although detection of unsafe conditions in this design is actually external to the executive, the executive is responsible for enforcing safety policy and deciding on the appropriate mechanisms to be used for recovery. The facilities of the safety executive might actually be implemented as a safety 'kernel' in the style of security kernels (e.g. Feiertag and Neumann (1979), Popek *et al.* (1979)), as part of the real-time executive or operating system, as a separate and concurrent task, or even distributed throughout the application code (although this last approach has several drawbacks). Separation allows centralisation and encapsulation of safety mechanisms with the concomitant advantages of reusability and possible

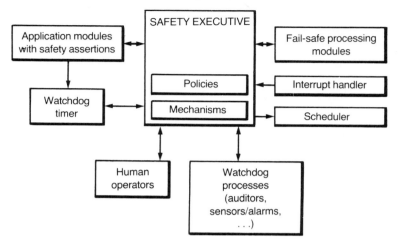

Fig. 7.4 A run-time safety environment.

formal verification of the executive. Reuse of code between systems and special verification and validation effort will help to ensure the required high reliability of the executive. If procedures and responsibility for safety are spread throughout a large program, it is difficult to ensure that safety has been adequately and reliably handled. Separation of the safety executive facilities may also help to minimise common failure modes.

As can be seen in Fig. 7.4, control can be passed to the executive from the application code, the interrupt handler, watchdog timers or watchdog processes. It is assumed that the application code contains software fault tolerance features to attempt recovery from software faults. However, this may not be possible (i.e. the fault tolerance facilities may fail) or it may be determined that a correct output cannot be produced within prescribed time limits. Even if application software recovery is attempted, it may be necessary for the safety executive to take some concurrent action in parallel with the recovery procedures. For example, it may be necessary to ensure containment of any possible radiation or chemical leakage while attempting software recovery. Although it can be argued that fault tolerance procedures will ensure that the computer never directs the system into an unsafe state, this is overly optimistic. A software error may not necessarily be readily or immediately apparent after it occurs, e.g. a small error in a closed loop system may require hours to build up to a value which exceeds prescribed safety tolerance limits. Furthermore, control actions which depend upon the incremental state of the system (such as torquing a gyro or a stepping motor), or which involve time, cannot be recovered through rollback procedures.

Exception handling procedures or safety assertions may be used to detect safety related problems and to pass control to the safety executive. Exception handling facilities are provided in most recent real-time programming languages. Every complex system can be viewed as being composed of multiple levels of abstraction. The primary goal of exception handling is to make a failure transparent to higher levels. Barring this, the system should be put in a consistent state so that recovery is possible. The failure is then reported to a higher level which can initiate error handling action and, hopefully, make the failure transparent to even higher levels (including the environment).

Some researchers have argued against using exception handling to recover from 'unanticipated' software errors (Melliar-Smith and Randell, 1975). Although the published examples of exception handling have primarily used built-in exceptions, this does not imply that the technique is limited in this way. The 'exception condition' (the condition to be tested to detect an erroneous state) can usually be any Boolean expression on the state, including an acceptance test or comparison (vote) (Leveson, 1983).

One way the executive may be passed control is through the use of 'safety assertions' (Leveson and Shimeall, 1983) which are embedded in the code. Safety assertions are Boolean expressions on the relevant parts of the computer system state (e.g. variable values, relationships between variables, input-output signals, time) to determine if the values are reasonable or are within safe bounds. One possible format is:

assert *<identifier>* : *<condition>*
 [**before** *<real number>* *<time unit>*]
 [**on failure do**
  assert *<identifier>* : *<condition>*
  assert *<identifier>* : *<condition>*
  ... **od**]

The *<identifier>* is a unique identifier for the assertion which is used by the safety executive to identify the fault. The *<condition>* is a Boolean expression. The optional **before** clause is used to indicate that a watchdog timer should be set. The time units can be any appropriate unit for the application involved, such as seconds or milliseconds, and the *<real number>* indicates how many of these units must pass before the assertion is considered to be violated. In a system where efficiency is important and execution time is under tight constraints, only a minimum number of assertions should be checked each time through the code. The 'top level' assertions are general checks to detect faults. If one of these top level assertions fails, then supplementary assertions can be used to diagnose the fault more fully and thus acquire information necessary for recovery. In the assertion format proposed above, the first assertion will always be checked. Only if this assertion fails will the assertions in the '**on failure do**' block be evaluated and the identifiers of all true assertions be passed to the safety executive.

Watchdog processes, alarms, signals, interrupts, etc., can also be used to monitor both the controlled system for hazardous conditions and to monitor the computer-controller, including both the hardware and software. Although the application modules can and should contain self-monitoring facilities, there is reason for concern when a component checks itself for errors. A basic principle of system safety is to eliminate single-point failure modes from the system design. For example, a multi-point failure mode exists if the hazard results only if *both* the application program and the monitor program 'fail'. This is also another argument for providing safety recovery functions which are separate from the application code modules.

Once given control, the safety executive can initiate recovery or fail-safe procedures, interact with the scheduler and communicate with human operators. Backward recovery techniques basically involve returning the system to a prior state (hopefully one which precedes the fault) and then going forward again with an alternate piece of code. There is no attempt to diagnose the particular fault that caused the error nor to assess the extent of any other damage the fault may have caused. Forward recovery includes techniques which attempt to 'repair' the faulty state. This may involve an internal state of the computer or, in the case of embedded systems, the state of the controlled system. Forward recovery techniques may return the system to a 'correct' state or, if that is not possible, contain or minimise the effects of the failure.

Examples of forward recovery techniques include using redundancy in data structures (Taylor, Morgan and Black, 1980), dynamically changing the flow of control, ignoring single-cycle errors which will be corrected on the next iteration, changing to a reduced capability control mode, etc. Since the safety executive will get control when either an unsafe state is detected externally or an internal routine has been unable to recover successfully within required time limits, most of the recovery techniques used will involve forward attempts to avoid or repair a hazard.

When an unsafe state is detected, recovery to a safe or less hazardous state is necessary. Safety recovery routines need to ensure that the system is in or enters a known, predictable, and safe state and to provide for orderly shutdown or reduced system capability. Non-normal control modes for a process control system may include:

- *Partial shutdown*: the system has partial or degraded functionality.
- *Hold*: no functionality is provided, but steps are taken to maintain safety or to limit the amount of damage.
- *Emergency shutdown*: the system is shut down completely.
- *Manual or externally controlled*: the system continues to function, but control is switched to a source external to the computer – the computer may be responsible for a smooth transition.
- *Restart*: the system is in a transitional state from non-normal to normal.

One type of recovery which may be needed involves dynamically changing the flow of control. In real-time systems, it is often the case that criticality of tasks may change during processing and may depend upon run-time environmental conditions. If peak system overload is increasing the response time above some critical point, run-time reconfiguration of the system may be achieved by delaying or temporarily eliminating non-critical functions. Note that system overload may be caused or increased by internal conditions such as excessive attempts to perform backward recovery. Some aspects of deadline scheduling have been explored by Campbell, Horton, and Belford (1979).

Another important task of the safety executive is to provide information to human operators about the state of the system and the state of the recovery actions. Unfortunate incidents have occurred or been exacerbated in the past due to inadequacies in the human/computer interface (e.g. Three Mile Island). Although appropriate action in the event of a detected hazard might be to signal for human help (such as signalling the nurse's station in a hospital or a controller in an air traffic control system), effective human intervention often depends on obtaining adequate information about the state of the problem. It is especially important to keep operators informed when things are going wrong. The whole question of optimal ways for the human and computer to work together is an important topic for future research.

CONCLUSIONS

There is much more to be learned about how to build safe computer controlled systems. This chapter has tried to outline some of what is known or has been suggested to date. Some of these approaches have been tested and used extensively while others are still in the development stage. Much important work remains to be done in extending and testing these proposed techniques and in developing new ones.

REFERENCES

Ben-Ari, M. (1982). *Principles of Concurrent Programming*, Prentice-Hall International, Englewood Cliffs, New Jersey.

Boebert, W. E. (1980). 'Formal Verification of Embedded Software'. *ACM Software Eng. Notes*, **5**, No. 3, 41–42.

Boehm, B. W., McClean, R. L. and Urfig, D. B. (1975). 'Some Experiments with Automated Aids to the Design of Large-Scale Reliable Software'. *IEEE Trans. on Soft. Eng.*, **SE-1**, No. 2, 125–133.

Campbell, R. H., Horton, K. H. and Belford, G. G. (1979). 'Simulations of a Fault-Tolerant Deadline Mechanism'. *Proc. of the Ninth Sym. on Fault Tolerant Comp.*, 95–101.

Dennis, J. B. and Van Horn, E. C. (1966). 'Programming Semantics for Multiprogrammed Computations'. *Comm. of the ACM*, **3**, No. 4, 143–155.

Dijkstra, E. (1976). *A Discipline of Programming*. Prentice-Hall, Englewood Cliffs, New Jersey.

Dunham, J. R. and Knight, J. C. (editors). (1981). 'Production of Reliable Flight-crucial Software'. *Proc. of Validation Methods Res. for Fault-Tolerant Avionics and Cont. Sys. Sub-Working-Group Meeting*, Research Triangle Park, North Carolina, NASA Conference Publication 2222.

Endres, A. B. (1975). 'An Analysis of Errors and Their Causes in Software Systems', *IEEE Trans. on Soft. Eng.*, **SE-1**, No. 2, 140–149.

Ericson, C. A. (1981). 'Software and System Safety'. *Proc. 5th Int. System Safety Conf.*, Denver, **1**, Part 1, III-B-1 to III-B-11.

Feiertag, R. J. and Neumann, P. G. (1979). 'The Foundations of a Provably Secure Operating System (PSOS)'. *Proc. NCC*, AFIPS Press, 329–334.

Frola, F. R. and Miller, C. O. (1984). *System Safety in Aircraft Management*, Logistics Management Institute, Washington D.C.

Fuller, J. G. (1984). 'Death by Robot'. *Omni*, **6**, No. 6, 45–46, 97–102.

Griggs, J. G. (1981). 'A Method of Software Safety Analysis'. *Proc. 5th Int. System Safety Conf.*, Denver, **1**, Part 1, III-D-1 to III-D-18.

Hecht, H. and Hecht, M. (1982). 'Use of Fault Trees for the Design of Recovery Blocks'. *Proc. of 12th Sym. on Fault Tolerant Comp.*, Santa Monica, 134–139.

Hoare, C. A. R. (1969). 'An Axiomatic Basis for Computer Programming'. *Comm. of the ACM*, **12**, No. 10, 576–580, 583.

Iyer, R. K. and Velardi, P. (1983). *A Statistical Study of Hardware Related Software Errors in MVS*. CEC Tech. Rep. No. 83–12, Center for Reliable Computing, Stanford University, Menlo Park, California.

Johnson, W. G. (1980). *MORT Safety Assurance Systems*, Marcel Dekker, Inc., New York.

Kletz, T. (1983). 'Human Problems with Computer Control'. *Hazard Prevention* (The Journal of the System Safety Society), 24–26.

Leveson, N. G. (1983). 'Software Fault Tolerance: The Case for Forward Recovery'. *AIAA Conf. on Comp. in Aerospace*, Oct.

Leveson, N. G. and Harvey, P. R. (1983). 'Analyzing Software Safety'. *IEEE Trans. on Software Eng.*, **SE-9**, No. 5, 569–579.

Leveson, N. G. and Shimeall, T. J. (1983). 'Safety Assertions for Process-Control Systems'. *Proc. 13th Int. Conf. on Fault-Tolerant Comp.*, Milan, 236–240.

Leveson, N. G. and Stolzy, J. L. (1983). 'Analyzing Ada Programs using Fault Trees'. *IEEE Trans. on Reliability*.

Leveson, N. G. and Stolzy, J. L. (1985). 'Analyzing Safety and Fault Tolerance using Time Petri Nets'. *TAPSOFT: Joint Conf. on Theory and Prac. of Software Dev.*, Berlin.

Lipow, M. (1979). 'Prediction of Software Errors'. *J. of Sys. and Soft.*, **1**, 71–75.

McIntee, J. W. (1983). *Fault Tree Technique as Applied to Software (SOFT TREE)*, BMO/AWS, Norton Air Force Base, California.

Melliar-Smith, P. M. and Randell, B. (1975). 'Software Reliability: The Role of Programmed Exception Handling'. *SIGPLAN Notices*, **12**, No. 3, 95–100.

Mineck, D. W., Derr, R. E., Lykken, L. O. and Hall, J. C. (1972). 'Avionic Flight Control System for the Lockheed L-1011 Tristar'. *SAE Aerospace Conf. and Guidance Sys. Meeting No. 30*, San Diego, California, 27–29.

Peterson, J. L. (1981). *Petri Net Theory and the Modeling of Systems*, Prentice Hall, Englewood Cliffs.

Popek, G. J., Kampe, M., Kline, C. S., Stoughton, A., Urban, M. and Walton, E. J. (1979). 'UCLA Secure Unix.'. *Proc. NCC*, AFIPS Press, 355–364.

Rouse, W. B. (1981). 'Human-Computer Interaction in the Control of Dynamic Systems'. *ACM Comp. Surveys*, **13**, No. 1, 71–99.

Taylor, J. R. (1982). *Fault Tree and Cause Consequence Analysis for Control*

Software Validation, RISO-M-2326, Riso National Laboratory, Roskilde, Denmark.

Taylor, D. J., Morgan, D. E. and Black, J. P. (1980). 'Redundancy in Data Structures: Improving Software Fault Tolerance'. *IEEE Trans. on Software Eng.*, **SE-6**, No. 6, 585–594.

Ternhem, K. E. (1981). 'Automatic Complacency'. *Flight Crew*, Winter, 34–35.

Vesely, W. E., Goldberg, F. F., Roberts, N. H. and Haasl, D. F. (1981). *Fault Tree Handbook*, NUREG-0492, U.S. Nuclear Regulatory Commission.

CHAPTER 8

Software reliability prediction

B. Littlewood

(Centre for Software Reliability, The City University, London)

Methods of measuring and predicting the reliability of software form a small but important branch of the new field of quantitative software studies. The general objective in all this work is to progress towards a scientific and engineering discipline, and away from the current anecdotal and often unsystematic approach.

Reliability problems associated with software are becoming more acute. Advances in hardware capability, and lowering of hardware costs, encourage the development of larger and more complex software systems. Physical failures of computer systems become proportionately less important to users than software failures. There is a temptation to use software to supplant hardware in applications which are often safety critical: nuclear reactor safety systems, civil airliner flight control.

To meet these challenges, new software development practices are evolving, but it is unlikely that improvements here will ever be as dramatic as those which have occurred in hardware over the last decade. All the more reason, then, that we can make rational choice based upon objective criteria.

In the following pages a general conceptual model is first presented, and then some detailed techniques for measuring software reliability are described. Some recent work, which aids user choice among the many competing models, follows. A final section indicates limitations of existing techniques and gives pointers to future developments.

A CONCEPTUAL MODEL OF THE SOFTWARE FAILURE PROCESS

Although there are similarities in appearance between failure data obtained from hardware and software systems, there are important conceptual differences which necessitate the use of different modelling techniques. There is, for example, a sense in which the operation of software is completely deterministic. If we know that a set of input conditions caused a failure in the past, we can be certain that they will cause the same program to fail in the future. Similarly, inputs which can be correctly processed now will be correctly processed for all time. For hardware the situation is quite different. Hardware devices suffer from physical degradation as time passes, and it is not possible to guarantee that the response to a particular input will remain constant. It is this random process of degradation, usually stimulated by the input process ('environment'), which requires that we use probabilistic techniques to describe hardware failure behaviour. Since this argument does not apply to software, it is instructive to examine in a little detail the nature of the software failure process.

Table 8.1 shows some fairly typical software failure data. This program was executing in a user environment, and faults were fixed when they showed themselves as software failures. Only the *execution times* between such failures are recorded, so the relationship to calendar time is unknown and complex. There are several striking features in the data. In the first place, the numbers show large random variability: predicting the next observation

Table 8.1 Execution times in seconds between successive failures. Read left to right in rows. (Ref. 1, where this data is referred to as Project 1.)

3	30	113	81	115
9	2	91	112	15
138	50	77	24	108
88	670	120	26	114
325	55	242	68	422
180	10	1146	600	15
36	4	0	8	227
65	176	58	457	300
97	263	452	255	197
193	6	79	816	1351
148	21	233	134	357
193	236	31	369	748
0	232	330	365	1222
543	10	16	529	379
44	129	810	290	300
529	281	160	828	1011
445	296	1755	1064	1783
860	983	707	33	868
724	2323	2930	1461	843
12	261	1800	865	1435
30	143	109	0	3110
1247	943	700	875	245
729	1897	447	386	446
122	990	948	1082	22
75	482	5509	100	10
1071	371	790	6150	3321
1045	648	5485	1160	1864
4116				

at any point in this series seems a daunting task. However, it is fairly obvious that the reliability of the program is *growing*, since there is a clear tendency for later inter-failure times to be greater than earlier ones.

What is the reason for the times between failures being unpredictable? Consider the simple input-program-output model of Fig. 8.1. Here I, the input space, represents the totality of all possible inputs. Use of the software involves selection of points from this space to be processed by the program, p, in order to produce points of the output space, O. The program is thus a mapping $p: I \rightarrow O$.

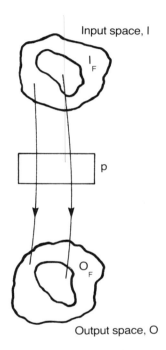

Fig. 8.1 O_F is the image set of I_F under the mapping p.

For most applications, the input space I will be extremely large and probably of large dimension. It is unlikely that a detailed description of I will be available, much less of the mechanism by which successive points in I are selected during use.

A failure is detected whenever the output resulting from the processing of a particular input violates the specification. The totality of all the inputs which the program is unable to process correctly is shown in Fig. 8.1 as the subset I_F.

The central assumption in most of the existing software reliability models is that I_F is encountered *purely randomly* when the program runs in its use environment. That is, the execution times between successive failures are independent random variables which are exponentially distributed. This random selection of inputs is the first source of the unpredictability in data sets such as Table 8.1.

This unpredictability would be present even if the program were not fixed when a failure occurred. If after a failure the program were restarted at a new point in I, it would run for a certain time until encountering I_F again. This execution time could reasonably be assumed to be independent of others and to have the *same* exponential distribution.

In practice, though, we shall have the much more interesting situation in which the fault causing the failure is fixed (or a fix is attempted). Figure 8.2 shows what happens in this case. Here I_F is shown partitioned by dotted lines. Each subset of I_F in this partitioning represents a *single fault* present in the program. Notice that, in most cases, each fault will comprise very many input cases, i.e. the repair of a fault will cause many input cases to become correctly executable. However, not all faults will be of the same 'size', in the sense of the likelihood of being encountered during a particular period of execution. In the figure, area can be taken as representative of this 'size'.

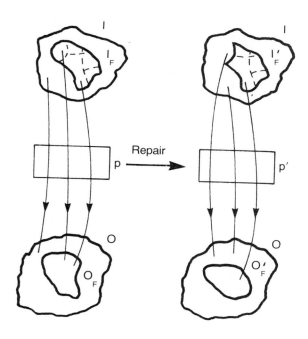

Fig. 8.2 The effect of a single fix.

When a failure occurs, it could have been caused by any one of the faults represented by the partition of I_F. Some of these (the 'larger' ones) are more likely candidates, and the repair of these 'larger' ones will cause a greater improvement in the reliability of the software.

In Fig. 8.2 the effect of removing a fault is shown as transforming the program p into a new program, p'. I_F becomes I_F' through the elimination of the subset of I_F corresponding to the removed fault. O_F becomes O_F', which is no larger than O_F and will often be smaller.

In order to have a conceptual model which describes what happens when we see data such as that in Table 8.1, we can generalise the above argument. The successive fixes correspond to a *sequence of programs*, $p(1)$, $p(2)$, $p(3)$, . . . with corresponding failure subsets $I_F(1)$, $I_F(2)$, $I_F(3)$, . . . of I. Although we informally talk of fixing a single program, in fact the fixing process generates a sequence of different programs.

The reliability growth is now characterised by changes in the magnitude of $I_F(i)$ as i increases. In the above it has been assumed that these changes always make $I_F(i)$ smaller, i.e. $I_F(i + 1) \subset I_F(i)$. A more general formulation would allow for the possibility of imperfect fixing. This could occur if the fix is simply ineffective, in which case $I_F(i + 1) = I_F(i)$; or, more realistically, a new fault is introduced and the old fault subset of I_F is transformed into a *new* subset of I_F'. Fortunately, the detailed modelling of the failure process only involves the I_F's via their magnitude. Most models make the reasonable assumption that these sizes decrease, at least stochastically.

The important point is that there are *two sources of randomness* in the failure process. The first source is the mechanism which selects successive inputs during execution. The second level of uncertainty is in the sequence of sizes of the successive faults removed.

SOME SOFTWARE RELIABILITY MODELS

The raw data available to a user of one of these models will be a sequence of execution times, t_1, t_2, . . . t_{i-1} between successive failures. These observed times can be regarded as realisations of random variables T_1, T_2, . . . T_{i-1}. The objective is to use the available data to make intelligent predictions about future behaviour, i.e. about the unobserved future T_i, T_{i+1}, ... Notice that measurement of the *current* reliability of the software is in fact a prediction, since it involves the random variable T_i.

A user would like to have a complete probabilistic description of the future T_i, T_{i+1}, ... From this it would be possible, in principle, to obtain any reliability measures of interest. Examples of these measures, for current reliability, are:

(a) the reliability function

$$R_i(t) \equiv P\{T_i > t\} \tag{1}$$

which represents the chance that the program will now execute without failure for a time exceeding t. This measure is particularly useful in contexts where a natural 'mission time' exists. For example, in the next generation of civil airliners it has been suggested that software play a flight critical role. Figures proposed for the reliability of such software assume $t = 10$ hours and $R(10) = 10^{-9}$.

(b) The rate of occurrence of failures (ROCOF)

$$\lambda(\tau) \equiv \lim_{\delta\tau \to 0} \frac{P\{\text{failure in } (\tau, \tau + \delta\tau)\}}{\delta\tau} \tag{2}$$

where τ represents the *calendar time* now. If, for example, the $(i - 1)$th failure has just been fixed, and the program set running, then

$$\lambda(\tau) \equiv f_i(0) \tag{3}$$

where $f_i(t)$ is the probability density function of the random variable T_i.

(c) The mean time between failures (MTBF)

$$E(T_i) = \int_0^\infty t f_i(t) \mathrm{d}t \tag{4}$$

This is a measure which should be used with some caution, since there is evidence that in certain contexts it does not exist.[3] That is, the function $f_i(t)$ has a 'fat'tail' and the integral does not converge. In such a case certain naive numerical procedures could produce meaningless results.

Similar measures to these can be used for longer term prediction. In addition, other measures come into use here: for example, the distribution of the (random variable) time to achieve a specified target reliability.

Although we loosely talk of software reliability models, this terminology is a little misleading. In order to predict future behaviour $(T_i, T_{i+1}, \ldots)$ from past data $(t_1, t_2, \ldots t_{i-1})$ we need:

(i) the *probabilistic model* which specifies the distribution of any subset of $\{T_j\}$ conditional on a (unknown) parameter α;

(ii) a *statistical inference procedure* for α when we have data (realisations of Ts);

(iii) a *prediction procedure* combining (i) and (ii) to allow us to make probability statements about future Ts.

The quality of any predictions will depend on all three legs of this triad. Later in the chapter we shall consider ways in which the performance of the complete prediction system, (i)–(iii), can be examined. We now consider several models in some detail.

JELINSKI–MORANDA, MUSA (JM)

The Jelinski–Moranda[4] model appears to be the earliest reliability growth model specifically designed for software rather than hardware. The model due to Shooman[5] is identical and seems to arise from independent work at roughly the same time. The Musa model[6] appeared later with extra refinements, but is essentially the same as JM.

The JM model assumes that T_1, T_2, ... are independent random variables with exponential probability density functions

$$p(t_i | \lambda_i) = \lambda_i e^{-\lambda_i t_i} \qquad t_i > 0 \tag{5}$$

and

$$\lambda_i = (N-i+1)\phi \tag{6}$$

The rationale for the model is as follows. The program begins life (debugging) containing N faults. The removal of a fault occurs instantaneously at a failure (i.e. the time taken to carry out a fix is ignored), and this causes the rate of occurrence of failures to reduce by an amount ϕ. Thus ϕ can be taken to represent the size of a fault in our conceptual model.

The unknown parameters of the model are estimated by maximum likelihood, and these estimates, $\hat{N}$ and $\hat{\phi}$, are substituted into appropriate mathematical expressions, derived from the model, in order to obtain predictions. Thus, for example, when $t_1, t_2, \ldots t_{i-1}$ are the observed data, the predicted reliability, (1), is

$$\hat{R}_i(t) = e^{-(\hat{N}-i+1)\hat{\phi}t} \tag{7}$$

A major criticism of this model is that it assumes that all faults contribute equally to the unreliability of a program. This seems to be very implausible, and recent empirical studies[7,8] suggest that the magnitudes of the ϕs corresponding to different faults are orders of magnitude different. Recent work[9] suggests that using this model in a context where the ϕs are really very variable in magnitude will result in optimistic predictions.

In terms of the earlier conceptual model, it will be seen that JM only represents the first source of randomness in the failure process: equation (5) represents the uncertainty arising in the selection of inputs. The changes in the size of the input subset I_F are modelled *deterministically* via equation (6).

BAYESIAN JELINSKI–MORANDA (BJM)

This model arises because of a conjecture that the poor predictive performance of JM may be due to the maximum likelihood inference procedure. The BJM model differs slightly from JM, being parameterised as $(\lambda, \phi) \in \mathbb{R}^+ \times \mathbb{R}^+$ with $\lambda \equiv N\phi$. Here λ can be regarded as the initial rate of occurrence of failures, and ϕ has the same interpretation as before. The modelling difference is that λ is not constrained to be an integer multiple of ϕ.

The Bayesian analysis of the model proceeds as follows (see Ref. 11 for details). We start with a prior distribution for (λ, ϕ). In Refs. 9 and 10 this is taken to be the 'ignorance' prior distribution. Given data $t_1, \ldots t_{i-1}$ the posterior distribution for (λ, ϕ) is calculated

$$p(\lambda, \phi | t_1, \ldots t_{i-1}) \tag{8}$$

Bayesian predictions[12] are then made in the usual way. For example, the current reliability function is

$$\bar{R}_i(t) = \iint R_i(t | \lambda, \phi) p(\lambda, \phi | t_1 \ldots t_{i-1}) d\lambda d\phi \tag{9}$$

where the conditional reliability is

$$R_i(t \mid \lambda, \phi) = e^{-(\lambda - [i-1]\phi)t} \qquad (10)$$

It turns out that BJM performs better than JM,[9,10] but still gives optimistic predictions. Although the Bayesian inference procedure is better than maximum likelihood, the model itself is based on such unrealistic assumptions that it seems incapable of producing good results.

LITTLEWOOD–VERRALL (LV)
This is the first model[13] to represent both the sources of randomness of the general conceptual model. As in JM and BJM, the first source of randomness comes from the assumption that T_1, T_2, ... are independent random variables with probability density functions

$$p(t_i \mid \lambda_i) = \lambda_i e^{-\lambda_i t_i} \qquad (11)$$

The second source of randomness is modelled by taking $\{\lambda_i\}$ to be a sequence of independent random variables with

$$p(\lambda_i) = \frac{[\psi(i)]^\alpha \lambda_i^{\alpha-1} e^{-\psi(i)\lambda_i}}{\Gamma(\alpha)} \qquad (12)$$

i.e. a gamma distribution with parameters $\psi(i)$, α.

The function $\psi(i)$ determines the reliability growth. If $\psi(i)$ is an increasing function of i, it is easy to show that the $\{\lambda_i\}$ sequence is *stochastically* decreasing. This contrasts with the JM case, where $\{\lambda_i\}$ is deterministically decreasing.

A parametric family is chosen for $\psi(i)$, and this choice is made by the user. The simplest choice is

$$\psi(i, \beta) = \beta_1 + \beta_2 i \qquad (13)$$

and this seems to give satisfactory results in general. Estimation of α and β is by maximum likelihood and predictions are made by substitution. Thus the reliability after seeing the inter-failure times t_1, t_2, ... t_{i-1} is

$$\tilde{R}_i(t) = \left[\frac{\psi(i, \hat{\beta})}{t + \psi(i, \hat{\beta})} \right]^{\hat{\alpha}} \qquad (14)$$

where $\hat{\alpha}$, $\hat{\beta}$ are the maximum likelihood estimates.

KEILLER–LITTLEWOOD (KL)
KL[9,10] is similar to LV, except that reliability growth is induced via the shape parameter of the gamma distribution for the $\{\lambda_i\}$ rates. That is

$$p(\lambda_i) = \frac{\beta^{\psi(i)} \lambda_i^{\psi(i)-1} e^{-\beta \lambda_i}}{\Gamma(\psi(i))} \qquad (15)$$

Here reliability growth, represented by stochastically decreasing λ_i, occurs when $\psi(i)$ is a decreasing function of i. Again, choice of a parametric family for $\psi(i)$ is under the control of the user. It has been found that a family of the type

$$\psi(i, \alpha) = (\alpha_1 + \alpha_2 i)^{-1} \tag{16}$$

gives acceptable results with most data sets. Estimation of the unknown parameters, α, β is by maximum likelihood. The reliability after observing inter-failure times t_1, t_2, ... t_{i-1} is then estimated as

$$\tilde{R}_i(t) = \left[\frac{\hat{\beta}}{t + \hat{\beta}} \right]^{\psi(i, \hat{\alpha})} \tag{17}$$

LITTLEWOOD

This model[14] attempts to overcome the major criticism of the JM model: that all faults have equal size and, consequently, the debugging process is treated purely deterministically. It assumes that a program begins life with N faults, that a particular fault (the ith) makes a contribution Φ_i to the overall rate of occurrence of failures, and that the Φ_i are independent random variables with a Gamma (α, β) distribution.

As the program executes, there is a tendency for the larger Φ_i to be detected and eliminated earlier than smaller ones. That is, earlier fixes tend to have a more beneficial effect upon the reliability of the software than later ones.

Estimation of the parameters, N, α, β is again by maximum likelihood. The estimated current reliability based upon data t_1, t_2, ... t_{i-1} is then

$$\hat{R}_i(t) = \left(\frac{\hat{\beta} + \tau}{\hat{\beta} + \tau + t} \right)^{(\hat{N} - i + 1)\hat{\alpha}} \tag{18}$$

where

$$\tau = \sum_{j=1}^{i-1} t_j \tag{19}$$

is total elapsed execution time.

DUANE

The Duane model arises from hardware reliability studies. Duane[15] claimed to have observed in several disparate applications that the reliability growth in complex hardware systems showed the ROCOF having a power law form in operating time. Crow[16] took this empirical observation and added the assumption that the failure process was a non-homogeneous Poisson process (NHPP), rate

$$kbt^{b-1} \qquad (k, b, t > 0) \tag{20}$$

There is a sense in which the NHPP is inappropriate for software reliability growth (and the reliability growth in hardware due to discrete design changes). We know that it is the fixes which change the reliability, and these occur at a finite number of known times. The reliability presumably remains constant between fixes. A model which has a continuously decreasing rate, such as equation (20), must therefore be 'wrong'.

However, these models could be close to event-altered rate models of the type discussed earlier, and they are considerably more tractable mathematically. It is interesting that the Jelinski–Moranda and Littlewood models become exactly NHPP when the parameter N is treated as a random variable with a Poisson distribution.[17]

This class of model is a wide one, and it seems likely that with an appropriate choice of rate function it will be able to represent the software failure process quite accurately. Recent work has suggested new rate functions,[17,18] but there is little evidence so far of the quality of prediction.

EXAMPLE

All the models in the previous section, with varying degrees of success, attempt to satisfy the requirements of the general conceptual model of the software failure process. They differ from one another in significant detail, and a user would probably have some difficulty in choosing a 'best buy' *a priori*. A little experience in using the different models shows that their predictions can differ quite dramatically. Consider, as an example, the analysis by JM and LV models of the data given in Table 8.1.

Figure 8.3 shows plots of successive median estimates, at five point intervals, of the current time-to-failure distribution. That is, the median of $\bar{F}_i(t)$, the predictive distribution for T_i, based on data t_1, t_2, ... t_{i-1}, is plotted for JM and LV with i increasing in steps of five.

Although both sets of predictions show reliability growth, there are dramatic differences between them. The JM medians give a consistently more optimistic picture of the reliability of the program than do those of LV. A user of these two models on this data set might reasonably enquire as to which, if either, was close to reality.

It is noticeable that the JM medians fluctuate in value more than those of LV, which show steady monotonic increase. Whether this variation in reliability is real, or a reflection of the 'noisiness' of JM predictions, is a matter for conjecture.

The disparate results of Fig. 8.3 are representative of the behaviour of software reliability predictions coming from different models using real failure data. Results of this kind are probably the main reason why potential users are deterred from using software reliability prediction systems. Although the assumptions underlying the different models vary in their plausibility, it is invariably the case that no single model can be regarded as true. A user cannot, therefore, choose a model *a priori* in the confident belief that its predictions will accord with the failure process of his software.

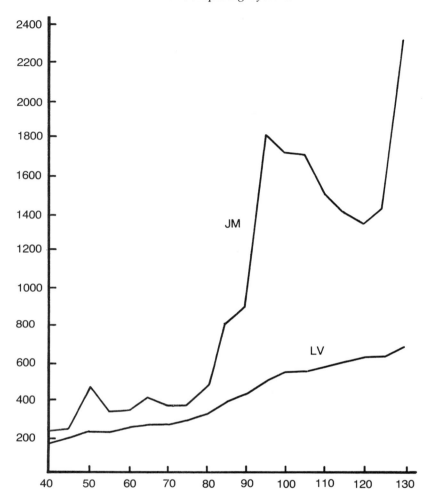

Fig. 8.3 Median predictions of LV and JM models. Data as in Table 8.1.

My own belief is that this is unlikely ever to be possible. The creation of software is a social process involving the solution of unique intellectual problems. If our understanding of the human contribution to the process improves, we shall be left with an irreducible open-endedness in the novelty of applications which motivate the writing of programs.

Faced with disagreements like those of Fig. 8.3, then, we should not only ask whether JM is *universally* a better (or worse) model than LV. Rather, we should seek to learn whether it is predicting close to reality *in this particular case*. In the next section, some investigative techniques are described which allow a user to examine the quality of predictions on a single data set. Such devices enable poor past predictions to be detected, so that current predictions can be regarded with suspicion.

ANALYSIS OF PREDICTIVE QUALITY

Consider the simplest prediction of all, concerning current reliability. Having observed t_1, t_2, ... t_{i-1} we want to predict the random variable T_i. More precisely, we want a good estimate of

$$F_i(t) \equiv P(T_i < t) \qquad (21)$$

If we have a prediction system, of the type described earlier, we can calculate from the data t_1, t_2, ... t_{i-1} a predictor

$$\tilde{F}_i(t) \qquad (22)$$

A user is interested in the 'closeness' of $\tilde{F}_i(t)$ to $F_i(t)$. Notice that the accuracy of other useful measures, such as rate of occurrence of failures, mean time to failure, etc., will depend upon this closeness.

Although the discussion here will concern only this problem of one-step-ahead prediction, some of the results generalise in an obvious way to longer term prediction.

Clearly, the difficulty of analysing the closeness of $\tilde{F}_i$ to F_i arises from our never knowing, even at a later stage, the true F_i. If this were to become available at some time after the prediction had been made, it would be possible to use measures of closeness based upon *entropy* and *information*.[19]

In the software reliability growth case, the only information we shall obtain will be a single realisation of the random variable T_i. That is, after making the prediction $\tilde{F}_i(t)$ based upon the observed t_1, t_2, ... t_{i-1}, we shall eventually see t_i, which is a sample of size one from the true distribution $F_i(t)$. All analysis of the quality of the predictions must be based upon these pairs $\{\tilde{F}_i(t), t_i\}$.

Informally, a user should examine a sequence of $\{\tilde{F}_i(t), t_i\}$ pairs to see whether there is any evidence that the t_is are not from the $\tilde{F}_i(t)$ distributions. If such evidence is found, it suggests that there are differences between $\tilde{F}_i(t)$ and $F_i(t)$, i.e. that the predictions are not in accord with actual behaviour.

More formally, consider

$$u_i = \tilde{F}_i(t_i) \qquad (23)$$

This is a *probability integral transform* of the observed t_i, using the previously calculated predictor $\tilde{F}_i$ based on t_1, t_2, ... t_{i-1}. If $\tilde{F}_i$ is a perfect predictor, i.e. it is identical to the true F_i, then the u_i will be realisations of independent, identically distributed (iid) uniform random variables on $(0, 1)$: U_i are iid $U(0, 1)$ random variables. The closeness of the u_is to realisations of iid $U(0, 1)$ random variables represents the closeness of $\{\tilde{F}_i\}$ to $\{F_i\}$.[20]

There are various ways in which the $\{u_i\}$ sequence can be examined in order to seek evidence of poor predictive quality.

THE u-PLOT

Since the u_is should look like a random sample from $U(0, 1)$ if the prediction system is working well, the first thing to examine is whether they seem uniformly distributed. Figure 8.4 shows how to draw the *sample cumulant distribution function* (cdf) of the u_is: the u-plot. The cdf of $U(0, 1)$ is the line of unit slope through the origin. A large deviation between these two would suggest a large deviation between $\{\bar{F}_i(t)\}$ and the true $\{F_i(t)\}$. The Kolmogorov distance, the maximum vertical distance between the two, is often used as a convenient measure of deviation.

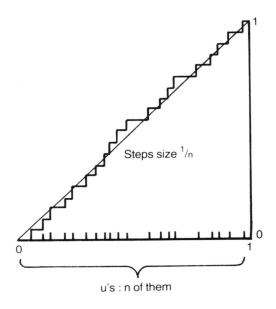

Fig. 8.4 Method of drawing u-plot.

Figure 8.5 shows the u-plots for our example: JM and LV predictions based on the data of Table 8.1. Here the predictions are for $\bar{F}_{36}(t)$ through $\bar{F}_{135}(t)$. The Kolmogorov distances are 0.170 (JM) and 0.144 (LV). In the appropriate tables of the Kolmogorov distribution the JM result is significant at the 1% level, LV only at the 5% level.

From this evidence we can conclude that neither is performing very well, although LV seems significantly better than JM. The detailed plots of Fig. 8.5, however, contain more information than this. It can be seen that the JM plot is almost everywhere above the line of unit slope (the u_is tend to be too small), whilst that of LV is almost everywhere below the line (the u_is tend to be too large). Now u_i represents the predicted probability that $T_i < t_i$, therefore consistently too small u_is suggest that the predictions are underestimating the chance of small ts: the predictions are too optimistic. Conversely, too large u_is represent pessimistic predictions.

There is evidence from Fig. 8.5, then, that the truth might lie between the predictions emanating from these two models *for this particular data*. Thus, for example, the true median plot might lie between the two plots

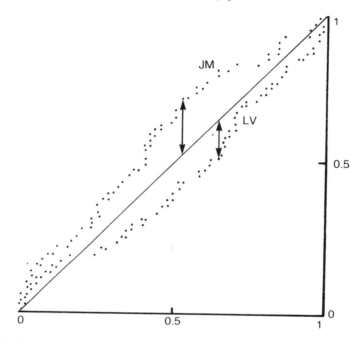

Fig. 8.5 LV, JM u-plots, data of Table 8.1. Steps omitted for clarity. Note that these are reproduced from line-printer plots and do not correspond exactly to the true plot.

shown in Fig. 8.3. A conservative user could use LV and be reasonably confident that actual behaviour would show *no worse* reliability than that predicted.

THE y-PLOT

The u-plot treats the u_is as a random sample, and investigates the (assumed) common distribution for departures from uniformity. The natural ordering of the u_is disappears in the procedure, and this raises questions about its efficiency in detecting when predictions differ from reality in a non-stationary way. If, for example, the early predictions were pessimistic and later ones optimistic, it is possible that the two types of error would cancel out to produce a spuriously 'good' u-plot.

This kind of effect can be detected by examining the $\{u_i\}$ sequence for trend: it ought to be trend-free. Figure 8.6 shows how this can be done. Since each u_i is defined on $(0, 1)$, the sequence u_i (Stage 1 in Fig. 8.6) will look 'super-regular'. The transformation $x_i = -\ell n(1 - u_i)$ will produce a realisation of iid unit exponential random variables if the $\{u_i\}$ are a realisation of iid $U(0, 1)$ random variables. That is, Stage 2 of Fig. 8.6 should look like a homogeneous Poisson process. A simple test for this (against the alternative hypothesis that there is trend present) is to

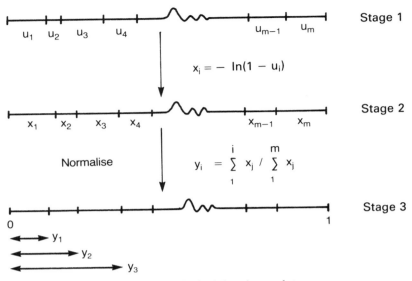

Fig. 8.6 Method of drawing y-plot.

normalise (Stage 3 in Fig. 8.6) and plot as in the section on the u-plot (page 156).[21]

Figure 8.7 shows the effect of this procedure on the JM and LV predictions of the data of Table 8.1. The Kolmogorov distances are 0.120 (JM) and 0.110 (LV), neither of which is significant at the 10% level.

A closer examination of the JM plot suggests that it is very close to linearity in the early stages, i.e. until about $i = 90$ (see broken line). This implies that the overall optimism of these predictions (see u-plot) arises chiefly from the later stages. Since these are based upon larger data vectors, the result is surprising.

CONCLUSION

It should be emphasised that the purpose of techniques such as the above is not to seek out a universally good model. They should, instead, be seen as investigative devices to help a user discriminate between different sets of predictions on data corresponding to the reliability growth of a single program. Recent studies have used these techniques[10] to analyse the performance of several models on several data sets. From this evidence it is clear that no single model can be trusted to perform well on all data sets, although some models perform sufficiently badly with enough consistency to suggest that they should only be used with great care. This empirical observation underlines the need for analysis of predictive quality whenever software reliability models are used.

Computer packages are available to carry out the analysis described here. Users can thus easily adopt an eclectic approach to reliability

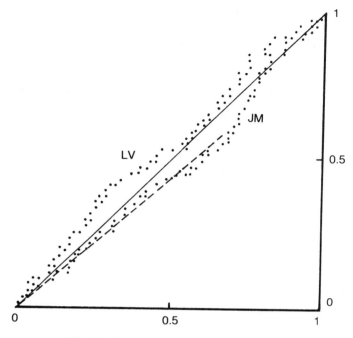

Fig. 8.7 LV, JM y-plots, data of Table 8.1.

prediction: using several models on each data set and selecting the predictions which have performed best in the past on that data.

These techniques are not complete and this is an active research area. It can be shown, for example, that a model can have good u- and y-plots and yet give poor predictions because of 'noise': i.e. the predictions are very variable as the sample size increases. There is evidence in the median plot of Fig. 8.3 that JM is such a model. Although simple plots can sometimes detect noise, they do not provide an objective measure to enable comparisons to be made between models. Some current research being conducted by the author is using the ideas of *prequential likelihood*[19] to investigate these issues.

DISCUSSION

The software reliability models considered here are only the early stages of a comprehensive reliability theory of software. They are deficient in some fairly obvious ways which future research must address.

In certain real-time control applications, for example, the conceptual model discussed here can be misleading. It is implicitly assumed that, after a failure, the program restarts execution at a point in the input space, I, which is distant from the point at which the failure occurred. This is not important in many contexts, but can be vital in safety-critical control.

Consider, for example, an avionics system[22] which is flight-critical. If an input case causes a failure, it is likely that the immediately following input cases will also cause failure, since these will be 'close' to the original one in the input space. Repair, of course, is not possible in this application. Failures are therefore likely to be seen in clusters, rather than singly. Even if the aerodynamic stability of the aircraft is sufficient for it to tolerate single failures, it will not be able to recover from sufficiently large clusters. In a case like this, it is important to consider the detailed structure of the failure process, rather than simply the rate of occurrence of failures.

The models treated here are essentially 'black box' ones: they do not take account of explanatory variables. In practice, there is often a great deal of extra information available which ought to contribute to better reliability modelling. Knowledge of the internal structure of the software, for example, can only be incorporated in relatively naive ways.[23] Complexity measures, and measures relating to software development methodology, are still contentious,[24] but are potentially fruitful research areas.[25]

Although it is usual to discuss *the* reliability of a program, it is clear that user-perceived reliability will often depend upon the type and severity of the use environment. It is well known that operating system reliability, for example, is lower in highly varied scientific use than in routine accounting applications. In fact, it is likely that certain classes of faults cannot show themselves in some use environments. This means that a supplier of software, seeing only failure data obtained by pooling from disparate users, may obtain a misleading impression of individual customers' experiences. Again, it is necessary to find appropriate metrics for type and severity of use before better models can be constructed.

Issues of data collection remain problematical in this area. The poor quality of most collected data attests to the difficulties which have been experienced. However, some of these difficulties can be overcome by setting up a suitable failure reporting mechanism at an early stage. The chief technical difficulty arises from the requirement that the data must be collected in an environment which is typical of the use environment. If the real use environment is not available, this means that random testing must be carried out with a probability profile representing the use environment. (Notice that 'random testing' does not mean equally likely selection of test cases from the input set: this involves use of a uniform distribution over the input set, and is usually very unrealistic.) It is often thought that such random testing is very inefficient,[26] but recent work suggests that this may not always be the case.[27] In any case, conventional testing procedures must always leave some doubt that parts of the input space have been covered with low probability.[28] Such regions may contain faults having high frequency and great importance to users. The only testing procedure currently known which ranks fault detection probabilities in the same way as user-perceived occurrence rates is random testing.

In the last few years there has been a growing interest in software reliability, and it is probable that solutions to many of these problems will soon be found. The programs for research in information technology which have been established recently in Japan, the USA, France, Europe and the UK should facilitate these advances.[25]

REFERENCES

1. Musa, J. D. (1979). *Software Reliability Data*. Report available from Data and Analysis Center for Software, Rome Air Development Center, Rome, NY.
2. Dunham, J. R. and Knight, J. C. (Eds.). (1982). *Production of Reliable Flight-Crucial Software*. NASA Conference Publication 2222.
3. Littlewood, B. (1979). 'How to Measure Software Reliability and How Not to'. *IEEE Trans. Reliability*, **R-28**, 3, 103–110.
4. Jelinski, Z. and Moranda, P. B. (1972). 'Software Reliability Research', in *Statistical Computer Performance Evaluation*. (W. Freiberger, ed.). Academic Press, New York, 465–484.
5. Shooman, M. (1973). 'Operational Testing and Software Reliability During Program Development'. *Record, 1973 IEEE Symp. Computer Software Reliability*. New York, NY, April 30–May 2, 51–57.
6. Musa, J. D. (1975). 'A Theory of Software Reliability and its Application'. *IEEE Trans. Software Eng.*, **SE-1**, 3, 312–327.
7. Nagel, P. M. and Skrivan, J. A. (1982). *Software Reliability: Repetitive Run Experimentation and Modelling*. NASA Contractor Report 165836.
8. Nagel, P. M., Scholz, F. W. and Skrivan, J. A. (1984). *Software Reliability: Additional Investigations into Modelling with Replicated Experiments*. NASA Contractor Report 172378.
9. Keiller, P. A., Littlewood, B., Miller, D. R. and Sofer, A. (1983). 'On the Quality of Software Reliability Predictions'. *Proc. NATO ASI on Electronic Systems Effectiveness and Life Cycle Costing*. Norwich, UK, 1982, Springer, 441–460.
10. Keiller, P. A., Littlewood, B., Miller, D. R. and Sofer, A. (1983). 'Comparison of Software Reliability Predictions'. *Proc. FTCS 13* (13th Annual International Symposium on Fault-Tolerant Computing), 128–134.
11. Littlewood, B. and Sofer, A. *A Bayesian Modification to the Jelinski-Moranda Software Reliability Growth Model*, unpublished manuscript.
12. Aitchison, J. and Dunsmore, I. R. (1975). *Statistical Prediction Analysis*. Cambridge University Press, Cambridge.
13. Littlewood, B. and Verrall, J. L. (1973). 'A Bayesian Reliability Growth Model for Computer Software'. *J. Royal Statist. Soc.*, **C (Applied Statistics) 22**, 332–346.
14. Littlewood, B. (1981). 'Stochastic Reliability Growth: a Model for Fault-removal in Computer Programs and Hardware Designs'. *IEEE Trans. Reliability*, **R-30**, 4, 313–320.
15. Duane, J. T. (1964). 'Learning Curve Approach to Reliability Monitoring'. *IEEE Trans. Aerospace*, **2**, 563–566.
16. Crow, L. H. (1977). *Confidence Interval Procedures for Reliability Growth Analysis*. Tech. Report No. 197, US Army Material Systems Analysis Activity, Aberdeen, Md.
17. Littlewood, B. (1984). 'Rationale for a Modified Duane Model'. *IEEE Trans.*

Reliability, **R-33**, No. 2, 157–159.

18. Musa, J. D. and Okumoto, K. (1984). 'A Logarithmic Poisson Execution Time Model for Software Reliability Measurement', *Proc. 7th Inter. Conf. on Software Eng.* Orlando, Florida, March 26–29.

19. Akaike, H. (1982). *Prediction and Entropy*. MRC Technical Summary Report, Mathematics Research Center, University of Wisconsin, Madison.

20. Dawid, A. P. (1984). 'Statistical Theory: the Prequential Approach', *J. Royal Statist. Soc.*, A, **147**, 278–292.

21. Cox, D. R. and Lewis, P. A. W. (1966). *Statistical Analysis of Series of Events*, Methuen, London.

22. Migneault, E. Private communication.

23. Littlewood, B. (1979). 'Software Reliability Model for Modular Program Structure'. *IEEE Trans. Reliability*, **R-28**, 3, 241–246.

24. Dale, C. J. and Harris, L. N. (1981). *Reliability Aspects of Microprocessor Systems*. British Aerospace Dynamics Group, ST-25358.

25. Centre for Software Reliability (1984). *Software Reliability and Metrics Programme*. The Alvey Directorate, London.

26. Myers, G. J. (1979). *The Art of Software Testing*. Wiley, New York.

27. Duran, J. W. and Ntafos, S. C. (1984). 'An Evaluation of Random Testing'. *IEEE Trans. Software Eng.* **SE-10**, 438–444.

CHAPTER 9

Commercial resilient systems

A. P. Smith

(*Information Technology Ltd*)

Fault tolerance techniques have been applied in the computer industry since the earliest days, but always as the responsibility of the programmer. Recently, however, there has been a spate of product announcements by commercial companies offering products which appear to take that responsibility away from the programmer.

As in the very early days of the motor industry, there are almost as many different design approaches as there are competing companies, and naturally each extols its own particular product virtues in its own glossy brochures.

The reader is recommended to study these brochures and draw his own conclusions but reading this chapter first may help to explain some of the reasoning behind commercially available products.

The first thing to understand is that a commercial company is totally driven by market pressures. Hence, the company's products are designed to meet the needs of a particular market sector and to sell profitably. These basic marketing factors apply to resilient computers just as surely as they apply to any High Street consumer goods. The significance is this: probably no commercially available resilient computers come up to an academic definition of full resilience, but neither do they need to as long as they are meeting the resilience requirements of the market sector they are operating in. Furthermore, a perfectly resilient system might be so expensive that its market would be tiny and hence not profitable.

The broadest market sector in terms of computer application has become business or commercial applications and this is where most computer companies are now aiming their resilient computer products. In particular they are aimed at on-line transaction processing, where the key task is to keep an on-line database up-to-date minute-by-minute by capturing details of 'transactions' as they occur, entered at multiple on-line VDUs.

A good example is a nationwide on-line order processing system totally integrated with stock control and accounting. The arrival of new stock in a warehouse in one part of the country is immediately reflected in the database, and the new stock position can be inspected as part of an 'order enquiry' transaction seconds later at the other end of the country. Such systems demand a degree of resilience and become the natural market for purveyors of resilient computer systems.

THE MOVE TO PACKAGING

The computer industry is still young but throughout its life there has been a steady and consistent movement towards packaging of its technology. The movement has been consistently away from bespoke solutions for specific applications towards packaged solutions for generalised applications.

An evolutionary trend is clear. The first computers were pure hardware designed for specific tasks. Very soon came the pressure for software and the concept of re-programming the same standard set of hardware for different tasks. The first of these programming languages were very low level with a clear one-to-one relationship between the hardware and the program instructions. People soon tired of re-writing the same set of low level instructions and invented high level languages. In a sense, these offered packaging of low level instructions into more understandable high level instructions.

With high level languages came the art of application programming with the skill of interpreting human requirements and instructing the computer more or less to meet that requirement. But there came a realisation that one man's accounts system was very similar to the next man's and so the applications software package was born.

The batch computer age provided relative calm until a new black art arrived – the art of the 'real-time programmer'. The programmer able to master the extra dimensions of time and random behaviour of on-line human users was a rare animal, fiercely hunted in the job columns. The industry's packaged response was to introduce transaction processing as teleprocessing (TP) monitors – systems software that took the responsibility for the most critical real-time aspects of the system away from the programmer. Today, very few computer users would consider writing VDU-handling routines from scratch!

Fault tolerance is the latest step in the evolution. As more and more people have become more and more dependent on computers, so the clamour for fault tolerance has increased. A couple more dimensions have been added to the programmer's task – coping with concurrent real-time events and coping with things going wrong – randomly! Once again, programmers with those skills are rare and once again the industry is responding with packaged solutions. The move this time is from 'programming for fault tolerance' to 'using fault tolerant systems'.

THE COMPROMISE

Before considering how successful the industry has been in packaging fault tolerance it is worth casting a historical eye over the industry's past achievements.

We have seen a steady move away from bespoke solutions to packaged solutions. In that movement, the industry has been in pursuit of a dream, a dream desired by the users and promised by the suppliers. The dream has been the belief that 'de-skilling' the design of systems would overcome the shortage of experienced skilled programmers.

In reality, the industry has arrived at a compromise. High level languages did not eliminate programming skills; TP monitors did not eliminate the need for good systems design; and, most significantly, applications software packages did not suit all applications. In that last example, the common compromise has been a tailored package. A tailored package provides generalised solutions, but tailoring is needed to fit each particular application.

There is an exact parallel with the new packaged offerings for fault tolerant computing. As with the early applications packages, there are those in the industry who resent their arrival. They will claim that they offer nothing that cannot be achieved by good programming anyway. Others will acclaim their arrival as the perfect answer to everyone's prayers. The glossy brochure of one brand new computer supplier claims that the user need be 'totally unaware of the problems of fault tolerance'.

The answer, of course, will be somewhere in the middle of those two extremes – in other words, tailored packages.

RELIABILITY, AVAILABILITY OR RESILIENCE

Before considering packages further it is worth clarifying the above three terms.

As organisations became more dependent on computers in the 1960s and 1970s they demanded reliability. In much the same way as a taxi driver might demand a reliable car, the business manager could be heard saying 'If I'm going to run my business on a computer, it had better be reliable.' By reliable he meant, as did the taxi driver, 'not go wrong very often'.

In the early days, computers generally did go wrong and that led people to introduce a measure of reliability – the availability figure. This was a weapon of both attack and defence and became the argumentative mainstay of most DP Department/User Department liaison meetings!

By the 1970s, availability had become a contractual term to be found in most industry supplier contracts – 'availability shall be not less than 95%' or similar. Availability was dependent on both Mean Time Between Failure (reliability) and Mean Time To Repair. As computers became inherently more reliable, so more emphasis was placed on Mean Time To Repair. Fast response maintenance contracts became the order of the day.

Resilience or fault tolerance is different again. Advocates of resilience accept that things go wrong and then aim to minimise the effect when the inevitable occurs. Instead of MTBF or MTTR, the real measure of resilience is HPI – Hassle Per Incident!

As an example, any computer system achieving 99% availability must be considered highly reliable. But that might mean 99 days working followed by a fault that takes a whole day to fix. If the computer was running on-line sales terminals that would be a disaster. On the other hand, a system might fail every 99 minutes but each time take only 1 minute to recover; again 99% availability, but obviously highly unreliable. If there was no lasting effect after each 1 minute of down-time, however, that system could be termed resilient – to a degree.

There are degrees of resilience, both in terms of faults tolerated and the disruption when faults do occur. In selecting 'packaged fault tolerance' one needs to decide the degree of resilience required for the particular business or organisation. To return to the analogy of the taxi driver, having bought a reliable car he builds in some resilience by carrying a spare wheel. A puncture on a lonely road will now cause him a little inconvenience rather than a few hours lost business.

DESIGN ASPECTS

When looking at the different commercial products available, there are noticeable differences in approach and these basically reflect some fundamental decisions that the product designers must have taken. These fundamental decisions are summarised below.

REDUNDANT OR NON-REDUNDANT?

Does the application justify, and can the user afford, partly or completely redundant systems? That is, equipment used only during emergencies. Our taxi driver carries a redundant spare wheel; he cannot justify carrying a spare engine, nor can he afford to carry a spare taxi towed on a trailer behind the first one!

Many computer installations provide resilience (of sorts) by having a stand-by system.

TRANSPARENT OR NON-TRANSPARENT?

Is the user to be aware that something has gone wrong? Will he have to do anything? The taxi driver had to stop and spend a few minutes changing the wheel. Perhaps he should have two wheels already mounted on each stub axle. If one tyre punctures he can drive on unawares. At least two commercial suppliers offer a computer equivalent of this analogy.

Both Tandem and ITL MOMENTUM provide mirror (or duplicate) disk facilities so that a catastrophic disk failure causes no effect on the user at the time it occurs.

HARDWARE, SOFTWARE OR SYSTEM?

There are many ways to achieve resilience. The main tools may be hardware striving for inherent fault tolerance; or software making non-resilient hardware appear resilient; or it may be a combination of both, taking a system view.

SKILLED OR DE-SKILLED?

The designer must have clearly in mind what sort of people will both program the computer and use the resultant system. Some designs leave the most critical aspects of implementation to the programmer, albeit with good documentation to guide him. A bad programmer can quickly nullify all the resilience features built into the rest of the system! On the other hand, some of the new designs claim to be totally foolproof.

SPECIFIC OR GENERAL?

Finally, the designer of fault tolerant systems must decide whether his design is to meet a specific application or is for general use. Clearly the latter is far more difficult, as the design will be meeting as yet unseen and undefined conditions.

TRADITIONAL APPROACHES

The traditional approach to fault tolerance over the years has been to develop turnkey solutions to specific problems. The applications that were most prominent were process control, military command and control systems and communications control computers. In every case the application justified the expense both of redundant equipment and of once-off development costs.

Most often the system was implemented using multiple identical minicomputers working in parallel, i.e. running the same software. The emphasis was very much on protection of hardware and of the programs running within the hardware. If a processor failed, the program or process would continue on the parallel duplicated processor.

The philosophy was not perfect; a software fault could crash the two synchronised processors – in synchronism! On the other hand, as the system was often carrying out a specific task repeatedly, the software could be reasonably well tested.

Tandem was the first design to challenge this approach. This was done with a 'new' design of minicomputer with critical components and data paths duplicated internally rather than externally. Furthermore, the hardware was equipped with software tools to allow a skilled designer to tackle a range of problems. In this sense it was also designed for generalised applications. In practice, the first applications were in communications, particularly moving money as banks became ever more automated. As with the traditional approach, the design emphasis was on protecting hardware and programs, but there was now also more emphasis on protecting data.

ITL announced MOMENTUM some years later as a second alternative offering a 'generalised' approach to resilience. Although also offering a full non-stop transaction processing, the design approach was quite different. MOMENTUM uses mainly software to provide resilience to otherwise standard hardware. There is another key difference. Uniquely, MOMEN-

TUM allows resilience to be added in stages, building up gradually from non-resilient to fully fault tolerant.

This unique aspect brought resilience to new applications. Whereas people buying Tandem definitely require resilience and are committed to paying for it, ITL MOMENTUM customers are often unaware of resilience and cannot justify full resilience at the start of their projects, although they may need it later.

Most ITL MOMENTUM applications are in commercial transaction processing with user software written in COBOL. Compared with the traditional approach to resilience, the design emphasis of MOMENTUM is inverted. First priority is protection of the database, followed by programs, and finally hardware. Resilience of the hardware is in fact added as an option, only if the application justifies it.

WHERE WERE THE OTHERS?

For several years Tandem and later ITL MOMENTUM went unchallenged by the major manufacturers. Why was this? The answer lies in the 'cleanliness' of the manufacturers' hardware and software range. Tandem started from scratch with a clean sheet of paper. Most of the other major manufacturers had developed their ranges over a decade or so and had a matrix of inconsistent products. Typically there might be several types of hardware. Running across these might be several different operating systems. Below that might be several database management systems and then several TP monitors, not even all under the manufacturer's control. The first three dimensions of this matrix are shown in Fig. 9.1.

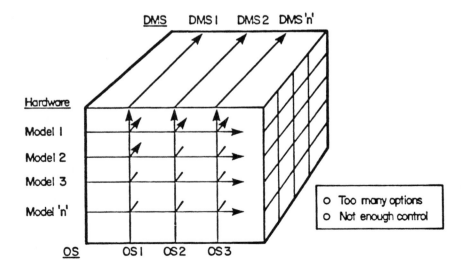

Fig. 9.1 Where to apply resilience.

Deciding where to apply resilience in that matrix proved too difficult. One of the basic rules of resilience is that it must consistently cover all critical components of the operating software. ITL achieved MOMENTUM only because, largely by chance, they had one consistent hardware range and one operating system, and all systems software was developed by their own staff in one integrated team.

NEWCOMERS TO THE MARKET

There are three reasons why more companies have joined battle in the market for resilient computer systems – market size, new technology and a certain degree of opportunistic marketing.

THE MARKET
Several independent US market research organisations produced very optimistic assessments of the market for fault tolerant systems. Two that received wide coverage were the Strategic Incorporated Report and the ITOM Report[1]. (Both are recommended reading.) Both saw a market rising ten-fold in five years. Such a goldmine could no longer be resisted by the world's manufacturers!

TECHNOLOGY
In five or six years there has been tremendous change in computer technology with the arrival of the micro. The availability of powerful cheap microprocessor building blocks has allowed the conception of designs that would have been far too expensive using conventional minicomputer architecture. Almost without exception, the newcomers to the market are based on multiple-micro technology. Redundancy can now be afforded!

OPPORTUNISTIC MARKETING
Sometimes there is very little new in the techniques used. As publicity about fault tolerance has grown, many companies have woken up to realise the similarities between the 'new fangled' concept of resilience and 'what they've been doing for years'. Most of these have specialised in a particular application that required fault tolerance. Some of these companies have quickly applied a name to their methods and attempted to generalise the application. Others have viewed their current products through rose-tinted spectacles and optimistically explained that fault tolerant systems could be built using them; so, stretching a point, perhaps they could be considered fault tolerant.

THE DIFFERENT TECHNIQUES USED

As in the early days of the motorcar, there are almost as many designs as there are suppliers. However, the different designs can be classified into a number of broad categories. These are shown diagrammatically in Figs.

9.2–9.7. When assessing manufacturers' packages it may help to classify them first.

REDUNDANT MINI
In these systems, also known as 'hot standby' systems, the entire system is duplicated and both sides run identical software. Both sides receive all input data and process that data in parallel. If one side fails, the other continues immediately. Because both sides are synchronised, the inter-processor link must be very fast, operating essentially at internal databus speed.

One obvious drawback of these architectures is that catastrophic software failure related to input data may crash both sides simultaneously.

There are many variants of the 'hot standby' approach with varying degrees of redundancy and protection. Amongst others, CAP and Honeywell offer 'hot standby' systems.

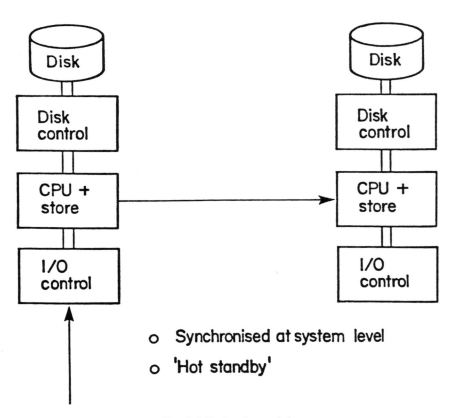

Fig. 9.2 Redundant mini.

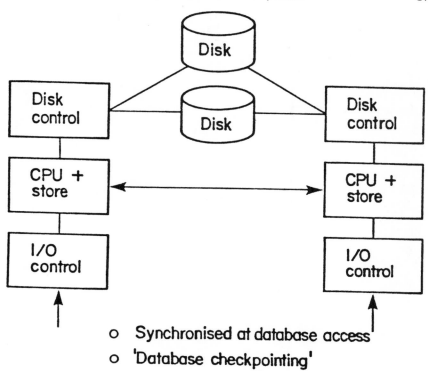

o Synchronised at database access
o 'Database checkpointing'

Fig. 9.3 Cooperating mini.

COOPERATING MINI

In these systems, duplicated minis are again used but this time they operate asynchronously. Each one independently processes its own data but keeps a friendly eye on its cooperating partner. In particular, the two partners cooperate whenever the database is updated, ensuring that the other could take recovery action if either failed. Similarly, action can be taken to roll back and re-start programs in progress at time of failure.

One possible criticism of the approach is that in fall-back mode there is less processor power available and inevitably reduced performance. On the other hand, in normal mode the second processor is available for useful work and is not redundant.

At present, only one implementation of this approach is commercially available – ITL MOMENTUM. It is possible that both IBM and DEC will take a similar approach with future products.

DUAL BUS MINI

These systems were the first to try to provide inherent resilience in the hardware design. Critical hardware components are duplicated throughout the system, connected via a duplicated high speed data bus. Tandem is the

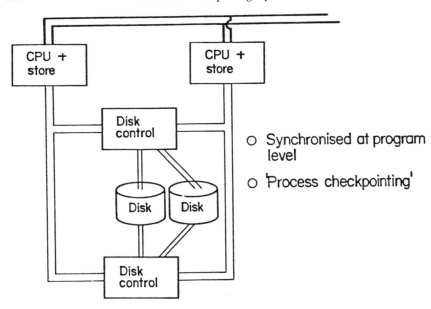

o Synchronised at program level

o 'Process checkpointing'

Fig. 9.4 Dual bus mini.

best known exponent of this approach, although there are others. As with the cooperating mini approach, there is a tendency to checkpoint programs and keep them in step.

An early criticism of this approach was that nervous or incompetent programmers could include too much 'checkpointing' with resultant poor performance.

REDUNDANT MULTI-MICRO

The arrival of cheap micro components has encouraged designers to re-introduce redundancy as a concept. Interestingly, these designers have criticised Tandem as being too software-based; instead they are striving for an ideal of total inherent hardware resilience.

They argue that if the hardware cannot go wrong, then there is no requirement for the programmer to consider resilience factors at all. STRATUS is a classic new design of this school. There is redundancy on each circuitboard with circuits duplicated and self-checking on the board. The processor boards themselves are duplicated to work in redundant synchronism – referred to by STRATUS as 'tight lock-step'. There could be one flaw in the design: it may be that an operating system fatal crash could crash the synchronised processors. Operating systems are notoriously prone to crashing during their early years and it is not clear to the author how the system would cope.

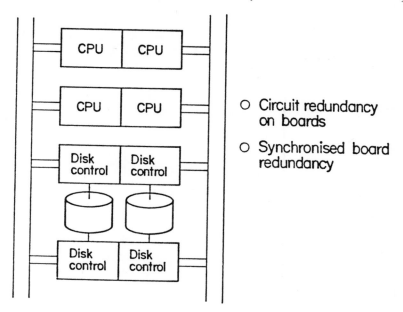

Fig. 9.5 Redundant multi-micro – inherent hardware resilience.

NON-REDUNDANT MULTI-MICRO

Another interesting approach based on availability of cheap microprocessor power is to cluster multiple microcomputers together to share a total processing task. The aim is to provide resilience without performance degradation. In normal use, each micro takes its share of work under control of a master. If one micro fails, its current work is re-assigned to another. SYNAPSE N+1 is a classic design of this school. If *n* micros are needed for the job, *n*+1 are provided, allowing full performance even if one fails. The SYNAPSE design is interesting in that all the micros share one large block of common store – a very obvious common point of failure that could stop the entire system. This is recognised by SYNAPSE who allow the system to stop, reconfigure and re-start if a store fault occurs. More worrying is the fact that a single copy of the operating system is apparently used. Again, it is not obvious to the author how operating system failure is handled.

REDUNDANT MULTI-MICRO VOTING

Included for completeness is the redundant voting approach. Voting implies an odd number of identically operating processors, in practice three. Total processor and store are triplicated. This approach does not lend itself to disk-based systems simply because current disk technology provides only dual-ported disk drives! This limits the application somewhat,

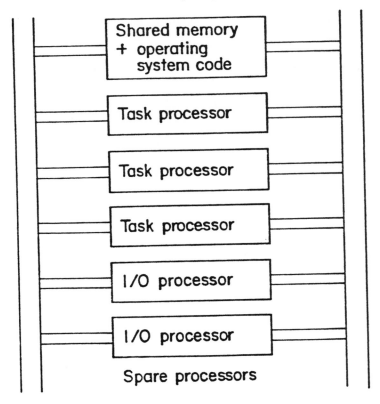

Fig. 9.6 Non-redundant multi-micro – inherent hardware resilience.

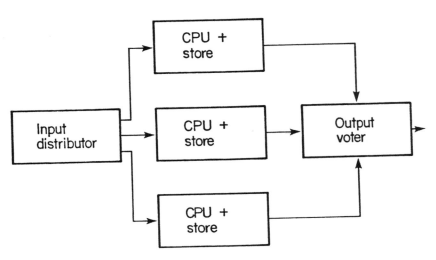

Fig. 9.7 Redundant multi-micro voting.

probably to process control only. August Systems is the only supplier that is obviously basing its product on this approach.

THE SUPPLIERS

Listed in Fig. 9.8 are all companies who have made recent press announcements concerning fault tolerant products. The vast majority are American companies and very few products are yet ready for market. Even fewer are yet available in Europe.

o	ABACUS	'Quitless'	o	IBM	
o	AUGUST	'It-Can't-Fail'	o	IPL	
o	AUTECH	'Faultproof'	o	PARALLEL	(AURAGEN)
o	CAP	'CAPTEC'	o	PARALLEL	
o	CCI		o	SEQUOIA	
o	CHORUS		o	STRATUS	
o	CTL	'MOMENTUM'	o	SYNAPSE	'N + I'
o	DEC		o	SYNTECH	'Non-Fail'
o	DOSC	'FailSafe'	o	SYNTREX	'Always Up'
o	FORMATION		o	TANDEM	'Non-Stop'
o	GEAC		o	TOLERANT	
o	HONEYWELL		o	TRILOGY	
o	HP	'1000 Systemsafe'			

Fig. 9.8 The newcomers.

Not all the suppliers are tackling the same market or applications. Figure 9.9 is a broad classification of supplier by main application. In addition to process control, other specific applications include banking cluster controllers, telephone exchange controllers and fast-food check-out controllers!

Two giants that have started to make product noises are DEC and IBM. DEC has announced a generalised architecture for loosely connecting multiple processors and will claim fault tolerant systems can be built from that architecture. In the USA, IBM has announced its intention to add fault tolerant features to the Series 1 mini. As with ITL's MOMENTUM, the approach seems to be that of dual systems cooperating on database updates.

HOW COMPLETE A PACKAGE?

A perfectly fault tolerant system would tolerate faults of any kind. A

```
┌─────────────────────────────┐   ┌─────────────────────────────┐
│  Process control            │   │  Other specific             │
│  AUGUST                     │   │  ABACUS                     │
│  AUTECH                     │   │  CCI                        │
│  CHORUS                     │   │  SYNTECH                    │
│  HP 1000                    │   │  SYNTREX                    │
│  CAPTEC                     │   │  DOSC                       │
│                             │   │  BELL 3B20D                 │
│                             │   │  GEAC                       │
└─────────────────────────────┘   └─────────────────────────────┘

┌─────────────────────────────┐   ┌─────────────────────────────┐
│  Mainframe/compatibles      │   │  On-line TP                 │
│  DEC SYSTEM 20              │   │  AURAGEN (PARALLEL)         │
│  FORMATION F/4000           │   │  CTL MOMENTUM               │
│  IPL                        │   │  HONEYWELL TPS              │
│  TRILOGY                    │   │  IBM SERIES 1               │
│                             │   │  PARALLEL                   │
│                             │   │  SEQUOIA                    │
│                             │   │  STRATUS                    │
│                             │   │  SYNAPSE                    │
│                             │   │  TANDEM                     │
│                             │   │  TTS                        │
└─────────────────────────────┘   └─────────────────────────────┘
```

Fig. 9.9 The newcomers by category.

perfectly packaged, perfectly fault tolerant system would also provide all its fault tolerance in a manner totally transparent to the programmers and the users. Regrettably, life isn't like that! When assessing a packaged fault tolerant product, the user must decide how complete a package he needs and how complete a package he is being sold.

At the lowest level are hardware tools – hardware that the competent designer can use to build fault tolerant systems. Dual-ported disk drives have been promoted by some as offering fault tolerance!

At the next level come fault tolerant hardware systems – packaged combinations of hardware with defined modes of use to achieve fault tolerance. Such packages may use terms such as 'no single point of hardware failure'. In other words, any component failure will cause no problem. However, such systems may rely very much on the programmer's skill and may be vulnerable to software failure.

Next to consider is the operating system. What happens if the operating system fails? Industry experience suggests that new operating systems may take years to stabilise. At first sight, most of the newcomers appear to have ignored this problem.

Next is the data management system. Protecting programs and ensuring that they continue or re-start is only part of the solution; it is also necessary to protect the database and ensure that it remains totally consistent whatever the failure, particularly with on-line database updating. Some designers are suggesting that multiple workstations connected via local area networks provide inherent resilience. Few of these designs consider what happens to a shared access database.

Next comes the transaction processing software. Having protected both programs and database, does the system protect the users at their VDU screens? Does it tell them what's happening and does it allow them to continue their work without duplicating or omitting transactions? Does the system maintain a true audit trail of transactions – whatever the failure? Does it maintain the correct order of database updates if there is a failure?

On top of the TP monitor comes bespoke applications software, the software written by the actual users, outside the control of the system supplier. User-written software fails! How will the system cope? Will the system protect itself, the users, the database and other programs from the program failure? Will it re-start the program when it is in use by multiple users? Does the packaging extend to applications packages? In addition to non-stop hardware and software, is there a non-stop accounts package and non-stop production control packages?

Finally, is the system user-proof? Is the system robust? When the implementation is complete, must the system be operated in a special way? This is the most difficult area but systems will certainly vary in their tolerance.

SUMMARY

There are now several commercially packaged 'resilient computers' on the market, using a number of different design approaches. Not all systems are full non-stop – not all need to be! The systems available vary widely in what they offer and how much skill is required to drive them.

Most of the new products appear to concentrate on making the hardware fault tolerant and perhaps underestimate the software aspects. Few offer complete fault tolerance.

REFERENCE

1. Serlin, O. (1982). *Fault Tolerant Systems*, ITOM Int. Co.

CHAPTER 10

The Tandem Non-Stop system

C. I. Dimmer

(*SPL International*)

FIRST INTO THE MARKETPLACE

Tandem Computers Incorporated, manufacturers of the Non-Stop range of computers, were the first company to produce and sell off-the-shelf fault tolerant computer systems. Prior to Tandem's arrival in 1977, fault tolerant systems had primarily been the domain of specialist systems houses building bespoke systems using multiple minicomputers.

Tandem was the first company to grasp the tremendous commercial opportunity that existed as a result of increasing demand for high availability on-line transaction processing systems. Tandem's founders correctly recognised the increasing reliance of many organisations upon such high availability and reliability systems. Of particular importance were those organisations whose very business depended upon on-line transaction processing and communications, such as banks, airlines, financial institutions. So convinced were they that in 1974 they founded Tandem specifically to design, manufacture and market the Non-Stop computer range.

That decision was probably the single most significant event in the history of the fault tolerant system market. For almost five years (1977–1982) Tandem enjoyed an unchallenged position, and both Tandem and the fault tolerant market grew explosively. Very positive market predictions attracted venture capital and a flock of other new companies entered the fault tolerant system marketplace, some to fail, others to find their own market niche, but none to copy directly Tandem's approach. Tandem, nevertheless, remain the dominant force in what they might reasonably claim to be 'their' market.

It is significant that Tandem's marketing and software product emphasis evolved as their products, the marketplace and their competitors' products matured. This chapter examines both the fundamental fault tolerant techniques utilised in the Non-Stop systems and the subsequent extensions thereto. The more recent changes in emphasis are covered in the sections entitled Transaction Processing Environment and Extensions for Networking.

FUNDAMENTALS, OBJECTIVES AND CONSTRAINTS

In the mid 1970s it was not cost effective to use static hardware redundancy (i.e. N-Modular Redundancy, or NMR) for on-line transaction processing (OLTP) systems. However, dynamic redundancy, which relies upon using an alternative resource after a fault is detected, was both cost effective and appropriate, particularly since OLTP systems could comfortably tolerate error detection and recovery times of a second or two.

Dynamic hardware redundancy implies having alternative devices available to handle the work of failed devices. Provided that this work can be rescheduled amongst the remaining devices in an adequately timely manner, then there is no fundamental reason for these alternative devices to be idle spares. This enables them to be used in both normal and fault toleration circumstances, and permits what is sometimes called *productive redundancy*. This reasoning materially influenced Tandem's choice of custom designed loosely coupled minicomputers as their basic architecture.

Tandem's key design objectives were:

- No single hardware failure should stop the system
- Hardware elements should be maintainable with the system on-line
- Database integrity should be assured
- The system should be modularly extensible without incurring application software changes.

HARDWARE ARCHITECTURE OVERVIEW

Traditional fault tolerant schemes using standard (non-fault-tolerant) minicomputers usually involved two separate computers with some form of interconnection between them, with peripherals optionally connected to one or both computers. Tandem effectively took this as their starting point. By applying rigorously the test that no single point of failure should jeopardise the system, they arrived at the generic design shown in Fig. 10.1.

Examination of Fig. 10.1 reveals that:

- There are two independent computers
- There are two independent data paths to everything
- Each peripheral controller is dual ported and can be accessed by either computer
- Each computer has its own power supply which also redundantly powers the peripheral controllers connected thereto.

Such a design is capable of meeting the resilience to single point of failure criterion, provided adequate fault containment measures are engineered into the hardware. Tandem, as we shall see, devoted much effort in this area.

Modular expansibility was another of Tandem's major objectives, so great attention was paid to the design of the interconnection between the computers. This resulted in a design utilising a fast dual interprocessor bus structure called Dynabus, which can best be likened to a duplicated very

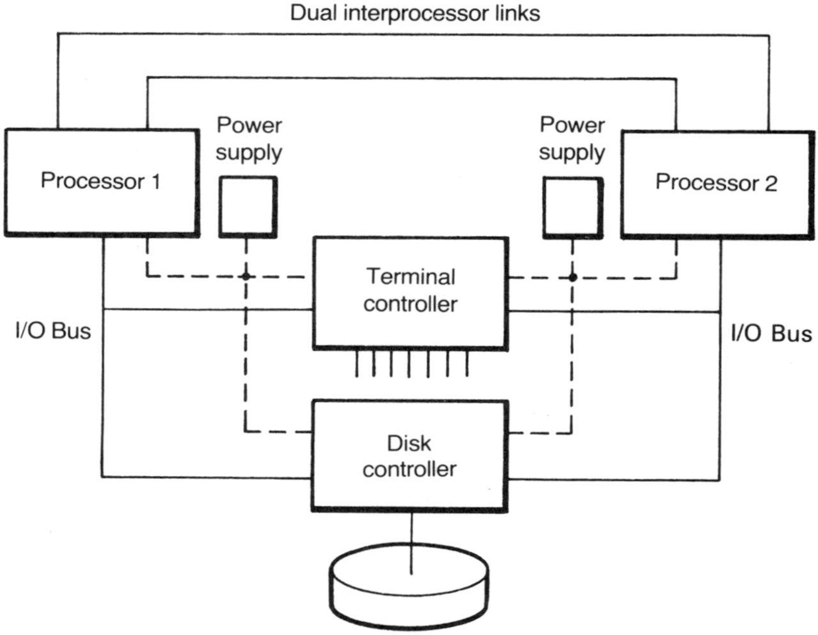

Fig. 10.1. Generic fault-tolerant design.

high performance local area network, owing to its extensive electrical isolation and message passing orientation. This isolation is necessary so that neither a bus failure nor a processor failure can crash other processors attached to the bus.

In practice, probably the two most critical pieces of hardware design in the Non-Stop system are the Dynabus control circuitry and the dual-ported interfaces to the peripheral device controllers. In each case it must be possible to disconnect a processor from an errant Dynabus or a peripheral controller from errant input/output (I/O) bus.

Dynabus is therefore capable of supporting substantially more than a mere two attached computers. The Tandem design admits the connection of between two and sixteen processors to form a single system. A typical configuration comprising three processors is depicted in Fig. 10.2. Notice how peripheral controllers may be strung between any pair of I/O busses; pairing of processors and peripherals is not necessary.

Database integrity was another very important consideration in the design of the system. Rotating magnetic disks, being the primary form of on-line non-volatile mass storage, were given special consideration. Disk 'crashes' usually destroy data, so multiple copies of the data on separate disks are required to survive disk failure. Tandem elected to use a dual-disk approach for achieving data integrity where two distinct disk drives are maintained as mirror images of each other. Tandem call this approach

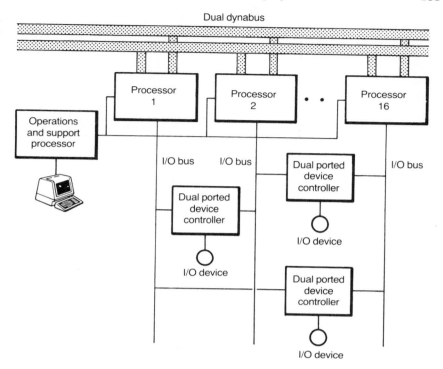

Fig. 10.2. Typical Tandem Non-Stop system.

mirrored volumes. Owing to the inevitable occurrence of surface defects in the magnetic coating of a disk, unusable patches of the disk surface (a recognised feature of high density disks) occur in different places on each disk. Therefore mirrored disks are not quite what they appear at first sight. A typical mirrored disk volume hardware configuration is shown in Fig. 10.3.

Such a configuration is resilient to failure of either disk controller, either disk drive, and any one data path. Notice how dual-ported disk drives again require the same careful design to protect a disk drive from permanent seizure by an errant disk controller.

KEY HARDWARE FEATURES

A Tandem system (or node) comprises a local network of two to sixteen processors, connected by Dynabus dual interprocessor busses (see Fig. 10.2).

Each processor comprises a power supply, interface logic for Dynabus control, a microprogrammed CPU, main memory, and a microprogrammed I/O channel driving a single block-multiplexed I/O bus (see Fig. 10.4).

I/O device controllers are dual-ported and attached to any two separate I/O channels, thus providing two alternative paths to each device controller

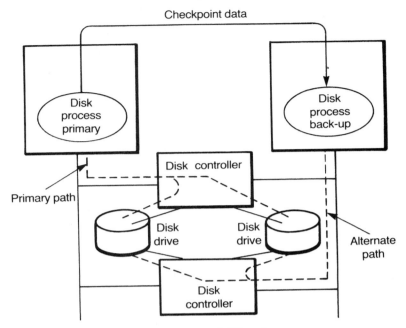

Fig. 10.3. Mirrored disk volumes.

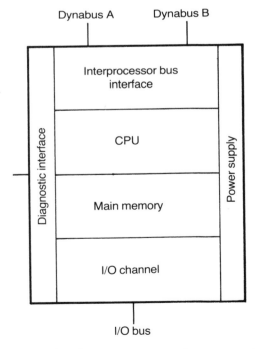

Fig. 10.4. Non-Stop processor – main components.

(see Fig. 10.2). An I/O channel can accommodate up to 32 device controllers, each with up to eight devices.

The power supplies within the system are arranged so that each processor has its own power supply, whilst non-redundant I/O controllers and interprocessor bus controllers are redundantly powered from two independent sources (see Fig. 10.1).

Individual assemblies such as processors, I/O controllers and power supplies may be powered down, repaired and returned to service whilst the rest of the system continues operation, albeit at a reduced level of fault tolerance.

To assist in on-line maintenance and fault location an Operations and Support Processor (OSP) is attached to all the processors in a system. The OSP provides local and remote (via a modem) control and diagnosis of the system (see Fig. 10.2).

Other mechanisms which contribute towards fault tolerance include main memory with error correction circuitry, optional battery back-up for main memory, power fail recovery, a two-state processor (privileged and non-privileged), I/O channel overrun protection and a redundant cooling system.

SUMMARY OF HARDWARE CONCEPTS

We have now examined the fundamental concepts which characterise the hardware design of the Non-Stop system. We have already observed that dynamic redundancy involves re-trying a failed operation using an alternative resource. Tandem control the use of alternative resources by software, and in the next section we shall examine how Tandem's unique combination of hardware and software together provide a fault tolerant environment.

SOFTWARE ARCHITECTURE

We begin our examination of the software architecture by considering how a process (a running program) survives failure of the processor in which it is running. This will lead on to an examination of the features in the Tandem operating system which together contribute to a manageable fault tolerant environment.

PROCESS PAIRS

The fundamental software technique deployed by Tandem to achieve fault tolerance is the use of *process pairs* to provide non-stop processes. A process pair consists of two copies of a process each residing in a separate processor (Fig. 10.5). One copy of the process, the 'primary', is actively executing, whilst the other copy, the 'back-up', is quiescent, but ready to take over should the primary fail.

To keep the back-up process up-to-date, the primary process selectively checkpoints its state variables (i.e. sends a copy of all critical data) to its

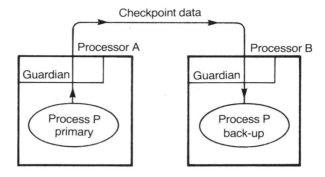

Fig. 10.5. Checkpointing data between non-stop process pairs.

back-up copy. Unlike more conventional systems this checkpoint is not to disk but to the corresponding memory locations in the process image of the back-up. The checkpoint data is transported synchronously by a secure message-passing system over the interprocessor bus. The initiation of a checkpoint is under the programmatic control of the primary process. By this means the back-up process is kept in a state where it is ready to take over should the primary process fail, e.g. as a result of processor failure.

TOLERATING PROCESSOR FAILURE

Once every second, each processor broadcasts over the interprocessor bus an 'I'm alive' message (Fig. 10.6). All processors monitor these messages and should one not arrive within two seconds the listeners assume the non-transmitting processor has failed. This failure exception is the stimulus to despatch any back-up processes whose primary copy resides in the failed processor (Fig. 10.7). At this point the back-up processes become the (new) primaries, and the non-stop process pair reduces to a stoppable

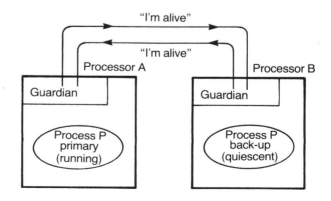

Fig. 10.6. Processors regularly transmit 'I'm alive' messages.

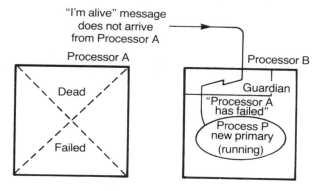

Fig. 10.7. Processor failure causes back-up process to take over.

single process. By this means the non-stop workload of the failed processor may be taken over by process back-ups residing in various processors.

It is well to remember how much fault tolerance Tandem were attempting to provide, namely 'survival of any single point of failure'. So, we will not explore the possibilities of having our new primaries create new back-ups elsewhere, which is indeed possible but generally less useful than it appears owing to I/O process and I/O path limitations which are addressed later.

When the failed processor is returned to service the unexpected arrival of its 'I'm alive' message triggers another exception which can be monitored by the patient new primaries and used as the stimulus to re-create a new back-up in the processor where the original primary ran (Fig. 10.8). At this time the process pair becomes fully fault tolerant again. When the roles of new back-up and new primary are reversed, status quo will have been restored (Fig. 10.5), the process pairs residing in their planned processors and the configuration in its optimally balanced state.

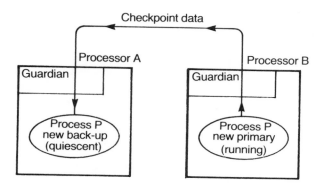

Fig. 10.8 Process-pair re-established following repair of failed processor.

GUARDIAN OPERATING SYSTEM

It is the Tandem operating system, euphemistically named Guardian, which is responsible for providing the environment in which process pairs exist. Guardian supports process creation and destruction, monitors the state of other processors, and notifies processes of processor failure or restoration. It also handles alternative I/O paths and provides the many other services customarily provided by a multiprogramming operating system.

Each processor in a system runs its own copy of Guardian. Since processors communicate exclusively by message passing over Dynabus, each copy of Guardian is well protected from interference by any of its siblings. The use of message passing contributes very materially to damage confinement following a fault.

Within Guardian are four main components:

- The Kernel, which is a process scheduler
- The Message System which supports interprocess communication (over the interprocessor bus if necessary)
- System Processes (e.g. virtual memory manager, I/O device control)
- The File System.

To the user the most important component is the file system, which provides a single interface between user processes and the outside world. The file system hides the physical location of both I/O devices (really system processes) and executing application processes. Thus, application processes interact only through the file system using a global file naming scheme. This naming scheme is in reality a process naming scheme, so that – for example – the files which reside on a particular disk are accessed by communicating with the device process which has responsibility for controlling that disk.

By this means a process Px (Fig. 10.9) running in processor A can communicate with a terminal Ty attached to processor B simply by opening Ty as a read-write file. The file system determines that terminal Ty is controlled by a device process residing in processor B and transparently routes messages to that process. To the user process it would make no difference if terminal Ty were a device attached locally to processor A.

These facilities, provided by the file system to hide the details of process location, are clearly vital to support transparent process migration as a result of a fault. Remember that when a processor fails, not only do the fault tolerant user processes located therein migrate elsewhere, but so too must any device processes previously responsible for controlling attached peripheral devices.

I/O DEVICE CONTROL PROCESSES

This category of system process is a constrained case of the process pair approach. Since an I/O device controller is dual-ported, it can only be connected to exactly two processors. In these two processors must reside

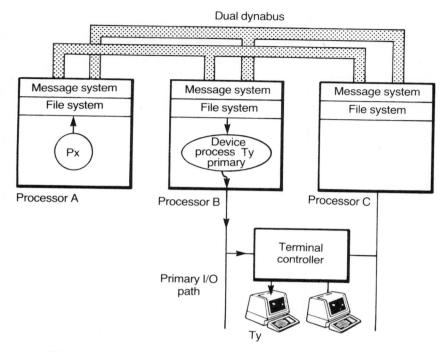

Fig. 10.9. The filing system determines how to access a peripheral.

the device control process pair. In this case, should one processor fail there is no opportunity to create a new back-up elsewhere, since only one path remains to the device controller, and that path is by definition already controlled by the back-up process. In a fault-free state the operating system can periodically alternate the roles of the process pair, to ensure that the alternative I/O path is functional (see Fig. 10.10).

The detailed low level checkpointing strategy used by this category of process differs slightly from that used by normal user processes. This is a consequence of Tandem's quest for operating system efficiency and the very practical need to recognise that some I/O operations (e.g. unit record operations) are inherently non-retryable. Control of mirrored disks is still exercised by a normal disk process pair, the primary writing to both disk drives.

Returning to our previous example (Fig. 10.9), it can now be appreciated that the operating system has to deal with the consequences of both processor and I/O path failure, both of which are masked from the user by the filing system. In both cases the affected process will migrate to other processors as far as message passing is concerned. Now we can appreciate what a major contribution the filing system makes by concealing these locational changes from user processes.

I/O device configuration is established via an operating system gener-

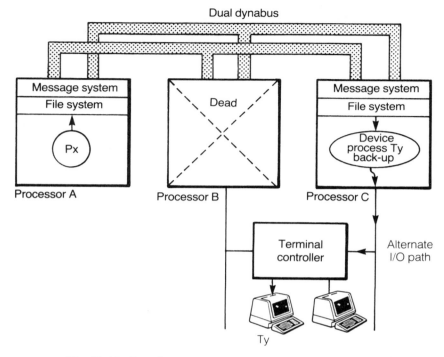

Fig. 10.10. Guardian hides I/O path failure and rerouting.

ation process, which records the allocation of process pairs to processors and constructs the system's logical device tables.

MESSAGE SYSTEM
Underpinning the entire filing system is the message system. This system provides the secure transmission of small error-checked packets of data over the dual interprocessor busses from one processor to another. If there is a failure of either bus then the other will be used, the message system transparently recovering from such faults. Normally – unlike other duplicated system resources – both interprocessor busses are used to effectively increase the bandwidth of the interprocessor data path.

FAULT TOLERANCE – SUMMARY OF BASIC APPROACH
Tandem utilises a minimally redundant processing and I/O system deploying dynamic hardware redundancy to tolerate faults. The power supplies exhibit planned partial static redundancy (dual supplies to non-redundant devices). The primary fault tolerance mechanism is to maintain process availability by means of non-stop process pairs, and through this to be able to exploit alternative I/O paths.

Practically, the entire approach stands or falls on the assumption that the operating system, system processes and user processes are themselves fault free. Needless to say, this is rarely the case, but an adequate approximation can be achieved. Tandem aid this by imposing copious interface checks on all calls to the operating system for services, to detect and prevent damage to the system by errant application processes. Additionally, although we will not examine the processor internal architecture in detail, user processes run in a paged virtual-memory regime with full interprocess memory protection.

Furthermore, the entire operating system is treated as trusted code which is company confidential to Tandem. Customers are therefore not able to tamper with the operating system internals; thus they are saved from the possibility of wrecking Tandem's careful work to achieve a highly reliable system through the symbiosis of the Guardian operating system and the Non-Stop hardware.

The result is an environment which can support both stoppable single processes and non-stop process pairs. Both categories benefit from the system's use of I/O device control process pairs to tolerate I/O path failures.

BOUNDARY CONSIDERATIONS

Fault tolerance only extends to the boundary of the system. If the user can provide dual independent power sources, the Non-Stop system can exploit them. If not, then an uninterruptible power supply (or supplies!) will need to be considered if the utility power supply reliability is inadequate to support the desired system availability.

A failure of one of the simpler multi-line communications controllers may disable one or more communications lines, so users need to ensure that enough spare ports exist on each controller to be able to tolerate the failure of any one controller. More sophisticated controllers isolate individual lines so that a failure only affects one line. To date, it appears not to be cost effective to push the boundary of the fault tolerant environment outwards any further for point-to-point lines driving a single terminal.

SHORTCOMING OF BASIC APPROACH

Tandem's original scheme for on-line transaction processing was that users would develop a single-thread non-stop process pair and replicate the process pair for each terminal to be supported; a back-drop of checkpointing, record locking and so forth would handle concurrency and provide fault tolerance.

Unfortunately there were two major drawbacks with this approach. First, checkpoints are problematic for three reasons:

- Checkpointing inadequate data causes the integrity of a process pair to be invalidated

- Checkpointing excessive data causes the system throughput to be reduced
- Checkpoints are difficult to optimise, tedious to test, and require skilled programming resources.

Second, large numbers of processes give rise to poor system resource utilisation. For example, excessive context swaps consume large amounts of CPU time, and memory utilisation (e.g. for buffer space) cannot be centrally optimised.

TRANSACTION PROCESSING ENVIRONMENT

Tandem's response to improving system resource utilisation, whilst simultaneously simplifying program development, was the production of a transaction processing monitor called Pathway.

Pathway provides a ready written, replicable, non-stop, multi-threaded multi-terminal control program (TCP). Screen handling is managed by user-provided modules, written in a COBOL-like language, which are interpreted by the TCP. The TCP services a user defined number of terminals and despatches transactions to replicable single-thread, stop-pable, server processes, which perform the real application work and respond to the TCP. If a server process fails, the Tandem supplied TCP will arrange to reprocess the transaction from the last TCP issued checkpoint for that transaction.

By this means, all non-stop coding is avoided by most users, provided the Pathway design rules can be followed (e.g. context-free servers). This liberates on-line transaction processing users from the highly skilled task of designing non-stop processes, and the tedious task of restart-testing at each checkpoint.

TRANSACTION MONITORING FACILITY

Tandem's second product to assist developers of on-line transaction processing systems is TMF (Transaction Monitoring Facility) which addresses database consistency and recoverability. TMF may be used without Pathway, since it provides the basic mechanisms to handle concurrent transactions. TMF provides a concurrency control mechanism that prevents individual transactions from seeing the uncommitted data produced by other concurrent transactions.

The provision of two system calls signifying 'begin transaction' and 'end transaction' and a set of design rules regarding file and record locking and unlocking protocols, enables the user to construct secure transactions. The mechanism involved is a transparent log-before and log-after file update policy, producing mirrored audit trails on disk. Thus when a transaction fails to complete, perhaps because of a deadlock, it can be backed out and its (perhaps partial) effect undone by reference to the before-images on the audit trail.

Especially significant is that this will work in a networked distributed processing environment. Files must be declared to be audited individually, in which case TMF will maintain an audit trail for them.

Additionally, if a catastrophic system crash occurs, the after-images on the audit trail(s) can be used, following reconstitution of the disk(s) from the latest disk dump(s), to effect a roll-forward recovery. Alternatively, if the disks are intact, incomplete transactions may simply be backed out by means of roll-back recovery, using the before-images from the audit trails.

TMF provides a full set of facilities for managing on-line disk-to-tape dumps, and the regular dumping of audit trail files from disk to tape, together with a cataloguing system for dump media control. After a system crash, TMF plays a major part in managing the restart of the system, instructing operators which tapes to mount, if necessary, and controlling the recovery procedure.

It should be noted that TMF's features are in addition to the basic on-line 'revive' of a mirrored disk volume, whereby a failed disk volume can be replaced and copied on-line from its surviving sibling, albeit at a reduced level of fault tolerance.

The combination of Pathway and TMF provides a secure distributed transaction processing environment with (for many applications) no need for the user to write non-stop programs. Together they address many of the early difficulties encountered when implementing on-line transaction processing systems directly with non-stop process pairs.

The crucial lesson to be learnt here is that even a fault tolerant system will totally fail sometimes, and there has to be a way to recover afterwards. TMF typifies the measures needed to achieve this. Some other fault tolerant system suppliers appeared intially to believe erroneously that this sort of facility was unnecessary!

EXTENSIONS FOR NETWORKING

Users seeking to construct large reliable networks will find that Tandem has extended its fault tolerant concepts to networks of Non-Stop systems. A network may comprise up to 255 nodes, each node comprising a Non-Stop system with between two and sixteen processors. Networks may use a variety of different physical interconnection media, depending upon the distances involved and the channel capacity or bandwidth required. For large sites with multiple nodes, duplicated fibre optic links are available. For longer distances, conventional communications lines may be used. For even longer hauls, where regulations so permit and tariffs are advantageous, terrestrial communications satellite links can be used.

Irrespective of the physical communications media used, multiple paths are provided to each node, and a secure packet switching environment provided, supporting automatic best-path message routing and re-routing.

Once again it is the Guardian file system which unifies the network from the user process viewpoint. The file/process naming scheme is extended to accommodate processes anywhere in the network with the result that the entire network can be viewed as one large computing resource. Process pairs still have to exist with a node!

This extension of concepts for networking includes TMF, so a transaction may update files on multiple remote nodes with the same ease, transaction integrity and database integrity as if running on a single node. It is this clean extension of concepts which characterises Tandem's approach to networking.

STRENGTHS OF TANDEM'S APPROACH

Tandem's real strength derives from designing a fault tolerant system from scratch. The Non-Stop system is conservatively engineered, fully supported and demonstrably meets its design objectives by providing tolerance of any single point of hardware failure.

Using dynamic hardware redundancy forced Tandem to solve the interconnection problem between both processors and processes. Having done this, Tandem had also solved the graceful growth problem.

Database integrity requires more than just process integrity. TMF provides database integrity by quite distinct techniques, which are, nevertheless, implemented by mechanisms ultimately reliant upon non-stop process pairs.

The ability to construct a fault tolerant network with up to 255 nodes and 4080 processors is no mean feat in itself, and should in practice be adequate for many needs.

WEAKNESSES OF THE TANDEM APPROACH

The process pair technique only assures process survival if the processes themselves are fault free in their handling of recovery data, failure exceptions and process creation. This method of achieving fault tolerance is unattractive since it demands extra logic in the processes themselves. Furthermore, this extra logic cannot easily be added to existing non-fault-tolerant processes. Tandem's provision of Pathway illustrates the need to circumvent these difficulties, and liberate the on-line transaction processing user from intimate participation in the provision of fault tolerance to user processes.

Performing the design calculation necessary to establish a configuration of hardware and software which can be guaranteed to achieve the required throughput and response time in the presence of all single component failures, is not a task to be undertaken lightly, particularly for critical applications. To attempt this stage before a system has been thoroughly designed is inviting trouble.

If k processors are required to provide adequate processing and I/O capacity, then *n* processors (where $n = k + 1$) are required to provide this capacity in a fault tolerant environment. A system with *n* processors can exhibit $(n + 1)$ processor configurations, i.e. one configuration of *n* processors, plus *n* configurations of $(n - 1)$ processors. Thus there are $(n + 1)$ configurations for which viability and balance must be ensured. Balanced means that no resource is used beyond its planned level of utilisation. Folklore has it that for typical on-line transaction processing applications the critical resource to balance on Non-Stop systems is the processor loading attributable to the disk processes in each processor.

Determining how much hardware is needed, which processors peripheral controllers should be connected to, and how to distribute process pairs optimally across processors is a highly skilled task. Fortunately various techniques (some heuristic) now exist which give acceptable results for reasonably standard applications. Tandem have nevertheless had to expend considerable effort to augment these rules of thumb with numerical techniques. Given that the internal timings of Guardian, and any other environmental software products supplied by Tandem, can easily change with a new software release, any measurements of performance that are used as the basis of design calculations need to be kept up-to-date by Tandem and made available to users either directly or through the medium of calibrated models or other tools to support hardware sizing and configuring activities.

Graceful growth and fault tolerance are also commonly demanded attributes of very high availability systems whose acceptable non-availability is typically quoted in minutes per year. How does Tandem measure up to these more demanding requirements? Two further weaknesses emerge here. First, the unplanned-for addition of new hardware to a system currently requires a new operating system to be generated and the system to be reloaded. Second, consider the addition of new disk drives, with a view to moving files among drives to balance disk drive loading. Currently no facility exists to move files which are actively in use from one (mirrored) volume to another. Thus on-line system tuning and balancing is hampered.

These two weaknesses may appear insignificant in a commercial DP environment, where a system can usually be taken off-line by prior arrangement at pre-planned times. They are, however, potentially critical for a class of systems requiring on-line maintenance, enhancement and continuous availability.

Finally, preventative hardware maintenance may involve taking certain hardware modules off-line. Whilst they are off-line the system is running at a reduced level of fault tolerance.

SUMMARY OF MAJOR NON-STOP FEATURES

- Provides an environment tolerant to any single point of failure, and has been doing so since 1977

- Constructed from custom designed, loosely coupled 16/32-bit micro-programmed virtual-memory minicomputers
- Uses dual-ported device controllers, each attached to any two processors to provide redundant I/O paths
- Uses process pairs as both an internal (system) mechanism and as an application measure to achieve fault tolerance
- Provides specialised software to simplify significantly the development of on-line transaction processing software
- Employs selectively audited files with duplicated audit trails to provide database consistency and integrity
- Permits the construction of large, integrated, geographically distributed networks through incremental growth
- Invokes fault recovery within 2 s of a processor failure occurring
- Permits on-line repair of failed hardware modules without needing to shut down an entire system
- Supports remote engineering diagnosis of faults, and unattended operation of remote sites.

TANDEM AND THE COMPETITION

Since their first shipments in 1977 Tandem has surely made a major impact on the marketplace. Fault tolerance is now in demand, and so too are gracefully expansible systems. But where were the traditional vendors? Their lack of response was such that a flurry of new companies entered the market.

These late market entrants were able to reap the benefits of technological advances in microelectronics, such as 32-bit microprocessors, local area network support semiconductor chips, and high density memory circuits, which were unavailable to Tandem in 1974 when the first Non-Stop computer was designed.

With today's more dense circuits it is now feasible to provide static hardware redundancy, at a small fraction of the cost in 1974, when such an approach would have been unthinkable except for the most vital systems. These technological advances have permitted Tandem's competitors to exploit a variety of different hardware and software approaches to provide fault tolerant systems. Indeed, the number of different approaches makes meaningful classification and comparison a difficult task. However, some of the distinguishing characteristics include:

- The number of simultaneous failures sustainable without total system failure; claimed *vs.* actual
- Presence or absence of shared non-replicated resources (e.g. shared global memory)
- The mechanisms used to provide error detection, error recovery, fault isolation and damage confinement
- The degree of replication of on-line data

- Ability to recover from a total system crash without loss of data – even if the brochure says this will never happen!
- Use of electrically isolated local area networks *vs.* integrated busses as the system interconnection medium (i.e. interprocessor bus or its equivalent)
- Provision of redundant power supplies
- Provision for identification, removal, repair, reinsertion and testing of a failed hardware module without needing to power-down the entire system; this includes processors, non-redundant peripheral controllers, cooling systems and power supplies
- The number of redundant paths between critical components
- Static versus dynamic redundancy
- Static (manual) load balancing *vs.* dynamic (automatic) load balancing
- Time to detect an error
- Time to correct an error
- Need for a SYSGEN *vs.* automatic hardware configuration sensing
- Use of a custom processor *vs.* a widely used (industry standard) instruction set
- Use of a custom operating system *vs.* compatibility with a widely used (industry standard) operating system

MARKET OUTLOOK

There is no one ideal solution to fault tolerance. Inevitably it is a case of 'horses for courses'! The purely technical choice depends heavily on the minimum granularity of fault detection and recovery required by the application. So, prospective purchasers have to examine the different trade-offs within and between alternative systems. Where custom software is involved, careful assessment of any additional development costs attributable to fault tolerance should be made.

Of paramount importance is to be able to quantify fault tolerance requirements, and where the option exists to examine the cost repercussions of small perturbations to these requirements. This requires that a numerate approach to system requirements definition be adopted. System suppliers can, initially at least, only provide calculated mean time between failure (MTBF) figures for their systems. (Tandem has a real head-start here, being first into the market.) Mean time to repair (MTTR) should be available from all suppliers. If a proposed system must achieve some specified level of availability, then the software components of the system must also meet MTBF requirements, as well as the hardware. Again, it is reasonable to expect MTBF figures for any software components of the fault tolerant environment (suppliers, please note).

User implemented software fault tolerance can be considered as a separate technique to circumvent faults in application software, allowing the construction of application software to the desired level of reliability.

As yet, no special support has been provided for this by any major system supplier.

Increasing demand for fault tolerant systems potentially implies the need for greater skills in both system design and software implementation. Given the already onerous costs of system development, particularly software, we can expect suppliers to continue to conceal (or package) fault tolerance, providing users with simplified (i.e. familiar) execution models, thus alleviating the need for greater skills.

Similar considerations apply to the operability (system operator) and maintainability (hardware and software maintenance engineers) skills requirements; their tasks should not increase in complexity with the theoretical number of failure modes.

It would in some circumstances be very useful if fault tolerance were to be an 'independent' system attribute which could be selectively applied to an existing system, or critical component thereof, simply by plugging in additional redundant hardware or software to achieve the desired level of fault tolerance. But this is arguably too difficult for many users to handle. We can therefore expect to see the continuance of a stratified market. I will hazard one prediction though, which is that we shall witness the widespread availability of fault tolerant file servers for both stand-alone and networked personal computers in the very near future.

ACKNOWLEDGEMENTS
Tandem, Non-Stop, Guardian, Pathway and Dynabus are trademarks of Tandem Computers Incorporated.

CHAPTER 11

The MOMENTUM high resilience system

A. P. Smith
(Information Technology Ltd.)

The MOMENTUM architecture for resilient systems was developed by a British company, Information Technology Limited, and is marketed by them as the MOMENTUM 9000 range of business computers.

The MOMENTUM approach to resilience is unusual in that it was developed specifically to meet the growth of on-line commercial business applications. With that in mind, the design approach was pragmatic rather than academic and the result is a system that puts its main emphasis on the protection of the database and fast recovery from all sorts of failure situations, including total system failure and most imaginable software failures.

At the time of product launch, MOMENTUM was only the second generally available 'packaged' resilient computer: after Tandem and before STRATUS. It remains the only product that allows resilience to be added in stages as the user's dependence on the computer grows. Resilience, in effect, becomes another variable system parameter just like CPU power, store size, number of communications ports and so on.

This chapter gives an overview of the MOMENTUM concept, including a little of the marketing justification, and some of the technology. System architecture brochures are available from Information Technology Ltd., Winchester, England.

BASIC MARKETING JUSTIFICATION

The basic arguments used to justify entering the resilient systems market could be summarised as:

- Advances in computer technology over the last few years have brought many changes in the way business computers are used
- The growth of interactive computing means many more users have direct access to the computer, through the VDUs on their desks
- Greater use of communications services means users are spread over greater geographical areas
- Greatly improved, sophisticated software tools allow users to venture further into true on-line processing and updating
- Greater cost effectiveness and reliability – in both hardware and

software – allow organisations to computerise more and more aspects of their business.

All these changes have brought great benefits to the user, resulting from instant access to accurate information kept constantly ·up-to-date, with details of events captured as they occur.

With all these advantages, however, come some drawbacks. Corruption or inconsistencies in stored information may cause havoc. A computer breakdown may, at best, inconvenience many people at the same time. At worst, it may cause an organisation effectively to stop operating until service is resumed. It is considerations like these that lead people to look to systems which offer a very high degree of fault tolerance.

In the past, the options available to those needing such systems were very limited. For applications demanding continuous operation there was, in fact, only one expensive solution: the provision of very specialised configurations specially engineered for the particular job at hand. For the less demanding the solution was a standby system, standing idle most of the time. Either way, the solution was expensive, and involved a commitment to multiple systems and specialised design concepts from the start.

The basic aim of MOMENTUM was to create a non-stop system which did not require this specialised type of approach.

BASIC DESIGN CONCEPTS

The design aims behind MOMENTUM were:

- Resilient, non-stop systems were to be built from standard product hardware and software modules
- Business applications were to be programmed completely in COBOL, using normal application programming skills
- MOMENTUM could be added in stages if desired – from a small business system with a handful of VDUs right up to a large, non-stop configuration supporting over 100 simultaneous VDU users and multiple communications lines.

MOMENTUM FEATURES

MOMENTUM is a family of hardware and software options that may be combined into tailored, resilient systems. Each extends the resilience of the system against either hardware or software malfunction. In particular, disruption and inconvenience experienced by the VDU user is reduced to a minimum.

FAST RECOVERY AND DATABASE INTEGRITY

The ITL DMS Data Management System carries prime responsibility for database integrity. It includes, as standard, powerful facilities for checkpointing the progress of applications level software. Following a program failure, the database is quickly and automatically returned to a consistent state. If there is a computer malfunction, recovery to a consistent state is performed automatically when the system is re-started.

This is the lowest level of resilience, applying to all MOMENTUM systems, including single-processor configurations which are not otherwise resilient to processor failure, of course.

DUAL SYSTEMS

MOMENTUM dual systems extend the DMS Data Management System, allowing a database to be shared between two separate but closely coupled computer systems. Each has full on-line update access, communicating with, and checking, its partner through the MOMENTUM link (see Fig. 11.1)

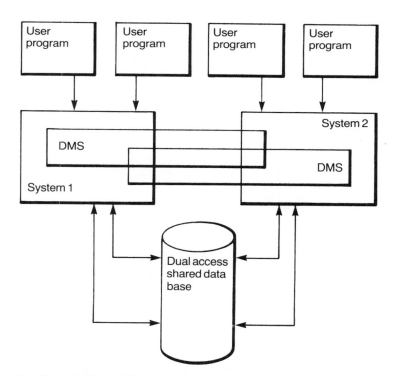

Fig. 11.1 Dual MOMENTUM systems run two separate copies of system software, operating asynchronously.

TRANSACTION PROCESSING

MOMENTUM may be used in conjunction with ITL's transaction processing software, TMS, to give transaction processing with fast recovery on single-processor configurations or continuous operation on dual systems, resilient against either hardware or software failure.

On single-processor systems, fast recovery after a total but transient system failure, such as power down/power up, takes around 90 s. On dual systems there is also protection against permanent failure of one half-system.

With no redundant hardware, each twin processor independently handles VDUs, processes transactions and updates the shared database (see Fig. 11.2). If one processor system fails, the other takes over the full workload of the failed system. Any update sequences in progress at the time of failure are completed. All transactions entered but not yet processed are transferred. As confirmation, VDU users switched from the failed system are informed of their progress, with a positive identification of the last transaction entered. They can then continue, knowing exactly where they were and which transactions have been successfully entered (see Fig. 11.3).

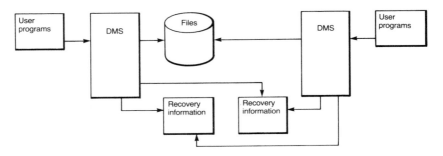

Fig. 11.2 Each half-system maintains database recovery information for both sides.

RECOVERY INFORMATION
MOMENTUM systems also have an optional memory board which provides 64 Kbyte of store, with on-board battery back-up. If present, it is used to hold recovery information without imposing extra disk overheads on performance. If not present, the same fast recovery mechanisms apply, but with recovery information held on disk.

MIRROR DISKS
The optional mirror disk facility allows the computer to continue working, unaffected even by catastrophic disk drive failure. Database updates are automatically applied in parallel to two mirror images of the data maintained on physically separate disk drives. Data is read from either disk drive. Following a disk failure, all transfers apply to the remaining disk drive. When the second disk is returned to service, DMS automatically brings it back into use, progressively updating its contents as a background activity. Any disk drive can be 'mirrored' – including the drive used by the operating system for virtual store transfers.

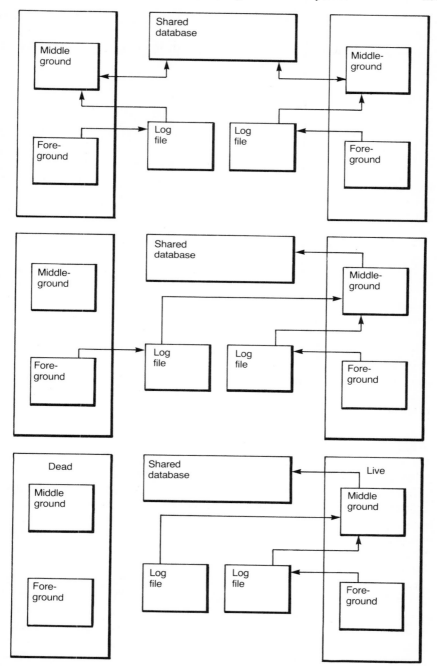

Fig. 11.3 Data flow and recovery through the TMS Transaction Processing Software.

OPERATION OF MOMENTUM

MOMENTUM systems are based on the DMS data management system and the multi-processor systems architecture of ITL'S MOMENTUM 9000 computers.

DATABASE MANAGEMENT

DMS is responsible for database integrity, provides facilities for multi-stream updating, resolves contention, and takes recovery action in the event of user-program failure.

Data can be protected against contention by locking – both at file and record level. Programs accessing locked records are queued until the lock is released. DMS checks for, and resolves, any 'deadly embrace' situations. If a program fails while it is holding locked records, DMS automatically releases the locks as part of its fast recovery mechanism.

Database operations frequently involve many separate but related updates. For consistency, these updates must be applied as a complete set. The fast recovery option ensures automatic recovery to a consistent state, even when a hardware or software failure occurs in the midst of an update process. Following a checkpoint call, DMS maintains before-look copies of all records subsequently updated.

By monitoring the progress of updating programs, DMS can take control in case of program failure. It returns affected records to their state at the previous checkpoint, and releases any record locks held by the failed program. In case of hardware failure, as in a power cut, recovery information is safely protected. Recovery is effected when the system is restarted.

DUAL SYSTEM OPERATION

Another feature available as part of MOMENTUM is the MOMENTUM link which allows processing to continue after total failure of a processor, with uninterrupted access to the up-to-the-minute database. This link enables two otherwise independent computer systems to act together as an integrated dual system (see Fig. 11.5). Each has its own instruction processor, store, disk controllers and input/output processors. The disk drives are dual-ported units connected directly to disk controllers on both systems.

Each system runs under control of its own operating system, and each runs its own copy of DMS. However, it is the MOMENTUM link, physically resident in both systems, that controls and coordinates all access to the shared database. Using the link, DMS extends its responsibilities for database integrity. Both systems are allowed full update access and record-locking capability. DMS meanwhile guards against data contention and deadly embraces. Details of updates, changes to the database structure and current lock information are constantly exchanged, so that both systems hold up-to-date information on the current state of the database. The link

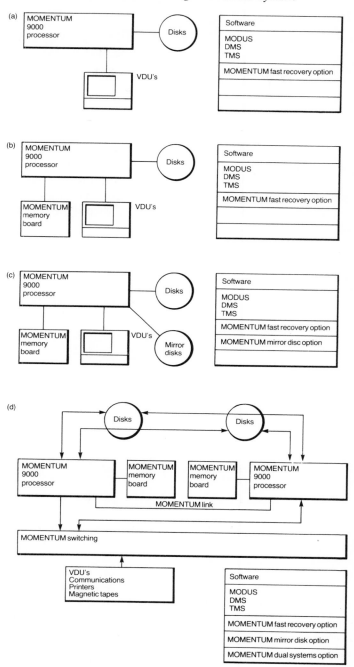

Fig. 11.4 Stages in adding resilience to an on-line system.

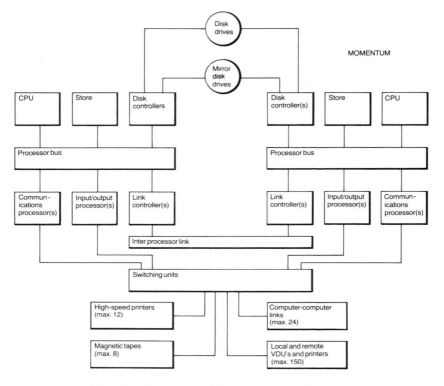

Fig. 11.5 Schematic of dual system configuration.

also has a system monitoring function, testing and reporting on both systems.

Following total failure of one system, DMS in the remaining system can take fast-recovery action. The database is returned to the consistent state of the previous checkpoint, and any record locks held by the failed system are released.

In normal use, the MOMENTUM link can provide performance benefits as well. Because traffic across the link is usually low volume, each system achieves high utilisation.

TP operations are managed by MOMENTUM using ITL's TMS software. TMS internal structure separates foreground VDU handling from middleground file updating. Between the two stages is the transaction log file, held on disk and containing completed transactions awaiting middleground processing.

Normally, transactions are fully processed by the system controlling the VDUs from which the transactions originated. In alternative mode, one system may be directed to process, in TMS middleground, transactions arising from the TMS foreground of both systems. In either mode, if one system suffers from total failure, TMS operating in the remaining system takes over the processing transactions in both log files. This includes completing any middleground processing in progress at time of failure. VDUs connected to the failed system may be switched to the remaining TMS system.

PERIPHERAL SWITCHING

The MOMENTUM range of peripheral switch units allows dynamic reconfiguring of terminals, peripherals and communication lines. The master switch controller houses power supplies and control electronics, plus up to sixteen individual switch units. Each unit switches devices either individually or in blocks between the twin controllers in a MOMENTUM dual configuration. Switches can be pre-set to particular distribution patterns with override capability to either system. The switches themselves are high reliability relay units able to maintain connections and switch settings during power breaks.

GROWTH PATHS

MOMENTUM is designed for easy upgrade. Resilience features can be added in stages, giving the ability to grow from a single-processor system up to the largest dual-processor configuration. Features of the growth path include the following:

- The MOMENTUM fast recovery system, available on both single and dual processor models
- The MOMENTUM memory board, available on both single- and dual-processor models, bringing important performance benefits to the fast recovery option
- The MOMENTUM mirror disk option, available on both single- and dual-processor models, allowing protection against disk failure even for small systems
- Any single processor configuration with 80 Mbyte or 300 Mbyte disk drives can be upgraded to a dual-processor configuration with the MOMENTUM link and appropriate MOMENTUM peripheral switches; the upgrade is effected on-site and all existing hardware and software is retained.

SYSTEM ARCHITECTURE

The MOMENTUM 9000 system is based on a multiple microprocessor architecture with I/O processing completely separated from the CPU or instruction processor. At the heart of the system is a 32-bit, 64 Mbit/s bidirectional data bus. Connected to it are the main store and a number of communicating microprocessor based units – each with its own intelligence and each dedicated to a particular function.

The conventional CPU becomes an instruction processor. Separate, powerful microprocessors are used for such functions as disk control, magnetic tape control, diagnostics processor and I/O control. Depending on the characteristics of the controlled devices, different types of microprocessors are used.

The instruction processor itself is based on multiple bit-slice processors with a 56-bit wide microinstruction and microprocessor cycle time of 180 ns. This processing engine is microcoded to provide the MOMENTUM 9000 instruction set used by all MODUS family software.

Main store attached to the system bus is arranged and accessed as 32 bits data plus 7 bits parity, giving error detection to the bit level. This store is packaged as 512 Kbyte per board, with a maximum of 2 Mbyte per instruction processor.

The overall configuration is highly suited to interactive applications, with intelligence distributed throughout the system. Multiple microprocessors, each with its own store, cooperate to provide the overall performance of the system, while making adjustment of computing power to the application relatively simple.

One of these microprocessors is a single-board, self-contained diagnostic processor with 16 Kbyte of store and interface to floppy diskette drive. It has switched access to the executive console, and full DMA access to all other system components. Under fault conditions, it can load and run test programs, and progressively test the rest of the system. In normal use it serves as a floppy disk controller.

32-BIT EXTENDED-ARCHITECTURE (XA) OPTION

Early ITL computers were totally 16-bit minicomputers. Later models incorporated a 32-bit data bus for improved performance, but retained the 16-bit instruction set. MOMENTUM 9000 provides both 16-bit and 32-bit instructions. The instruction set used on earlier models has been retained for full software portability, and to it has been added an XA option designed to further improve performance in on-line transaction processing.

Extensions provided by the XA option comprise (a) a 32-bit arithmetic instruction set, (b) single- and double-length hardware floating point, (c) 8-, 16- and 32-bit block-move and block-fill instructions and (d) extended physical address range to 2 Mbyte. In addition, microcode assistance is provided to the executive software. Matching XA options in systems software and high level language compilers provide considerable performance gains.

UNIQUE I/O CONCEPT

Central to the power of the overall system architecture is the I/O architecture. Here too, ITL uses multiple microprocessors to provide the facilities needed for high performance, on-line transaction processing. I/O processing is implemented at two levels. Each Block Level Processor (BLP) manages data transport between the host processor store and up to

16 Character Level Processors (CLPs), each programmed to handle a particular set of peripherals or communication lines. In effect, the BLP 'front ends' the host computer, and the CLP cluster performs a similar role for the BLP.

Each BLP is a complete microcomputer on a board, with a 68B09 microprocessor, 16 Kbyte of store and its own multi-tasking executive. High speed DMA is used to access both the main system store and that in the CLPs. Each CLP is a similar single-board microcomputer, with its 68B09 microprocessor, 64 Kbyte of store and multi-tasking executive. It has enough power to handle not only the low level aspects of I/O, but more high level tasks as well. Thus, for a communications link to a mainframe, it handles all aspects of the protocol, passing only clean, processed data into the system.

In addition to interfacing standard peripherals and protocols, the CLP also provides an ideal mechanism for safely connecting special or new interfaces.

The maximum configuration is four BLPs per CPU, each with a maximum throughput of 20 000 fully processed characters per second, giving the system a maximum of 80 000 fully processed characters per second from connected communication lines, VDUs and printers. Up to 64 CLPs can be connected to each CPU, giving a theoretical maximum of 4 Mbyte of I/O store per CPU. In practice, configurations have typically from 20 to 200 character mode VDUs, plus anything up to a dozen or more different communications protocols running concurrently on many communications lines.

CHAPTER 12

The STRATUS computer system

D. Wilson
(*British Olivetti*)

The STRATUS S/32 Continuous Processing System is designed and manufactured by Stratus Computer Inc. of USA, founded in February, 1980.

It is aimed at on-line applications where reliability and availability are important. Olivetti are a stockholder in STRATUS and have a marketing and distribution agreement covering Western Europe, South Africa and South America. Olivetti market the equipment as the CPS 32 Continuous Processing System.

The S/32 is an interactive transaction oriented business processing system. Continuous processing is defined as uninterrupted operation without loss of data, performance degradation, and without special application programming. The S/32 system provides true continuous processing with a uniquely simple approach that eliminates the complexity associated with most other high reliability systems. These systems use software to detect failures and to back up and recover from failure, and generally involve application programmers with complex checkpointing and restart programs. The S/32 solution is a hardware approach which detects a failure or transient error at the point of failure, so that data is always protected from corruption and user checkpointing and restart programming are eliminated. The first delivery of an S/32 system was made in February, 1982, since when over 300 systems have been ordered or delivered worldwide.

The S/32 has a modular architecture. The basic system unit is the processing module, made up of the following elements:

- CPU with user and system processors
- Memory of up to 8 Mbyte
- Controllers
- Peripherals
- Power supplies.

Processing modules can be easily connected together to form a multi-module system using a high speed data link over coaxial cable. The S/32 operating system, VOS (Virtual Operating System), is designed to support on-line transactions with a distributed file system; it provides tools for the interactive development of application software competing with other processes, and it supports S/32 system networks.

Since the original FT200 model, STRATUS have announced the extended architecture (XA400 and XA600) systems. The XA600 system is claimed to be the most powerful on-line fault tolerant system available.

THE BASIC SYSTEM

The S/32 system is an interactive system oriented to transaction processing (see Fig. 12.1). It is available in various configurations ranging from 4 to 512 Mbyte of main memory and from 60 to 688100 Mbyte of disk storage. Tape drives, letter quality printers and 300, 600 and 900 lpm line printers can be attached. The system can connect up to 2048 communication lines with directly attached or remote terminals. The basic unit of computational processing in the S/32 is the processing module (PM). Figure 12.2 is an example of a processing module.

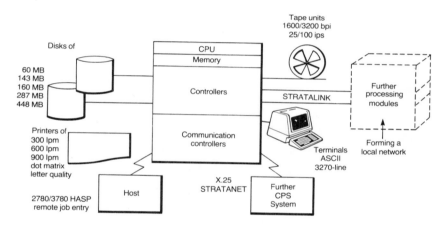

Fig. 12.1 A CPS/32 system.

Up to 32 processing modules can be included in an S/32 system (see Fig. 12.3), but because of the S/32's unique architecture, the user sees a single system no matter how many processing modules are present. The user can access files, devices and programs regardless of which module they are attached to. A user connected to one module can:

- run a program in another module
- access files in a third module
- and print the results on a printer connected to a fourth module

as easily as if all the operations were performed in one module.

The processing modules are connected by a high speed data path called the StrataLINK, forming a multiprocessor system. Processing modules can be located from several feet to several miles apart with the use of link repeaters. Expansion of a system's resources to include an additional

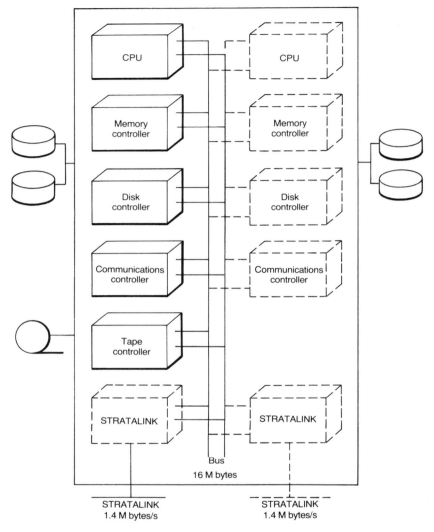

Fig. 12.2 Processing module, duplex version. All models.

module, more disk storage or additional memory requires no reprogramming or system regeneration, with no impact on users.

CONFIGURATION OF A LOCAL NETWORK
By using several processing modules, S/32 can be seen as a distributed system which effectively creates a local network comprising the individual processing modules. The system user can benefit from the possibility of distributed processing, which is typical of a local network, without needing specific software or specific network operating procedures.

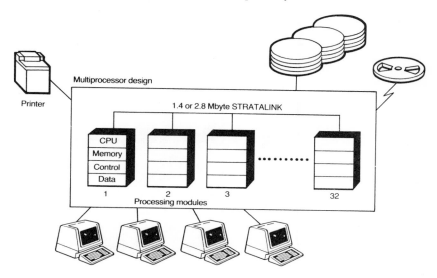

Fig. 12.3 CPS/32 system expandability.

CONFIGURATION OF A GEOGRAPHICAL NETWORK

S/32 systems can be connected together in a network using the StrataNET software package, which uses the X.25 communications protocol in handling messages between S/32 systems. A network presents a single view to the user. He can execute a program or access a file as easily on a remote S/32 system as on a local S/32 system. Figure 12.4 illustrates a simple network in which the operator logs into a system in Milan through a system in Paris, runs a program on it and prints the output on the Munich system.

GENERAL CONCEPTS

This section presents a description of the system characteristics in terms of:

- Reliability
- Serviceability
- Expandability.

RELIABILITY

The S/32 system adopts a hardware solution for guaranteeing reliability: a malfunction or a transitory error is signalled as soon as it occurs and does not affect the applications or data (continuous checking). The malfunctioning board is indicated so that it can be replaced. Processing continues on the partner board; this means that the system's features are not degraded in any way and error recovery routines which are costly in terms of space and effort are not required in the applications.

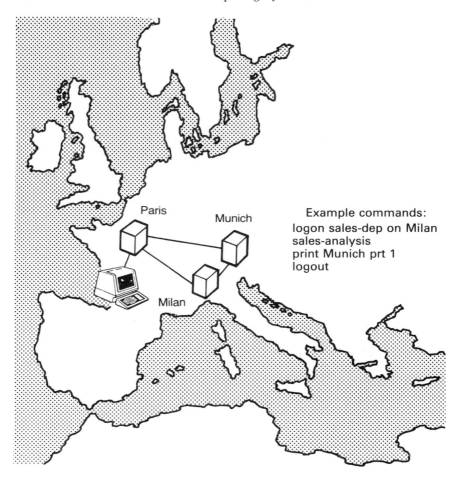

Example commands:
logon sales-dep on Milan
sales-analysis
print Munich prt 1
logout

Fig. 12.4 Example of a geographical network.

Continuous checking

All hardware operations are continuously checked on each board. This is accomplished by a number of different techniques. In most cases, a second set of identical circuitry is contained on the board. Both sets of circuitry perform every operation and the results are compared by hardware.

As shown in Fig. 12.2, a duplicate board performs the same operations as its partner. If the sets of logic circuitry on either board do not produce identical results, the failed board immediately shuts itself off while operation of the system continues uninterrupted with the partner board. Other major components, such as disk drives and power supplies, are also duplicated and operate in parallel with a partner.

This approach of continuous checking for both operational and data errors makes it possible to detect malfunctions as they occur. Operational integrity and data integrity are maintained. Figure 12.5 illustrates in a simple way how the checking process is performed in the disk controller, so that bad data is never sent on the bus or to the drive. Just before the data is sent the compare logic checks the results. If the comparison fails the data is not transferred, and the controller disconnects itself from the bus. The red light on the board is turned on and a maintenance interrupt is sent to the CPU.

The maintenance software receives all hardware maintenance interrupts and it determines the cause and nature of a malfunction. Transient errors result in the board being restarted. Permanent errors result in the board or device remaining out of service, an indication of the failure being sent to a selected terminal. All errors are logged in a system file for later analysis by

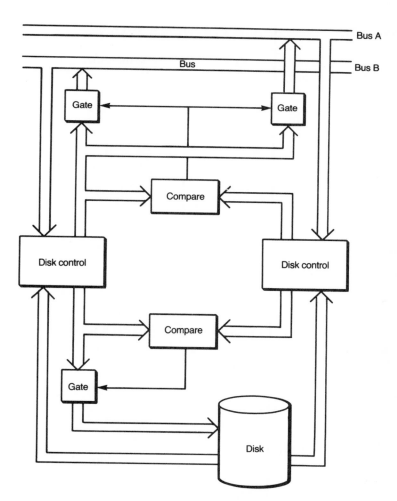

Fig. 12.5 Self-checking disk controller.

service personnel. This software runs concurrently with user applications and does not degrade system performance.

Continuous processing
The S/32 solution for continuous processing is based on two techniques:

- Continuous checking which is carried out on all versions of the system
- Duplexed components.

Component duplication means that every system board, or disk, can be duplicated (see Fig. 12.2), and that the same operations are carried out in parallel on the two elements of each pair. Each board is totally independent of its partner and contains its own checking logic and diagnostics. If a board's logic detects a malfunction or failure, the failed board is taken out of service before erroneous processing occurs or data is corrupted; processing continues with the duplexed partner.

In summary, the S/32 solution to continuous processing is a combination of hardware and software. Hardware detects malfunctions when they occur. Duplex hardware continues the processing with no human or program intervention. The maintenance software analyses errors and determines the type of failure.

SERVICEABILITY
Low cost serviceability is an integral part of the S/32 strategy. The goal is to minimise service costs, and the approach incorporates several considerations. They are:

- Power-up diagnostics
- Self-checking
- Board replacement
- Remote maintenance.

Power-up diagnostics
As a board is powered up, it executes an extensive set of diagnostic routines, and device controllers execute an additional test of each device. If diagnostics are not successfully completed, the red light on the cabinet's front panel, and the red light on the failed board are lit.

Self-checking hardware and error recovery
In the event of a failure the following events occur:

- A red light is lit on the failed board
- The operating system (VOS) is interrupted
- Maintenance software determines the type of failure
- Transient failures result in the board being restarted
- Permanent failures turn on a red light on the cabinet front panel, and send a message to a selected terminal.

In addition processing continues without interruption on the duplexed board. All these actions are performed without any application programming or operator intervention.

Board replacement

The CPS approach to in-line servicing means that the substitution of the failed board is easy. The benefits to a user are timely repair and low maintenance costs.

In addition, all duplexed boards and associated peripherals can be removed and replaced while the system continues to operate. When a duplexed component is replaced, it is brought to the same state as its partner by the operating system in conjunction with the hardware.

Remote maintenance

Every S/32 system has the capability for remote maintenance, in addition to the normal local maintenance operations. A 1200 baud modem is a part of the system and allows the off-site engineer, through use of the maintenance software, to determine the nature of a software or hardware failure, provide fixes and identify hardware corrective action.

MODULAR EXPANDABILITY

The S/32 system can be configured to the user's requirements. The minimum system configuration consists of a single processing module containing the following elements:

- CPU with 4 Mbyte of memory
- One disk
- Magnetic tape
- Two asynchronous communication lines
- One CRT terminal
- A line for remote diagnostics
- A calendar/clock.

The maximum capacity for each processing module is:

- 32 Mbyte of semiconductor memory (with battery back-up in case of power supply failure)
- 32 disk drives, each with a capacity of 60, 143, 287 or 484 Mbyte
- 128 asynchronous communication lines, or 64 synchronous communication lines
- 2 magnetic tape drives
- line and letter-quality printers.

First level expansion

Up to 32 processing modules can be connected to form a system using a StrataLINK. While the system is operating, processing modules and duplexed disks can be added without disruption. After powering up the module or disk, the user updates the configuration file with the names of new devices. No recompiling and no changes to the operating system are necessary.

Second level expansion

A second dimension of S/32 expansion is obtained by connecting S/32 systems together in a network, the number of nodes in a network being virtually unlimited. Networking próvides a logical expansion of resources while maintaining the single-user view of the system. The user can execute programs and access data anywhere in the network, as if the operations were being done locally.

The StrataNET software package allows for the switching of message traffic through private lines or public packet-switched networks using the standard X.25 protocol. StrataNET handles best path routing, re-routing of messages and node/line failures.

HARDWARE CHARACTERISTICS

This section describes the characteristics and capacities of a processing module.

BASIC HARDWARE COMPONENTS

A processing module contains several types of components, which can be configured in various ways.

The basic components are circuitboards, a 20-slot or 40-slot chassis, for circuitboards, power supplies, I/O devices, cabinets and cables. The disk drives, a tape drive, power supplies and chassis with circuitboards that make up a processing module may all be contained in one cabinet. If a processing module has more peripheral devices than fit in one cabinet, these components may be housed in adjacent cabinets.

The types of circuitboards are:

- Processor board
- Memory controller board
- Memory board
- Disk controller
- Communications controller board
- Magnetic tape controller board
- Programmable StrataBUS interface

In addition, communications line adapter boards plug in to one or more communications panels connected to the communications controller board.

THE PROCESSOR

Processor board

The FT200 processor board has two independent central processor units. The user processor and the executive processor handle interrupt signals from I/O devices, the clock and other components. For example, it is the executive processor that accesses the disk when a missing page fault occurs. The XA400 and XA600 models utilise the Motorola 68010 processor.

The XA400 is the first member of the family of new CPS 32 processors. This board fits into the same 20-slot chassis as the FT200 and has complete compatibility with FT200 software, controllers and peripherals. Four 68010s are used as non-specialised processors, each concurrently working on applications programs or operating system tasks.

A program can be independently scheduled on any of the four processors. Interrupts are reduced between processors using advanced gate array semi-custom logic chips, providing speed, power and space savings. The 68010 has advanced features including private instruction cache and on-chip virtual memory logic which enhance performance. Depending on the application, the XA400 will deliver between two and three times the processing power of the FT200, and has the same fully duplexed fault tolerant characteristics.

The XA600 currently occupies the top of the CPS 32 range. This CPU is engineered in a new 40-slot chassis and has increased memory capacity, to a total of 16 Mbyte duplexed. The XA600 uses six logical Motorola 68101s in a similar arrangement to the XA400. Each processor is unspecialised, and a program can run on any of the six. Interrupts are assigned to free processors using high speed gate array logic.

The XA600 also offers two extra features – each processor has 16 Kbyte of high speed cache memory assigned to it. This allows it to hold two pages of memory locally, giving fast access and minimising memory contention for pages of main memory. The XA600 board also extends the power of the Motorola 68010 instruction set by using microcoded arithmetic processors, providing floating point, BCD and trigonometric functions. Depending on the application mix, the XA600 will provide between three and five times the power of the basic FT200.

Data formats

The S/32 processor operates on:

- Bit data
- Byte data (8 bits)
- Double byte data (16 bits)
- Quadruple byte data (32 bits).

The stack

The processor has stack instructions for efficient procedure calls and context switches.

Registers
There are sixteen 32-bit processor registers, eight for data and eight for addresses.

Addressing
The processor can directly address 16 Mbyte of memory.

Instruction set
There is a form of each basic machine instruction type for each of the four machine data types and each of the addressing modes.

Main memory
A memory controller and the memory boards it controls are packaged as an integrated unit. A memory board contains 2 Mbyte of semiconductor memory fabricated from 64 Kbyte RAM chips. The memory cycle time is 375 ns. A memory controller can control either one or two memory boards, and a processing module can access one to four memory controllers. Therefore, the amount of main memory that a processing module can contain ranges from 2 Mbyte to 6 Mbyte.

The battery back-up circuit in a processing module guarantees to retain the memory and the state of the processor for a maximum of eight minutes after a power failure. If power is restored in that period, processing can continue without any loss of data.

Disks
The S/32 disks provide large capacity data storage for the S/32. Five different sizes of drives are offered. These use Winchester technology (60, 142, 150 and 484 Mbyte models). The fifth is a 287 Mbyte removable disk pack drive. All disks are formatted with fixed-length sectors of 2048 bytes.

Disks connect to a microprocessor-driven disk controller. A fixed disk controller can manage up to four disk drives of 60, 142 or 150 Mbyte or eight 484 Mbyte; a removable disk controller can support up to four of the 287 Mbyte drives. A total of six disk controllers of both types can be connected to a processing module. The fixed disks are rack-mounted in cabinets, with one or two disks in a processing module cabinet and up to six disks in each expansion cabinet. The removable disks are housed in single free standing cabinets connected to the controller by a 30 ft radial cable, with shorter cables 'daisy chaining' successive drives together.

Magnetic tape
A magnetic tape controller is required for each magnetic tape drive. A processing module can have three tape drives. Tape drives supported include 1600/3200 bpi streaming drives and 6250 bpi group code recorded (GCR) drives.

Communications

The communications controller, using microprogrammed technology, provides a high speed, intelligent interface for the communications environment. All terminal I/O is managed by the controller, which queues characters for transmission and writes received characters to main memory. CPU processing is interrupted only when a message completes, or a designated control character is received, or a line error condition is encountered. In addition, line protocols are handled by the controller.

A communications panel, connected to a communications controller, holds up to eight communications line adapter boards. Two communications panels can be connected to each communications controller. Each line adapter can handle one synchronous or two asynchronous communications lines.

A processing module can have up to 128 asynchronous communications lines, controlled by four communications controllers.

Asynchronous line adaptors are available in three versions:

(1) A full modem line card.
(2) A direct connection line card.
(3) A line card with a battery powered calendar/clock and single modem line.

This last adapter provides the time of day and the date for system initialisation, and a connection for remote support by maintenance personnel.

Synchronous communications are provided by two line adapters. The standard synchronous line adapter supports one synchronous line at up to 4800 bps. The SmartSynch line adapter supports one synchronous line at speeds of up to 56 000 bps.

StrataLINK

Every processing module of a multi-module S/32 system must contain a StrataLINK controller board. The data transfer rate of a StrataLINK is 1.4 Mbyte per second. A system can have two StrataLINKs, which doubles the data rate between modules.

Programmable StrataBUS Interface

The Programmable StrataBUS Interface (PSI) is a high speed interface between the S/32 and up to four custom peripheral devices. The PSI is a full sized printed circuitboard that plugs into the S/32 chassis. It contains the circuitry, storage and control logic that a user needs as an interface to both custom peripheral devices and the StrataBUS. Dual circuitry and comparison logic on the board prevent the PSI from putting incorrect data on the StrataBUS or the PSI bus. Data transfer on the PSI can occur at a rate up to 4 Mbyte/s. The PSI's Motorola 68000 processor and its 256 Kbyte of RAM facilitate custom software, which users can develop in COBOL, BASIC, PL/I, Pascal, FORTRAN or assembly language. User custom circuitry is contained on a user-supplied board external to the PSI.

THE SOFTWARE

The S/32 Virtual Operating System (VOS) provides a convenient environment for on-line interactive and batch processing. This section provides an overview of the VOS software.

PROCESS SCHEDULING

VOS decides which process to run on the basis of the process's priority. The amount of time a process has to run is influenced by how interactive the process is. In any extended interval of time, an interactive process gets many short CPU time slices, while a batch process gets a few long periods. A high priority process gives up the CPU to a lower priority process only when it is waiting for an I/O operation to finish; a ready process with a high priority prompts a low priority process.

The system administrator has a great deal of flexibility in setting the scheduling parameters.

THE USER INTERFACE

Command language

The VOS command language is the means by which a user interacts with VOS. Both interactive and batch users issue the same commands; the system administrator has certain additional commands available to administer the system. Normally there is no particular operator's console in a system; a user with the appropriate password may access any command from any terminal in the system.

VOS accepts every command in two forms:

(1) The lineal form, which is a line of text that begins with the name of the command and is followed by the command arguments. This form can be issued at any type of terminal.

(2) The CRT form, which the user invokes by typing the name of the command and pressing the 'display form' key. VOS displays a form on the screen, with default values in those fields that have them, and the user edits the form. The CRT form can only be issued from a CRT terminal.

Users can write their own commands and command macros to have a CRT form. VOS provides convenient software form-writing menu format commands and other CRT interfaces.

The screen editor accepts many powerful editing requests, which the user issues by pressing designated function keys on the terminal. Users can issue these same requests to edit both terminal input lines and CRT command forms. Furthermore, applications can be written to use these requests. These requests provide users with a consistent way of entering data in all environments.

Command abbreviations

Each user can create an interactive environment that meets his or her particular requirements. For example, the user can define a set of abbreviations for often used names and command arguments. The VOS abbreviations facility lets a user abbreviate any of the names and other words that can occur in commands. The user can include parameters in the definition of an abbreviation which VOS replaces with arguments when it processes the abbreviation.

Command macros

A user can collect any sequence of VOS commands and calls to application programs into a file, called a *command macro*, and issue the entire sequence by typing the name of the file. VOS has extended the flexibility and generality of the command macro by allowing a user to supply arguments when calling a macro.

The command processor reads the commands in a macro in sequence. It replaces all abbreviations in each command. Because VOS reads the commands in a macro from a file rather than one at a time from the user's terminal, the user has additional control over the sequence in which VOS can skip some commands in a macro if a file does not exist, or loop through a series of commands while files remain to be processed.

A macro known as a *start-up command macro* is a powerful VOS feature for setting up a user's environment. When a user logs in, VOS looks for a specifically named command macro associated with the user, and it executes the macro before giving control to the user. A start-up macro can, for example, set the characteristics of the user's terminal, change the current directory, display any memos for the user and run a specified program. The ability to run a program before the user has control allows a system administrator to restrict the user to a controlled interactive environment.

THE I/O SYSTEM

The I/O system manages all the input, storage and output of users' data. Its flexible methods of organising files in storage makes for easy and efficient access from any processing module in any system in the network. The techniques for input and output are efficient for the types of jobs most common in interactive commercial data processing. The variety and extent of the file and record locking modes allow applications programmers to achieve high performance in shared file applications.

Directory hierarchy

Files stored on the disks of a system are catalogued in a hierarchy of directories. A file catalogued in a directory is said to be contained in the directory, because from a user's point of view, reference to the file involves, directly, referring to the directory in which the file is catalogued. However, the actual locations on the disk of the directory and the file are not necessarily related.

A directory can also contain entries for other directories, which are called *subdirectories* because they are thought of as being subordinate to the containing directory. The subordinate relation defines the hierarchy of directories. The top directory on a disk – VOS allows only one – is called the *pack master directory* of the disk.

Referring to files and directories

One attribute of every file and directory is its name, supplied and modifiable by users. A user refers to a file or directory by this name in a program or when issuing VOS commands.

A file can be catalogued in only one directory, and a directory can be subordinate to only one directory. Within a directory, all the files and all the subdirectories must have different names from each other. However, many different files can have the same name as long as they are all contained in different directories. Thus, users can create and name files without worrying about name conflicts that might lead to ambiguity, as long as they maintain different names for the contents of any one directory.

There are convenient ways to shorten the path names of files that a user refers to continually.

Each I/O device also has a path name, which is composed of the system name and the name of the device. The device path name allows users and programs to refer explicitly to devices in the same way they refer to files. Device names must be unique within a system and must be different from all the pack master directory names (since they look like pack master directory path names). This naming convention allows unambiguous access to I/O devices anywhere in the network from any other location.

To achieve additional flexibility in referring to files and devices, VOS provides a way to associate real files and devices with named objects, called I/O ports, that act like virtual I/O devices. Associating a port with a file or device is called attaching the port to the file or device. After attaching a port, a user can access the attachment using the name of the port. All the VOS programming languages assume that file names in programs refer to ports with the same name. Thus a user attaches a port named in a program to any file just before executing the program; which file is processed need not be determined until then. Ports let programmers write their programs without specifying particular files or I/O devices to be processed.

File organisations and access modes

The file is the basic unit of storage in the system. A file consists of records, and records can be thought of as arrays of bytes. VOS imposes a logical limit on the size of every record of 32767 bytes. (The physical limit on the size of a file depends on the configuration of the hardware in a system.)

A file can have one of three organisations: sequential, relative, or fixed. The sequential and relative organisations support variable length records; records in a fixed file all have the same length.

Any VOS file can be indexed. A file can have any number of indexes, and, for COBOL, one of the file's indexes can be designated as its primary index.

VOS manages two kinds of indexes: *embedded-key indexes* and *separate-key indexes*. In an embedded-key index, keys are created by combining up to 64 fields of the records in the file. A separate-key index consists of keys defined independently of the values of the file records.

There are three file access modes: sequential, random and indexed. VOS allows any combination of file organisation and file access mode except random access to a sequential file.

VOS maintains and manages a large number of frames of main memory (a frame is 4096 bytes) as I/O buffers to be able to read and write data quickly between main memory and the disks. The buffer frames constitute a fast disk cache. Because of these buffer frames, a process accessing a file sequentially usually does not have to wait for disk I/O operations. When VOS reads a disk file block into a buffer in sequential access mode, it anticipates the user's need for the next file block. When the user needs to access another file block, in most cases VOS has already read it from the disk to a buffer frame.

The indexed access mode lets a user quickly access records in an indexed file in the order defined by the index. The user can also explicitly supply keys to select records in an arbitrary order.

File and record locking

VOS provides several file and record locking methods to make several types of processing efficient. A file 'can be locked for writing by a single process or locked for reading by one or more processes. A file can be locked when it is opened or later.

In cases where many processes need to access a file at the same time, programmers can use VOS's provisions for record management. A program can lock records, as well as files, for reading or writing. Furthermore, implicit record locking lets a program lock and process a sequence of records before unlocking any of the records. It is unnecessary for the program to specify all the records in the sequence before starting to process the first one.

I/O drivers

Two disks in a duplexed configuration contain identical data. When VOS reads a disk block, it reads from the disk whose access arm is closest to the block. When VOS writes a disk block, it writes to both disks. VOS has special provisions to keep disks that are in a duplexed configuration in a consistent state.

The second disk in a duplexed configuration can be brought on-line while VOS is using the first disk for normal processing. VOS reads blocks to both disks, and copies blocks from the first disk to the second concurrently with normal processing.

VOS uses sector and cylinder sorting to increase the rate of disk input and output when a burst of disk accesses occurs.

The VOS tape processing facility can read and write ANSI labelled tapes (Level 4), IBM labelled tapes and unlabelled tapes. The tape driver uses multi-block read-ahead and write-behind to increase the data transfer rate.

The asynchronous communications driver contains an extensive CRT terminal manager that provides fast responses to user input. The screen editing functions use the executive processor, thereby relieving the user processor of the burden of handling terminal interrupts.

FORMS MANAGEMENT SYSTEMS (FMS)

The VOS Forms Management System is a comprehensive facility for building, testing and using video display forms. It simplifies and standardises the creation, modification and testing of forms with an easy-to-use, interactive forms design utility.

At the nucleus of FMS are the EDIT FORM comand, which calls the forms editor, and the ACCEPT statement, an extension to all CPS 32 high level languages that controls the editing and transfer of forms between the terminal and the application program. Users design forms directly on their video terminals, defining how data will be displayed and edited on CPS 32 V101 terminals and other ASCII or IBM 3270-compatible terminals. Then the application programmer uses the ACCEPT statement to display a form and to accept validated input from the form.

The field attributes of a form are presented in a simple check list, thus eliminating the need to write tedious control sequences. Forms design is further simplified with a library feature for the cataloguing of commonly used field definitions with their attributes. In addition, FMS produces a form image file that can be printed and used in application programs.

VOS performs validation checks on input data fields, then waits for the operator to correct errors before transferring the data to the application program. Data field attributes can be modified dynamically at execution time. FMS provides commands to position the cursor at individual data fields and function key selections to allow conditional branching within an application program.

TRANSACTION PROCESSING FACILITY (TPF)

The VOS Transaction Processing Facility offers functions specialised to meet the demands of on-line transaction processing. It coordinates the receipt and dispatch of messages for an application communicating with a large number of terminals, and initiates a user processing routine receipt of a message from a terminal. TPF monitors the progress of each user routine and provides for the parallel execution of multiple transactions.

The Transaction Control Process (TCP) is logically divided into parts:

- Transaction requester program
- Forms and data validation
- VOS transaction monitor.

This combination of VOS TPF and user-supplied programs controls all physical terminal operation and performs data management, forms handling and transaction control.

A TCP can support up to two hundred terminals, which can be any combination of asynchronous terminals and IBM 3270-compatible terminals. Multiple TCPs can run concurrently within a processing module or within a CPS 32 system. This distribution of resources across processing modules provides high throughput for applications using hundreds of terminals.

Application programs with TPF

A transaction control program is written to manage one terminal, no matter how many terminals the program will control. The application program does not have to be aware of the existence of other concurrent uses of the same program or of other programs within the Transaction Control Process.

Application programs can be written in COBOL, BASIC, PL/I, FORTRAN or Pascal. All language features can be used, including I/O statements. Programs are compiled by the standard VOS compilers into optimised machine code identical to that produced when programs are executed by VOS in normal, single-user mode. Programs can be debugged in the Transaction Control Process using the S/32 interactive symbolic debugger.

TPF provides for the orderly growth of applications – without the need to reprogram or even to recompile – by flexibility in the use of message queues. There are two types of message queues used to communicate between tasks. Tasks are used to control terminals in a Monitor and Server Process. The Monitor Process initiates requests causing the Server Process to access files and generate a response. A single queue can connect any number of servers with any number of requesters (transaction control programs that use server processes).

Requester and server processes can reside anywhere within a system or anywhere within a network of systems. An application developed to run on a processing module can easily be run on several modules with no change to the programs.

File protection and priority control

TPF provides complete file protection for transactions, including transactions that involve updating data on multiple computer systems within a network. This protection ensures data integrity regardless of extended power failures, communications line failures, system software failures, application program errors and operator errors. The file protection features of TPF simplify the server program design by providing the functions that maintain data consistency and integrity during transaction processing.

The START, COMMIT and ABORT transaction commands ensure data consistency and integrity. START marks the beginning of a transaction, and COMMIT marks the end. When COMMIT is issued, the file updates are guaranteed to be completed regardless of failures due to any cause. The ABORT transaction results in all files being restored to their pre-START state. Since data can reside on a single processing module or can be distributed over many processing modules and systems, these commands provide data integrity independent of physical location. TPF and VOS ensure that the data remain consistent in the unlikely event of a failure.

Priority control of key transactions allows high priority transactions to be serviced before lower priority transactions. 'Round robin' task scheduling ensures uniform terminal response.

Integration with FMS

TPF is fully integrated with VOS Forms Management System. TPF/FMS can use any ASCII terminal or block mode terminal compatible with an IBM 3270 terminal. Application programs are independent of the terminal type.

SECURITY

VOS uses several methods to protect itself and user's programs and data from inadvertent misuse.

System access

System access protection is enforced by the log-in procedure. Every user of a S/32 system is registered in a system registration file. To gain access to the system, the user enters his or her name and password. System administrators can classify users into registration groups, with group membership partly controlling a user's access to system resources, files and programs.

The same registration file is checked when a user logs in from another system over the StrataNET.

Program protection

In the S/32 system, VOS prevents:

- One user's programs from accessing another user's address space
- A user's program from attempting to execute data or to write into executable code
- A user's program from reading or writing into VOS code and data.

Access control

Access control is a mechanism to specify which users can access a file or directory and to specify the type of access.

For a particular user, access to a file can be:

- Null, which denies all access to the file
- Execute, which lets the user execute a program but not read or write it
- Read, which lets the user read the file.
- Write, which lets the user write to the file.

The possible types of access to directories are:

- Null, which denies all access
- Status, which lets the user see the table of contents of the directory and some of the attributes of the contents
- Modify, which gives the user full access to all the contents.

Every time a user accesses a file or directory in the system, VOS checks the access.

MAINTENANCE

Hardware maintenance program
When a hardware error occurs on a board, the board turns on its red light and signals VOS with an interrupt. The hardware maintenance program runs a series of tests on the circuitboard, with the aim of determining the cause and nature of the error. The maintenance program also tests the comparator logic circuits at this time to ensure that they are working, since the comparator is needed to make the remainder of the tests. Then the maintenance programs tests the rest of the board.

If the tests show that the board is faulty, the maintenance program records the nature of the failure in the hardware error log and signals VOS that the circuitboard is unusable. It leaves the board's red light on, indicating that the board needs to be repaired. If the tests do not show that the board is faulty, then the error was transitory. The maintenance program enters a report in the hardware error log, turns off the board's red light and releases the board to VOS for further use.

Periodically, the maintenance program tests the comparator circuit-boards to ensure that all the boards are correctly checking their results. Although the tests commonly are performed once a day, the system administrator can set the frequency of the tests.

When a problem arises, a service engineer can call the system on the remote maintenance communications line to test the boards. By issuing commands to the hardware maintenance program, the engineer can perform some elementary tests on the boards.

Software maintenance program
The remote software maintenance facility allows S/32 software engineers to maintain VOS and other S/32 software remotely. If the software fails, a privileged user can examine it locally or remotely and then a software maintenance engineer can use the tools contained in VOS for debugging

S/32 software. If the engineer cannot solve the problem using these tools, he or she can copy parts of all the faulty software back to the service office, where more powerful tools are available. As with hardware testing, a software engineer attempts to repair the software concurrently with the normal operation of the system.

PROGRAMMING LANGUAGES AND PROGRAM DEVELOPMENT

VOS is designed to allow users to develop programs interactively. The system continues execution of application programs for some users while other users are writing and testing their programs. A user can write programs in any of the VOS programming languages: COBOL, BASIC, PL/I, FORTRAN, and Pascal. Parts of a large program can be compiled separately and bound into one executable program module; therefore, a user can write the parts in more than one language if appropriate.

VOS provides several development tools for program development:

- The VOS screen editor
- The binder
- Compilers for COBOL, BASIC, PL/I, FORTRAN, and Pascal
- The debugger.

The screen editor

A user creates and modifies source programs and other text files with the screen editor. The screen editor requests contain a subset of requests for word processing.

The binder

The binder combines a set of object modules, generated by the COBOL, BASIC, PL/I, FORTRAN and Pascal compilers, into an executable program module. It resolves references to external names in the set of object modules, and it can also search in a set of specified directories or in the system libraries for missing object modules. The binder chooses addresses for the code and data of the program in the user's virtual address space. The binder can also combine the symbol tables of separately compiled object modules into a table for the debugger, then put the table in the program module.

A user can specify the parameters that control the binder either in the bind command or in a binder control file. The user can thus set up an often used set of instructions to the binder in a single control file.

The compiler

The VOS compilers use state-of-the-art techniques to generate fast and compact code. They use a common optimiser and a common code generator.

VOS COBOL fully conforms to the full American National Standard COBOL (ANSI X3.23-1974). It is designed to meet the requirements of the Federal Information Processing Service COBOL Level 4 audit. VOS PL/I is a powerful programming language designed for commercial data processing and systems programming. It conforms to the proposed ANS PL/I(ANSI X3.74), but also has some useful S/32 extensions. PL/I is the VOS systems programming language. VOS BASIC is an extension of ANSI Minimal BASIC (ANSI X3.60-1978). It is intended for use in commercial data processing. VOS FORTRAN encompasses and is compatible with the full American National Standard FORTRAN (ANSI X3.9-1978). VOS Pascal is a complete implementation of Standard Pascal and conforms fully to the draft standard defined by the joint ANSI/IEEE Pascal Committee. Many extensions have been added to broaden the scope and applicability of the language.

A routine written in any VOS language can call routines written in other VOS languages and most of the VOS service subroutines.

The debugger
The VOS debugger allows debugging of programs written in any of the VOS languages. During a debugging session the debugger controls the execution of the program. Break points can be set in the program at source statements, specified either by statement number or relative to the current statement.

Database management systems (DBMS)
In addition to the comprehensive file management software available with the S/32, two DBMS products are available. These are:

- ORACLE relational database system
- RAPPORT relational database system.

COMMUNICATIONS
VOS encompasses a broad range of communication products. The following reflects some of the communication products available.

Protocol products
- Binary synchronous communications
- Financial ticker protocol
- SWIFT
- SDLC
- X.25.

Network products
- X.25 virtual circuits
- X.25 StrataNET.

Device-support products
- CPS 32 asynchronous terminals
- 3270 terminals
- X.29 virtual terminals
- User-supplied terminals
- User-supplied printers.

Emulation products
Using BSC:

- 3270 control units
- 2780 terminals
- 3780 terminals
- HASP workstations
- RJE facility.

Using SNA

- 3270 control units.

Described below are some of the communications products available.

Remote job entry
The VOS Remote Job Entry (RJE) facility emulates one of three IBM RJE terminals communicating with a remote host computer. The three terminals emulated are the IBM 2780, the IBM 3780 and the IBM HASP workstation.

X.25 networking
The X.25 Networking Facility provides for full-duplex communications between remote application programs. Application programs can be executing in the same S/32 processing module, or they can be on different modules in the same system or in different systems. An application could be in a non-S/32 system that supports the CCITT X.25 Level III standard.

The use of the X.25 Networking Facility provides for interprogram communication independent of hardware link, line speed and protocol. Optional extended addressing allows a CPS 32 application to 'call' another CPS 32 application anywhere in a public service or private network. Calls from other vendors' applications can be examined and dispatched appropriately under user control.

X.29 Virtual Terminals
The X.29 Virtual Terminal Facility offers communications between remote terminals and an S/32 system. The terminals can connect to a packet switching network through a dial-up line, and the traffic is routed to the appropriate S/32 host system. Alternatively, terminals can be locally concentrated in a packet assembler/disassembler (PAD) and connect to a host either through private lines or public data networks.

3270 control unit emulator

The S/32 3270 Emulator Facility enables S/32 application programs to communicate with an IBM-compatible host. The application programs appear to the IBM host as Binary Synchronous Communications (BSC) 3270 display stations (terminals). With an easy-to-use read/write interface, programs can read data from and pass data to teleprocessing applications executing on the host system. Using this facility, an application program can allow a user from a terminal to access local data or data stored at the host.

SUMMARY

CPS 32 provides a hardware-based approach to fault tolerant computing. Significant increases in power can be anticipated as further use is made of M68010 and M68020 chips. The CPS 32 system is fully supported in the UK by the Olivetti customer engineering service.

CHAPTER 13

August Systems industrial control computers

J. Wensley

(August Systems, Oregon)

Early uses of highly reliable computers occurred in the space program and in telephone exchange control. The need for high reliability in the space program is self-evident, where human life and very expensive equipment is dependent on the correct performance of control computers. It is not sufficient that the computer exhibits only high availability, but also that all control actions taken by the computer be correct and occur at the right time. We refer to the latter as *high integrity*. In telephone exchange control, some errors can be tolerated, for example a misplaced call. Individual telephone connections are subject to human misdialling and faulty performance of individual telephone sets. The important requirement is that the probability of an error be made acceptably low, and that the exchange continues to be available. The loss of service from an entire exchange would represent a severe economic and social disturbance.

Recent attention on highly available computers has focused very heavily on their use in transaction processing. Several companies offer products in that market. The typical buyer of such computers requires the high availability because essential business records are up-dated or accessed continuously on a transaction by transaction basis. The continuing integrity of the file system is of great importance, as well as the need for the system to be available when required. Examples include banking, airline reservations, financial institutions.

Computers used in industrial or process control have long used some form of redundancy of equipment, in order to maintain continued correct and safe operation. The most common example is the use of dual systems with either operator initiated or automatic switchover to the spare when the primary equipment fails. This presumes that the switch-over can be achieved quickly enough so that the process that is being controlled does not become unsafe. It is also necessary that failure of the primary system can be detected reliably and that the equipment used to effect the switch-over be itself highly reliable. In many cases these functions are assisted by a human operator. Control systems also use various forms of functional redundancy. A common form of this is to use one system for primary control, with a totally independent second system for monitor and safety shutdown. The assumption in such systems is that an unsafe (or undesirable) condition of the plant will only occur if both systems fail. The important parameters in control computers are high availability, high integrity, and real-time response. Of slightly lesser importance is the protection of data bases, because many control computers do not utilise them, and when used they are often not critical to plant safety.

The concept of fault tolerance is based on a recognition that individual parts of a system will be subject to random failures. Such failures can be due to internal causes such as diffusion of material within an LSI component or breakage of elements in the part. It can also be due to external causes such as vibration, high temperature, electromagnetic interference and the like. The idea of fault tolerance is to use extra equipment so that additional resources are available to take over the task of the failed part. With the increasing capability of modern electronic parts it is appropriate that the extra, or redundant, equipment be added in complete units such as processors or even complete computers. Examples exist of double, triple and greater replication depending on the reliability objectives for particular applications. While replication of units is a common feature, there are significant differences in the way in which the redundant resources are managed, i.e. how to accomplish such functions as error detection, fault location, switching in of spares, masking of errors, repair of failed units, etc.

While direct replication is appropriate to such units as processors and control units, the use of special coding techniques is very appropriate for data storage and data transmission units. It is common practice to use error detection and correction coding on random access memories, and the same technique can also be used on disk units and for data communication. The use of coding requires only a small amount of redundancy while giving very good protection against some of the more common types of faults in such units. Where extreme reliability is required then it is appropriate to combine coding and replication. A common example of this is to be found with disk data storage. Two disks are used to provide against extensive failure of either one, with coding being used to protect against some of the smaller errors, and also to resolve which unit is in error when a disagreement exists between the data from the two units.

DESIGN ISSUES

The August Systems Series 300 and Series 30 control computers are based on several design issues that differ in important ways from those of many other fault tolerant systems. The most important issue is the distinction that is made between reliability and availability. In many applications where fault tolerant computers are used, the reliability with which each transaction is processed is not extreme. Occasional errors can occur, with only minor annoyance. For example, in transaction processing, any one transaction can be initially subject to errors in data or operator actions. In telephone switching systems, one call connection is often in error due to user misdialling. In such systems the reliability of each transaction must be kept to a reasonable level, but it is not necessary to achieve extreme reliability. The important quality that is required in such systems is very high availability, i.e. the proportion of time during which service is denied to the user must be kept very low. A typical specification for telephone switching systems is that downtime be held to a few hours in a service life of a few decades.

In industrial control systems, an incorrect result produced by the computer can potentially cause damage to equipment, loss of product, and in extreme situations loss of life. It is therefore necessary that the probability of incorrect action be extremely low (which also implies that the availability be very high). This requirement for very high reliability places many constraints upon the design. For example, a design that occasionally produced errors and then later corrected them is unacceptable, even if the correction occurred within a few seconds. For a transaction processing application such a system could be acceptable.

Industrial control systems must operate in real time. The system must usually respond to process events in a fraction of a second. Furthermore, the time taken for processing the control algorithm must be deterministic and a constant. This rules out design approaches that are stochastic such as the use of virtual memory schemes or many well known operating systems. Usually all programs and data must be held in either RAM or ROM memory to provide for fast and deterministic access time.

Another requirement for control computers is the need to interface to many hundreds or thousands of process devices. Such devices are frequently very simple, such as switches or thermocouples, but their large number causes the input/output subsystem to be far larger than the central processing unit(s). This implies that faults are more likely to occur in the input/output units and the fault tolerance must therefore include those units.

Within any fault tolerant system, the objective is that the occurrence of a fault should produce no external effect. It is therefore possible that a fault could occur and remain hidden from the user. Such hidden or latent faults must be removed before further faults eventually occur that could exceed the ability of the fault tolerance techniques that are used. One technique that is sometimes used is to carry out periodic testing, usually involving diagnostic programs to uncover such latent faults. In a control environment such techniques can seldom be used, because the testing interferes with the running of the process. It is therefore necessary to employ other methods to uncover latent faults.

Control computers must be designed to meet far harsher environments than is normal in standard computer rooms. High temperature extremes can occur in many industrial plants or where the system is not housed in a building. It is thus necessary to introduce this factor at the design stage, and also to ensure adequate temperature testing during manufacture. Another important factor in the design and manufacture of control computers is the need to protect against external disturbances represented by vibration, moisture, corrosive atmospheres and electromagnetic disturbances (EMP and RFI). In the August Systems products, that protection is achieved by appropriate use of special cabinets (e.g. NEMA enclosures) that effectively create a protected environment for the electronics.

THE AUGUST SYSTEMS TMR CONTROL COMPUTER

HARDWARE STRUCTURE

The August Systems Series 300 is illustrated in Fig. 13.1. The processing function is carried out in the control computers. To provide high integrity, this function is triplicated, i.e. three independent processors each with its own memory are used to form the control computer modules (CCMs). These units carry out the logic and arithmetic calculations, conversion of process variables to and from engineering units, calibration of instruments, and control of the other elements in the system. The triplication of the processing function is used to ensure that a fault in a processor does not produce any corruption of control signals.

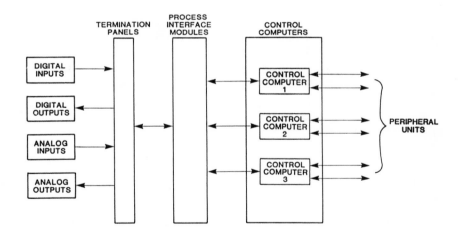

Fig. 13.1. The structure of the August Systems fault tolerant system.

While triplication of the processing function results in high integrity, it is necessary for the CCM to interface to the signals from the process or to the process. Signals from the process (i.e. from sensors) must be distributed to all three of the processing elements of the CCM. Signals from the CCM to the process (i.e. to actuators) must be transmitted in such a way that faulty data from one processing element in the CCM is properly masked by the remaining two processing elements so that a fault produces no incorrect control action. In addition, the process signals are frequently very numerous, so a capability must be provided to connect to a large number of process points, far larger than can ordinarily be achieved from a processing unit. These functions are carried out in the process interface module (PIM) which also carries out conversions between analogue and digital data.

While the CCMs and PIMs operate with voltage and current levels that are appropriate for modern electronics, it is necessary to convert such power levels to those appropriate for the process itself. Frequently, high voltage and high power signals within the process need to be switched or controlled. This function is carried out by the use of solid state relays housed in one or more termination modules (TMs). These TMs provide a convenient means for the large number of wires from the process to be terminated at the Series 300. Another feature of the TMs is that the solid state relays are optically isolated, thus protecting the control computer from the effect of high power erroneous signals from the process plant.

Control computer modules
The control computer modules are based upon the design concept of the SIFT computer.[1-4] The SIFT computer was designed for aircraft control and, in particular, for an advanced aircraft type that required a correctly functioning computer system for safe flight. The reliability requirements for that system were exceedingly stringent. Typically, the requirement is that the probability of failure per hour of flight should not exceed 10^{-10}. This translates approximately into a mean time before failure (MTBF) in excess of one million years. To achieve such a high reliability, a large number of processors were included to provide the necessary replication of computers, plus redundant units to be used when faults occurred. In its first embodiment, seven processors were used.

For control applications the reliability requirements, though severe, are not as stringent as those found in aircraft control. In general, they can be achieved by a structure containing three independent computing channels. Such a system is referred to as *triple modular redundant* (TMR). While the basic design of the August Systems Series 300 is such that more than three channels could be used in one installation, the reliability requirements seldom demand replication beyond three.

Each individual processor is based upon the Intel 8086 microprocessor. This choice of processing element is based upon design decisions concerned with processing power, memory addressability, and the availability of a large number of ancillary components that can be used to construct a complete computer module. The 8086 is a 16-bit microprocessor operating with a clock of 8 MHz and includes 20-bit memory addressing capability, a vectored interrupt capability and the use of stacks for program control.

Fault tolerance is achieved by each of the three processors being able to examine computational results from each of the other two channels. Thus, each channel receives three versions of the results of each critical calculation, one from its own calculation and one each from the other two processors. Following determination of these three results, software in each processor selects the majority value. If no faults have occurred, it can be expected that all three channels will produce the same result. In the event of a fault in one channel, this will be recognised by the voting software and an error will be reported, but will have no further effect upon the computation. This error report is used to trigger maintenance action on this faulty channel. The reading of critical data from the other two processors is accomplished by a *read only* connection. This connection enables each processor to determine values computed by the other two, but because it is read only, there is no possibility that a faulty channel can corrupt data in the other correctly functioning channels.

Input of the data is accomplished independently by each processor. Each channel thus receives an independent view concerning all inputs. Where it is necessary to protect against failure of an input device, then that device itself should be replicated and values from each of the replicated devices should be fed to all computational channels. Thus, each channel can independently carry out a vote of the individual sensors and determine both the correct value to be used, and, if there is a fault, to identify the faulty sensor.

When each channel has determined the output to be transmitted to the process, each of them sends its value to circuitry that carries out a hardware vote to remove any data from a faulty computational channel. The method by which this is achieved is described in more detail in the next subsection.

The mode of operation of the computational channels is that for critical calculations: they all carry out identically the same calculation and in the absence of faults will achieve identically the same results. These calculations are not carried out in a tightly synchronised manner, but the processors are loosely synchronised by software.

The process interface

It is necessary in a control computer system to interface the inputs and outputs of the computer to specific devices in the process equipment. This interfacing requires many functions to be accomplished, such as multiplexing a large number of inputs and outputs, distributing inputs to all the computing channels, carrying out voting of outputs to actuators, and conversion to and from signal levels used in the process equipment.

The multiplexing is required to enable a computer with a relatively small number of input/output channels to connect to many hundreds, or thousands, of process devices. This multiplexing is carried out in the process interface module. Each PIM contains three interface units, each connected to a computational channel. These interface units implement an independent bus (three in total) in each PIM. Each of these buses communicates with up to fifteen input/output cards. The principal input/output cards that are provided are: a 32-bit digital input, a 32-bit digital output, a 32-channel analogue input, and a 4-channel analogue output.

Up to fifteen PIMs can be included in a complete system; thus the maximum number of process points that can be monitored or controlled can be as high as 7200 (fifteen PIMs, each containing fifteen cards, each interfacing to up to 32 points). Thus, the relatively small number of input/output lines from the computer modules (24 in the case of the August Systems Series 300) can be multiplexed to a far larger number of processing points.

It is the responsibility of the PIM to take each input variable and feed that data independently to each of the computational channels via the three interface units in each PIM. This distribution of input data is carried out by routing this data to three independent circuits in the input card.

For output, it is necessary that the PIM remove all effects of a faulty computational channel. This is accomplished by a voter that carries out the logical 'majority function', shown in Fig. 13.2. Such a majority circuit must, however, be protected against faulty components within itself. A circuit for discrete outputs is illustrated in Fig. 13.3. It can be shown that each individual component of that circuit can experience failure without corrupting the output of that circuit, assuming that all data received from the three computational channels is correct. Thus, the combination of three computational channels and the output voter can survive an error in any computational channel, or a faulty component within the voter itself. A double fault, such that a computational unit fails and also that a component in the voter fails, is not always tolerated.

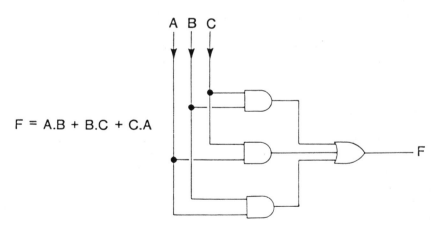

$$F = A.B + B.C + C.A$$

Fig. 13.2 The majority function.

Analogue voting of output data is far more complex. In the scheme used, the data from each computational channel is first converted to analogue form. Because of the inherent slight inaccuracy of digital-to-analogue convertors, the selection of two identical values may not be possible. However, satisfactory operation is achieved by a circuit that selects the middle of the three analogue values. Thus, if any computational channel is

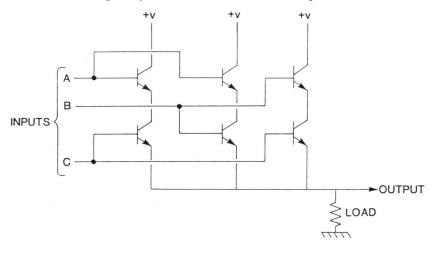

Fig. 13.3 A fault tolerant majority (voter) circuit.

at fault, so that it generates a totally incorrect value, then that value will be ignored because it will not be the middle value of the three. The design of a circuit to accomplish this voter is complicated by the need to incorporate the following two features:

(1) The circuit itself must be fault tolerant so that individual faults in the components cannot corrupt the output
(2) Accuracy and linearity of analogue data must be maintained.

Such a circuit represents a difficult design challenge and the complexity of that circuit is one of the reasons why the analogue output cards of the Series 300 only implement four output channels. Such a limitation on analogue output does not represent a significant problem in control systems, where in general the number of analogue output points is very small compared with analogue inputs and discrete inputs and outputs.

Process equipment frequently operates at voltage and power levels that are different from those used in computers. In addition, a.c. signals are used, as are current loop signals. The conversion of these different signal types to those appropriate for computing equipment (typically 5 V and 0 V) is accomplished by using solid state relays that also incorporate optical isolation. This isolation protects the circuitry of the control system from any induced high power transients on input or output lines. The solid state relays are incorporated in termination modules that also provide a convenient means for attaching user wiring to the system via appropriate terminals. The solid state relays have very good reliability characteristics and it is seldom necessary to provide fault tolerance for them. However, if it is desired to protect against failure of a solid state relay, this can be accomplished by connecting them as shown in Fig. 13.4. Here, the first connection scheme provides a voter function that will tolerate any of the

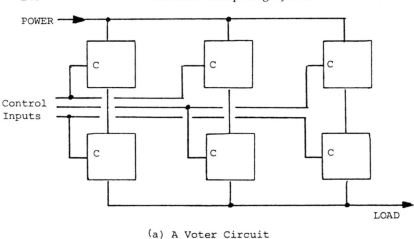

(a) A Voter Circuit

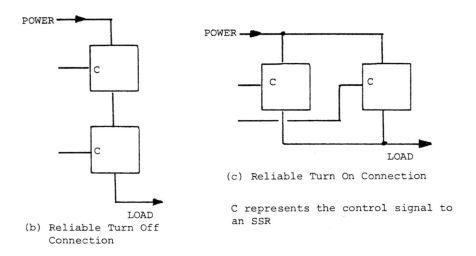

(c) Reliable Turn On Connection

C represents the control signal to an SSR

(b) Reliable Turn Off Connection

LOAD

Fig. 13.4 Circuit schemes to protect against failures in solid state relays (SSRs).

solid state relays failing in an open circuit or closed circuit manner. In Fig. 13.4(b), a simpler circuit is shown, utilising only two solid state relays. This connection scheme is used for a system in which it is necessary to turn off a process unit reliably. Thus, if one unit fails to turn off, the other unit properly accomplishes this function. Figure 13.4(c) illustrates the case where a process unit must be reliably turned on, even if one solid state relay fails in the open circuit mode. As mentioned above, such interconnections of multiple solid state relays are seldom necessary.

SOFTWARE ISSUES

The management of the redundancy in the structure described above is carried out by two major software systems: the Real Time Task Supervisor (RTTS) and the Process Interface Module Sub-System (PIMSS). Additional software is provided with the system to assist the control engineer in implementing his control algorithms, but as those do not impact the fault tolerance of the system they will not be addressed here. The primary design objective of both RTTS and PIMSS was to provide all the functions necessary for fault tolerant operation without the user of the system having to be aware of these functions. Ideally the user should be able to use the system as if it were a conventional single processor.

Real time task supervisor (RTTS)

The purpose of an operating system is to provide high level functions that augment the raw hardware capabilities of a computer system in order to make it more convenient to use. Many of the functions provided in RTTS are those found in virtually all operating systems. These include such functions as scheduling, dispatching, interrupt handling and the like. The detailed actions required to be performed to carry out these functions in general require a detailed understanding of the hardware of the system, such as the particular addressing of registers, timing relationships and the instruction set of the computer. These functions collectively provide a system with high level capabilities. One such capability is referred to as multi-tasking, in which the user can separately define a number of tasks that, in total, define his application. Tasks may be run on a regular periodic basis by specifying only the time period between each running of the tasks. Alternatively, tasks can be specified to run under the occurrence of a particular event. Such events can be hardware interrupts caused by some external signal, or software events, such as a request by one task for a different task to be run. The use of multiple tasks to accomplish a complete application has important advantages in the design of large, complex systems, because it enables the user to focus attention individually on particular components of his total system, with only limited attention being required on the interaction between tasks.

In addition to the more conventional facilities mentioned above, RTTS provides facilities that are found only in more advanced operating systems. An example of such a function is the mailbox and message facility. This facility provides a convenient and well controlled mechanism for tasks to communicate with each other by sending messages to mailboxes that are owned by another task. This message flow is accomplished without the user having to be concerned with such machine dependent factors as storage allocation, buffer allocation, timing relationships between tasks, etc.

As well as the functions described above that are found in conventional computer operating systems, the fault tolerance capabilities are also embedded in RTTS. The most obvious such facility is the voting capability whereby critical data in one computer of the triple is compared with the same data computed in the other two channels. In the event of a discrepancy, the erroneous value is ignored and an error report is issued, thus triggering maintenance actions to correct the faulty channel. This voting capability uses a lower level function to accomplish the communication of data between the three computing modules. The user need only be concerned with the voting within RTTS without concern for the detailed communication capability implied in this function.

A capability that is essential in providing fault tolerance is the ability to synchronise the operation of the three computing channels. Because the Series 300 contains three independent processing modules that contain independent clocking circuits, they will tend to operate at slightly different speeds. If the computing channels were not synchronised from time to time, they would slowly drift apart in time and would be at different stages in their calculations, and thus it could not be expected that successful voting would take place, even if there were no faults. Before voting on critical data, each of the computing channels therefore enters a synchronisation routine at the exit of which all of the computational channels are in close to the same state of execution. In the Series 300, no attempt is made to achieve tight synchronisation as used, for example, in computers that operate in 'lock step'. Rather, the computing channels are synchronised so that they are within about 50 μs of each other in their execution. Another function provided by the synchronisation routines is to separate the voting of critical data from modification of that data. The problem that is attacked here is that it is possible with no synchronisation that one computing channel will be ahead of the other two and will modify a piece of data before the others have voted on it. Thus, it would appear that the faster channel is faulty. This is prevented from occurring by resynchronising the computing channels between the voting operation and whatever operation modifies the data. This synchronisation ensures that all computing channels have completed their voting before any of them modifies the data. The design of synchronisation routines has been addressed in the fault tolerant literature.[5-7]

In fault tolerant computing systems, the intent is that the system as a whole will continue correct operation, even in the presence of a fault. In certain installations, the occurrence of a fault will trigger a maintenance or replacement action by the user, wherein the faulty unit is either repaired or replaced by a properly functioning unit. The replacement ideally should be carried out with the system still continuing to operate. It is necessary for this newly inserted unit to carry out a warm start operation. This operation attempts to set the newly inserted unit into the same state as the units that have been continuing to operate. This must be accomplished while the process continues to be controlled. The technical problem is that the newly inserted unit must capture all the data that defines the state of the system, while the other units are continuing to change that data. Simple copying of the state data from the good units to the newly inserted unit leaves the possibility of inconsistency between data items because some were changed after this copying process, while others were not. A primitive mechanism for achieving warm start is to temporarily halt the two good units while the new unit copies the state data. This simple mechanism may, in certain cases, be satisfactory, but for some systems this temporary shutting down of the control system even for a few milliseconds may be unsatisfactory.

It is therefore necessary to provide a more sophisticated system whereby the state data is copied from the good processors to the new one in small parts. After each part is copied, a test is then made to see if any modification to that part was carried out by the processors that were continuing execution. If no modification has occurred, then this part has been consistently copied. If modification has occurred during copying, then the copy is declared invalid and the copying action must be reinitiated. The breaking of the state data into parts is done on the basis that there is independence between the parts, so that consistency need only concern the data in one part, without concern for the state data in another part. In general, the parts are individually associated with a task. The effect is that over a short period of time the state data of each task is copied into the newly inserted processor which can then carry out the control algorithms associated with that task, thus maintaining the consistency of the data for that task.

To illustrate the hot replacement of input units we take as an example a single discrete input. Because of the small number of components associated with a single discrete input, it is usual to associate many such inputs on a single circuit card. To accomplish on-line repair the replacement of a single board effects repair of all 32 discrete inputs, some of which may not be faulty. The basic input circuit consists of triplicated electronics that receive process inputs and hold them in registers so they may be read by the three processors.

The technique for on-line repair is essentially very simple. All process input is wired to the active card, and also to the connector for an empty card slot adjacent to it. When on-line repair is required, a replacement card is inserted in the adjacent slot and therefore will receive all process input. Because the reading of the input card is controlled by the processor units, they must be notified that a new card is to be used. This is accomplished by the operator depressing a switch on the board. This causes an interrupt signal, the 'maintenance interrupt'. Upon receipt of this maintenance interrupt by all three processors, they are aware that a replacement board is to be used. At that time, all reading of the process input takes place through this new board and the old board which contains the fault is no longer used. It is now possible for the operator to remove the old board so that it may be repaired off-line. The system is now back to its fully fault tolerant form.

Two aspects of this process require particular attention if high reliability is to be achieved. Both are concerned with the possibility of operator error. The first such possible error is that an incorrect board type or an already faulty board was inserted by the operator. Protection against this is achieved by having the processing unit identify the board type and by carrying out a check of its functions before utilising it. The board type is checked by reading a small special register on the board that contains a signature defining its type. Correct functioning of the board is tested by the fact that the three independent circuits on the board should all yield identically the same data. During this sequence of operations, the operator is prompted concerning the switchover to the new board. Three light emitting diodes (LEDs) are incorporated on each board. Under normal operations the LEDs are not lit. When a fault in one of the three channels in a board is detected, one of the three LEDs will be lit, thus providing an indication to the operator as to which board contains a fault. When the replacement board is inserted, the three processors each light one of the three LEDs. When the maintenance switch is operated, the processor must first check out the new board and if it is correct, start using it. At this point, all three LEDs on the new board are turned off (one by each of the three processors) and the three LEDs on the old faulty board are all turned on. This is an indication to the operator that the old, faulty board may be removed. By these means the operator is prompted in correct board replacement.

Another possible operator error is that the wrong board slot may be used. In this event, the insertion of a new board into an incorrect slot will be detected by the processor. The processor is aware of which boards require repair because of a fault, and the system will not activate use of a board inserted in a wrong slot, thus preventing this potential operator error. All such incorrect operator actions, i.e. the use of a wrong board, the use of a faulty board, or the insertion of a board in the wrong slot, are also printed on an alarm printer so that detailed information to the operator is provided beyond the indications that were achieved through the LEDs.

The hot replacement of output units entails an important difference from input units. In the case of input units, it is a simple matter to interface them from the process to three processing channels by simple common connection. With output units, it is necessary that the circuit be designed in such a manner that a newly inserted replacement board has no effect on the output until it is set to the proper state by the processors.

Consider replacement of a discrete output board that uses a voter circuit based on the arrangement shown in Fig. 13.3. A new board of the same type is inserted in an adjacent card slot that is also wired in common to the process. This new board, at initiation, has all switches in the 'off' position, and thus will have no effect upon the output to the process. The processors first check that the board is of the right type and that it is inserted in the correct position to replace the board that contains a fault. The actuation of the maintenance switch causes an interrupt which then causes the processors to set the switches in the new board to the proper state for the process condition. At this point, the old board may be deactivated by opening all of its switches and the operator is informed of this condition by the processors turning 'off' the LEDs on the new board and turning them 'on' on the old board that is to be removed. It is then possible for the operator to remove the old board without having any effect upon the output to the process.

FURTHER DEVELOPMENT OF FAULT TOLERANT CONTROL COMPUTERS

It can be expected that fault tolerance will be incorporated into an ever increasing proportion of control computers. This is primarily due to two significant trends. The first is the continuing decrease in the cost of electronics. This continuing movement means that the increased hardware cost needed for replication only represents a small part of each total project cost. Other costs such as software, management and operations will dominate.

The second trend is that process equipment is being used for more and more critical processes. It is frequently the case that efficient operation of a plant is achieved when the process variables are very close to their safety limits. Small perturbations in these process variables can quickly put the process in an unsafe state, and therefore the need for reliable control becomes increasingly important.

The functionality of fault tolerant control computers will increase as the market expands and matures. It can be expected that more and more of the total system will be fault tolerant. An obvious trend will be to sensors and actuators that are designed to be either fault tolerant or at least fail-safe. Another area where fault tolerance is being introduced is in the communication subsystems that are being incorporated in distributed control systems.

Another field where advances can be expected is in techniques to deal with software faults. While replication is capable of properly handling random hardware faults, the use of the same software in each processor means that a software design fault will not be tolerated. The current techniques that are used to remove errors from programs mainly involve extensive testing and the use of good program design methodologies, e.g. structured design techniques. Continuing research on the topic of correctness proving of software yields the hope that in future programs can be proven correct by formal mathematical techniques, but such techniques are at present not economically practicable except in extreme cases. Two other techniques that are currently being researched involve the creation of more than one version of a program. With n-version software these multiple copies are all executed and the results compared to achieve error detection and correction. In the other technique, fault tolerant software, a single version is executed followed by an acceptance test of the results. If the test fails, then another program version is run. These techniques can potentially protect against software errors, but are difficult to design, particularly for large software projects such as operating systems.

REFERENCES

1. Wensley, J. H. (1972). 'SIFT – Software Implemented Fault Tolerance'. *Proc. Fall Joint Comp. Conf.*, 243–253.
2. Wensley, J. H. *et al.* (1976). 'The Design, Analysis and Verification of the SIFT Fault Tolerant System'. *Proc., 2nd Int. Conf. on Software Eng.*, 458–469.
3. Murray, N. D., Hopkins, A. L. and Wensley, J. H. (1977). 'Highly Reliable Microprocessors'. AGARDograph on *Integrity in Flight Control Systems*, No. 224.
4. Wensley, J. H. *et al.* (1974). 'SIFT: Design and Analysis of a Fault Tolerant Computer for Aircraft Control'. *Proc. of the IEEE*, **66**, No. 10, 1240–1255.
5. Davies, D. and Wakerly, J. P. (1978). 'Synchronization and Matching in Redundant Systems'. *IEEE Trans. on Computers*, **C-27**, No. 6, 531–539.
6. McConnell, S. R. and Siewiorek, D. P. (1981). 'Synchronization and Voting'. *IEEE Trans. on Computers*, **C-30**, No. 2, 161–164.
7. Frison, S. G. and Wensley, J. H. (1982). 'Interactive Consistency and its Impact on the Design of TMR Systems'. *Proc. of 12th IEEE Fault Tolerant Comp. Symp.*, 228–233.

Index

acceptability checks, 69–71
acceptance test, 74
access control, 226
active redundancy, 94–6
adjudication module, 68
Airbus A310, 75
Amdahl 470, 51
analogue voting, 238
anticipated faults, 26, 64
ARGUS system, 113
assertions, 132
'at most once' semantics, 116
atomic actions, 5, 6, 33, 36, 52,
    103, 104, 109, 111, 112
    nested, 109
    robust, 104, 110, 119
audit trail, 6, 190–91
    programs, 40
August Systems, 10, 175, 232–45
availability, 12, 165, 178, 193, 208,
    232, 234
AXE system, 50–51

back-up process, 183–5
baton, 136
battery back-up, 218
Berger codes, 30, 38
board replacement, 215
broadcast network, 80
broadcast protocols, 78
built-in-self-test, 15, 23

capabilities, 36, 48, 71, 136
cascade roll back, 105, 109
check sum, 28, 38
checking circuits, 32
checkpoint(ing), 6, 32, 49, 93, 96,
    119, 172, 182–90 *passim* 202
clock synchronisation, 31
code disjoint circuit, 34
codes, 27 *et seq.*
COMET program, 53
commit, 113
    algorithm, 112, 117–18
    two phase, 118
commitment, 93, 226
comparison logic, 219
complexity measures, 160
component faults, 2
consistency checking, 84
consistent state, 202

constant weight codes, 30
continuous
    checking, 212, 214
    operation, 198
    processing, 214
control
    computer modules, 236
    faults, 132
    systems, 234
cooperating mini, 171
crash
    -proof, 113
    -recovery, 111–12
    -resistance, 116, 119
cross check analysis, 134
cyclic redundancy check, 28, 34, 45

damage, 124
    assessment, 5, 44, 48, 52
data
    consistency, 226, 243
    corruption, 81
    integrity, 81, 84, 213, 225
    locking, 202
database integrity, 179–80, 192, 202
deadline mechanisms, 134, 141
defensive programming, 75
design
    diversity, 9, 67, 70, 98–9
    faults, 2, 3, 65–6, 100, 103, 245
        tolerance, 64, 68, 76
device controllers, 180
diagnosis, 50, 183
    remote, 194
    system, 44, 46
diagnostic
    checking, 7–8
    interface, 182
    routines, 214
    testing, 16, 227, 234
distributed
    program, 102
    systems, 102
domino effect, 85
dual
    bus mini, 171–2
    disk, 233
dual/dual, 31
dual-ported
    device controllers, 194
    disk drives, 176, 181

dual systems, 199, 202, 204, 232
Duane model, 152
duplexed
  components, 214–15
  discs, 223
duplicate board, 212
duplicated
  drives, 212
  power supplies, 212
  processor, 167
duty cycle, 92–3
Dynabus, 179–82, 186
dynamic redundancy, 31–2, 179, 183,
  188

emergency shutdown, 140
end-to-end
  network, 80
  protocols, 78
ENIAC, 17
entropy, 155
error
  correction, 27–8, 34, 95
    circuitry, 183
  detection, 4, 26–8, 32, 68–9, 233
  propagation, 12
  recovery, 6, 9, 12, 26, 43, 71–2, 74, 86,
    107, 114, 140, 214
errors, 2, 11
  latent, 13, 49
  operator, 243–4
  permanent, 213
  transient, 213
ESS, 36
ESS-1, 46, 50
ESS-1A, 10, 11
'exactly once' semantics, 115
exceptions, 192
  handling, 4, 8–9, 39, 106, 116, 139
  signals, 41, 44
exhaustive testing, 22
expert systems, 42

fail-safe, 87, 91, 122, 125, 132, 135,
  140
failure, 2, 11, 122
  atomicity, 102
  data, 145
  rate, 2
fault
  avoidance, 53
  coverage, 18
  isolation, 44
  latency, 18, 37
  location, 6, 14, 73, 183, 233
  model, 14, 25, 146–7
  removal, 13
  secure, 33–4
  tolerance, 3, 26, 53–4, 66, 68, 88,
    93, 125, 135, 138, 164–5, 196, 233,
    236, 245

tree, 128, 131–4
  analysis, 128, 132, 134–5
faults, 2, 3, 11, 13, 81
  anticipated, 26, 64
  component, 2
  control, 132
  design, 2, 3, 64–6, 100, 103, 245
    tolerance, 64, 68, 76
  intermittent, 94
  latent, 18, 37, 39, 65
  mutiple, 18
  permanent, 94–5
  physical, 13
fire codes, 34
flowcharts, 21, 40
function checks, 32

graceful degradation, 7, 50, 88, 140,
  173
Guardian system, 186, 192–3

Hamming
  codes, 82
  distance, 27–8
hardcore, 8, 33
hazards, 124–6, 134–7
  analysis, 126–8
Honeywell D-1000, 50
hot
  replacement, 243–4
  restart, 87–8
  standby, 49, 170
hybrid redundancy, 35

IBM
  704/709, 14
  3081, 21, 44
  S/360, 50
  S/370, 34, 51
information redundancy, 82
integrity, high, 232, 235
interface checks, 189
interference-free, 104
intermittent faults, 94

Jelinski-Moranda model, 149–59

Keiller-Littlewood model, 151

L1011, 126
lamp, 53
latent
  errors, 13, 49
  faults, 18, 37, 39, 65
link failure, 89
Littlewood model, 152–9
Littlewood-Verrall model, 151
logic fault simulation, 16
logging, 86, 190, 204, 213

maintenance, 227, 237, 242

remote, 215
processors, 18
majority
circuit, 238
value, 237
market
sector, 163
size, 169
marketing, 169
MARS, 98–9
matching circuits, 46
mean time between failures
see MTBF
mean time to repair (MTTR), 165–95
mirrored disks, 181–2, 187, 191, 200, 204–5
module, adjudication, 68
MOMENTUM 10, 166–8, 171, 197–207
monitor computers, 18, 137
MTBF, 2, 149, 165–95
multi-micro
non-redundant, 173–4
redundant, 172–3
Musa model, 149

N-version programming, 9, 74
NMR, 35
nested atomic action, 109
non-redundant multi-micro, 173–4

object manager, 103–4, 107, 111, 113
online
maintenance, 92, 183
repair, 243
operator error, 243–4

packaging, 164
tailored, 165
parity, 28, 29, 32, 34
check, 34, 38
matrix, 28–9
passive redundancy, 94–5
paths, multiple, 191
Pathway, 190–92
peripheral switching, 205
permanent erros, 213
permanent faults, 94–5
physical faults, 13
Pluribus, 10
power
fail recovery, 183
redundancy, 82–3
predictive quality, 155, 158
prequential likelihood, 159
process
migration, 186
pairs, 183–7, 189, 192–4
processor controllers, 18, 23, 40, 49, 232

processors, triplicated, 235
productive redundancy, 179
protection, 6, 36, 48, 71, 189, 226

quadded logic, 30

random testing, 21–2, 25, 46, 160 ·
rate of occurrence of failures
(ROCOF), 149, 152
real time
control systems, 159
environment, 91–2
response, 233
systems, 92, 122, 140
task scheduler (RTTS), 241
reconfiguration, 7–8, 39, 49–50, 141, 173
record locking, 189, 223
recoverable object, 107, 110–11
recovery, 53–4, 202
blocks, 9, 73, 103, 108, 112
cache, 6, 50, 108
data, 192
information, 200
lines, 85, 87
points, 85, 87, 107, 116
region, 107–108, 110, 112, 116
roll-back, 191
rectangular codes, 34
redundancy, 3, 9, 18, 26–7, 30–1, 49, 53, 67, 81, 95, 140, 166, 232–3, 241
active, 94–6
circuit, 18
dynamic, 31–2, 179, 183, 188
hybrid, 35
information, 82
passive, 94–5
power, 82–3
productive, 179
space, 82–3
static, 31, 35, 178, 188
temporal, 8
time, 82–3, 94–5
triple modular (TMR), 9, 30–31
35, 71, 97–8, 236
two-way, 31
redundant
coding, 82
mini, 170
multi-micro, 172–3
voting, 173–4
reference circuit, 21–2
reliability, 1–3, 12, 54, 89, 91, 122, 165, 211, 232, 234
function, 148
growth, 146, 148
modelling, 160
prediction, 149
remote
diagnosis, 194

maintenance, 215
procedure call (RPC), 103, 115
repair, 7, 48, 50
replaceable unit, 33, 44, 51
replacement, 242
  hot, 243–4
replication checks, 69–71
residue codes, 35
response time, 91–2
restart, 49–50, 140, 173
restorable action, 6
retry, 8, 12, 26, 43–4, 115
reversal check, 69
risk, 124, 126, 135
  assessment, 124
robust atomic action, 104, 110, 119
roll-back recovery, 191

safe state, 125, 136–7, 140
safety
  assertions, 138–9
  critical systems, 122–3, 125, 136
  executive, 137–40
  requirements, 125, 128
SAGE system, 32
Saturn V, 30
self-checking, 33, 100
  checkers, 36, 39
  components, 98–9
  hardware, 214
  repair, 32
  test, 15–16, 25, 33–4
    programs, 17
semipassive lines, 42
Shooman model, 149
SIFT computer, 10
signature, 15, 45–6, 136
  testing, 22
smallest replaceable units (SRU),
  96–7
software reliability models, 148
space
  redundancy, 82–3
  shuttle, 75
specification, 1, 2, 11, 40, 53, 74, 123,
  234
  errors, 127
spectral shaping, 29
stable storage, 106, 110–11, 119
stand-by
  spares, 7, 32
  system, 198
  unit, 46
Star computer, 10, 35, 40, 69
state consistency, 93
static redundancy, 31, 35, 178, 188
StrataBUS, 219
StrataLINK, 219
StrataNET, 211, 216
STRATUS SYSTEMS, 10, 31, 172, 197,
  208–31

structural checks, 32
stuck-at fault, 14, 16, 20–21, 33
survival attribute, 11
Synapse system, 173
synchronisation, 172, 242
  clock, 31
syndrome, 28, 41–2
system
  crash, 191
  diagnosis, 44, 46
  integrity, 13, 15, 26

t-fault diagnosable, 47
tailored packages, 165
Tandem systems, 10, 64, 166–8, 171,
  178–97
test patterns, 14–20 *passim*
testing, 3, 15–25 *passim*
Three Mile Island, 128, 141
time
  checking, 84
  redundancy, 82–3, 94–5
timeout, 26, 99, 115, 118
  counters, 84
TMR (triple modular redundancy), 9,
  30–31, 35, 71, 97–8, 236
transaction(s), 6, 162, 190–92, 200,
  204, 225
  processing, 162, 199, 206, 208–209,
    224, 233–4
transferency, 166
transient errors, 213
transient faults, 31, 94–5
triple modular redundancy
  see TMR
triplicated processors, 235
two-phase
  locking, 105, 109
  commit algorithm, 118

undesired event, 128
undirectional broadcast
  networks, 83
UNIVAC, 32
unrecoverable objects, 72

valid result, 94
validation checks, 224
VLSI, 18–20, 23, 30–31, 38, 67
voter(s), 9, 30–31, 97, 238
  circuit, 240
voting, 72, 75, 237, 242
  analogue, 237

warm start, 242–3
watchdog(s), 84
  processes, 138–9
  processors, 18
  timers, 32, 41, 138

X.25 protocol, 216, 230